BEND LIKE THE WILLOW

A Tale
of an Arab Promise

Susan Glasier

Glasier, Susan

BEND LIKE THE WILLOW
A Tale of an Arab Promise

Library and Archives Canada Cataloguing in Publication

Glasier, Susan, 1943-
    Bend like the willow : a tale of an Arab promise / Susan Glasier.

ISBN
Paperback: 978-1-927588-00-0
ebook: 0-978-1-77354-449-6

    1. Glasier, Susan, 1943- --Marriage. 2. Interethnic marriage--Algeria. 3. Algeria--History--1962-1990. 4. Algeria--Biography.
I. Title.

DT295.55.G53A3 2012   965.05'2092   C2012-906387-8

Published by: Susan Glasier
Distributed by PageMaster

Publication assistance and digital printing in Canada by

PUBLISHING
PageMasterPublishing.ca

Dedicated to

all of my children, grandchildren and

great-grandchildren,

both in and out of my life.

May this small piece of my memory lead each of you

to an understanding of your own place in the world.

 Acknowledgment

This book never could have happened without the encouragement, love and work of many people.

First and foremost, I would like to thank Elaine Cust, my untiring and forever hopeful editor, mentor and friend. Without her support and encouragement, I would have stopped trying long ago. I truly owe this book to her and can never repay her for her patience, kindness and hard work.

Thank you to my writing group, Dawn Curran, Iris McNiven, and Elaine Cust who worked through my book chapter by chapter, sometimes laughing, sometimes crying but ever patient and listening.

Thank heavens for the University of Alberta and their yearly Women's Words week, through which I took courses for many years and met many inspiring instructors and local writers. Debby Marshall, Lynn Coady, Janice Williamson, Carolyn Redl and Shirley Serviss – all played a part in my initial manuscript. I learned wonderful things from each of them.

I thank all my friends, relatives and strangers who acted as test readers of my many manuscripts. Your brutally honest comments helped more than you will ever know.

And last but certainly not least to my husband of the last twenty-five years, Robert, who sat through tears, hysteria and rages while I revisited a past he was not responsible for. He knew to hug me when I needed hugging, and he encouraged me when I lost hope, all the while whispering wise sayings in my ear that helped me see the light at the end of this tunnel.

And a special kind of gratitude is extended to my dear granddaughter, Alyssa, who read my entire manuscript in its earliest stages and burst into tears. Through the act of reading the entire epistle with such emotion, she helped me believe in myself and in my work. She is the reason I shall endure.

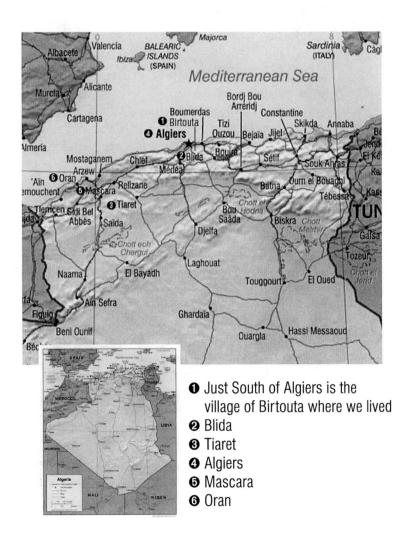

❶ Just South of Algiers is the village of Birtouta where we lived
❷ Blida
❸ Tiaret
❹ Algiers
❺ Mascara
❻ Oran

Table of Contents

 Prologue

Forty years ago, when I first began writing the story of my Algerian experience, my intentions were clear. I wanted to answer the many questions my children were asking about their absent Algerian father. Thirty years later I was getting the same questions from my grandchildren. "Grandma how could you, a strong self confident modern woman, ever find yourself in such a conservative country accepting a way of life that you would never tolerate today?"

It had become clear that simply telling my stories over and over again to family didn't really put things in context – didn't really tell the whole story in detail.

Because I always thought I would someday write this tale, I carried the pieces of it deep inside my soul, vowing never to forget what had happened to me. This act of remembering meant I never processed the grief of leaving a land and a life I had tried so hard to adapt to. As a consequence I have spent many years searching for myself in the world.

The day I began to write this tale in earnest was the day I began a healing journey. By finally writing it to its conclusion, I was able to heal my sorrow and to honour my experience. I am strong today because this experience taught me to "bend like the willow."

If there is one thing I want my children to take away from this tale, it's to look fondly on their father. He was a troubled man who lived through the horrors of war and hardship, and then sacrificed everything for the good of his country. In the end, he was destroyed by his own expectations and the dreams of what might have been. My hope is that his children will look at him with respect for his determination to honour his promise to my father: "I will look after your daughter and grandchildren. I promise." Had my Algerian husband not kept that promise, my life and the lives of my children would have been very different.

It is also my hope that others outside my family who come to read this story will read it as the unlikely love story between two people from different cultures, a love story that starts and ends with illusions and misinformation. It is an attempt to explain the layers of that relationship. A woman driven by the need to escape a suffocating mother and a man driven by guilt over his moment of passion gone wrong.

It should also be noted that while I believe all of my story to be true, some of it may have been distorted by time and memory. I have tried to be as accurate as possible but acknowledge that I have fabricated dialogue to make the story more readable. Therefore, parts of this tale may not be exactly as they occurred, but they are as accurate as I can remember. Some names have been changed for the sake of clarity and privacy.

PART ONE

Tucson, Arizona
1962 - 1966

 And So It Begins

"Okay, Mother," I sigh. "You win. Whatever you say."

My mother gives me her *that's my good little girl* smile, returns her eyes to the road and we continue on our way in silence.

Because every story needs a beginning, and because this is my story, I choose to begin it on September 9, 1962, the day before I start my first year of university. I am travelling from our military base home at Ft. Huachuca, Arizona, to the University of Arizona in Tucson in our 1960 red and white Desoto with my mother at the wheel.

My mother learned early in life that she had to fight for everything she wanted to accomplish. Her father died when she was three, and her brothers were five and eight. The family went from being well off to being poor in the space of a year. Her mother started to work sixteen-hour days. My mother ran the household from the time she was eight, becoming the good little girl, who not only went to school, but also did all the housework and cooked all the meals. She learned how to be in charge. When her brothers didn't do what she wanted, the only strategy that worked was to grab them by the hair and pull.

I learned early in my life that disagreeing with my mother is pointless. I do it anyway, but I always lose. She wants everything her way. She tells me what I can do and can't do and even who my friends should be. When I come home from school, I never know if she will be happy to see me or if she will scream at me. One minute she is happy and the next, she is so crazy. When she is crazy, she grabs me by the hair and pulls. She always tells me, if you don't want your hair pulled, *be a good little girl;* then she smiles her special *that's my good little girl smile* when I comply. I am so happy to be out of her house.

Abruptly, my mother takes her eyes off the road and looks at me, her expression electric. "I'm so excited for you, honey. My one and only baby, off to university. You can't imagine how I have dreamed of this all my life. I am so proud of you and all you have accomplished." Her large, round dark brown eyes fill with tears. "I would have given anything to go to a real university," she continues. "You'll love every moment. I know you will." She gazes at me, tears running down her face.

Oh god, more of my mother's crap. I have listened to her ravings for as long as I can remember, and this is just another version of how sad and unfortunate she thinks her upbringing was. I try not to roll my eyes, but I fail.

Her excited voice turns into her disappointed voice. Sighing loudly, she asks, "Can't you ever be happy about anything?" When my mother lashes out like that, her lips turn under and her whole body tightens. She reminds me of a cat ready to spring on some unsuspecting little mouse. "I just don't understand how you can't be at least a little excited about going off to university. It's a huge step up."

I can't help it. I roll my eyes again. A huge step up. All my mother ever cares about is a huge step up. What does that even mean? Why does my mother talk like that?

"Watch the road! You'll kill us both!" I shriek.

She swerves suddenly to avoid an oncoming car. "Damn!" escapes her pursed lips.

I inch my way to the far edge of the seat and push my face against the cool window. I focus on the silver wings that give character to this beast of a car. It is our first car with real air conditioning. I revel in the coolness and finally, relax into the silence and nestle down into the soft luxury of the leather seats. My heart beats in rhythm with the car – a rhythm that lulls the anxiety I feel at leaving home for the first time, the only worry I have that is more powerful than the desire to get away from the manipulations of my social-climbing, controlling mother.

An idea pops into my head – the sure-fire way to prevent my

mother from barrelling into my university life and taking it over as if it were she who was going to be living it. I sit up straight. I try to make my voice sound less annoyed than I feel. Calmly and quietly, as if it is an ordinary everyday request, I say, "Just drop me off at the dorm, Mom. I'll be fine."

In a saccharine voice, she responds, "Of course I'm not dropping you off at the dorm, dear. I want to see where you are going to live. Besides, I want to be sure your roommate is good enough for you." She emphasizes the *good enough* and then turns her eyes away from the road again. This time she stares at me, raising her eyebrows until I can see their hairy tips nearly join together.

I shake my head, disgustedly, but resist the temptation to argue with her again.

A few more miles of silence. Then, she glances down at the seat beside her. She reaches into the large stack of papers sitting there and picks up first one, then another. She barely glances at the road as she searches. Finally, she finds the one she wants. "Ah yes, here's the information on your roommate." Squinting, she holds up a paper from the stack. "It says here her name is Julia. Julia Stanton." She hesitates, and then runs the name, Julia, across her tongue and out her mouth almost like she is tasting it. "Ah," she says at last. "That's a good American name. I'm sure she will be just fine."

I glare at her. I can't let her know that I am just as concerned about who my roommate will be as she is. My annoyed voice returns. "If you are so sure she will be just fine, then drop me off at the dorm entrance, and let me do this by myself."

She stares at me in disbelief. "Why do you have to be so difficult, especially at a time like this?"

I study my mother. She is a beautiful woman with short, black, naturally curly hair, olive skin and full lips, which she keeps always carefully painted with bright red lipstick. She is small in stature, tiny boned, with long narrow fingers ending in nails carefully manicured and always painted in the same vibrant red as her lips. She has perky little breasts that she manages to make look bigger by accentuating her tiny waist, which she pulls in even smaller with one of the many matching cinch belts she owns.

Today, she is decked out in a white linen designer dress decorated profusely with large brightly coloured flowers. Her shoes are dyed to match the colours of the blue flowers that seem to tumble down its front.

Growing up poor gave my mother an obsessive need to hoard money and to surround herself with beautiful things. My father earns a good living for the three of us, and with my mother's budgeting skills, we appear to be wealthier than we really are. As a result, she draws friends, who under normal circumstances would be out of her social class. No one would guess that she shops at the Tucson Junior League Rummage Sale once a year for all her clothing and all of my father's and mine as well. She even buys her shoes there. My mother relishes this deception. Moving in the highest social circles and staying beautiful are the most important goals in my mother's life, and I resent her for both.

After what I am sure is the longest trip of my life, the university campus looms ahead and my mother follows the signs to Yavapai Dormitory. The dorm turns out to be one of the oldest buildings on campus with ivy on the walls and stone facings. I walk through the door with my baggage and my mother. A young woman sits at the long front desk with a neatly typed nametag pinned to her breast pocket identifying her as a Residence Aide. She asks my name and checks her official list.

"Yes," she says brightly. "Susan Glasier. Go down the hall on this floor and it's the last room on the right. Number 22."

My mother holds out her hand for the key, and the girl pauses and glances back and forth between us. I reach out too late. My mother has already snatched the key from the startled aide. We go down the hall in the direction of my room, me, in my sneakers, over-sized t-shirt and blue jeans, trudging along behind my high-heel-clicking mother.

The halls are wide and brightly colored, filled in every direction with other new students – all lugging numerous bags and bundles – and their parents. Part way down the hall, I notice, with grudging awe, how the crowd parts for my mother. She marches along like some self-important soldier on emergency duty and whoever jostles up against her or steps in front of her gets tossed to the side as if she has magical powers. Following along behind, I feel like the groupie of a movie star. If she weren't my mother, I would be thrilled. But she is my mother, and I feel embarrassed and more anxious than ever for her to get out of my life.

I hear her voice over the crowd. "Here we are, Sweetie. Number 22."

I am well behind her and continue pushing my way through the throngs of people. I am now half dragging my suitcases, so it is taking me longer than my mother thinks it should.

In mid-sentence, her demeanor changes. "Oh. For Pete's sake, hurry up," she bellows in a voice clearly heard by everyone in the hall.

People stop and let me by. I cringe.

By the time I get to the door of Room 22, my mother has already entered. She is standing in the middle of a brightly painted yellow-curtained space with a bunk bed against one wall and two desks along the opposite one. The end wall holds two small closets and two stacked dressers. The room feels welcoming and comfortable. I fling my bags on the floor next to the beds. The top bunk is already brightly decorated with a fuchsia quilt and matching pillow. Clothes hang in one of the closets and an ashtray containing three Newport Menthol filter-tipped cigarette butts sits on one of the desks. Bright pink lipstick stains encircle each butt.

I smile, in spite of my anger at my mother. How could anything be more perfect? Out of all the roommates I could have been given, what are the chances of getting one that smokes my brand?

Suddenly, the door bangs open and in strides a statuesque young woman. She holds out her hand to me. "Hi. Julia Stanton," she announces. "You must be Susan. Hope you don't mind, but I picked the upper bunk. I think it will be much more exciting than the lower one." She winks at me, and then laughs a deep outlandish laugh that starts from the centre of her soul.

I am not certain what she means by 'more exciting than the lower one' but there is definitely something grownup and mysterious about this girl. "It's okay. I prefer the lower one anyway." I answer quickly, anxious to be agreeable. I have never slept in a bunk bed, so I have no way of knowing if the top could be more exciting than the bottom. I smile at her as I take her warm hand and give it a firm squeeze. My mother has taught me that a handshake should be firm and solid. Julia smiles at me curiously and quickly removes her hand from mine.

She turns to the mirror behind the door, touching a comb to her brown curls. Checking her face, she announces, "I'm meeting my boyfriend any minute now, so I'll go and get out of your way. You can unpack and settle in." She picks up her purse and heads to the door, nodding politely to my mother who stands with her mouth agape, frowning.

As Julia starts down the hallway, I hear my mother begin, "Well, I never. What an ill-mannered rude little pip–"

"Shh," I interrupt. "Don't talk so loud. She'll hear you."

"Well, I don't care if she does. She walked right by me and never said a thing. She obviously has no respect for her elders, and – furthermore, did you see how big her chest is and how she sticks it out for the whole world to see?"

I can't believe what is coming out of my mother's mouth. I close the door quickly and whisper. "She wasn't rude or ill-mannered. She was just talking to me, not to you. And – what does her chest have to do with anything?" I shake my head. I want to shake my mother.

My mother stares at me for a few seconds and then responds, "Oh, you poor naïve thing. I'm not sure you are even ready for university. You have to pay attention to things about girls like that or you will be in trouble before you know it."

"Mother, what exactly do you mean by *in trouble?* Why do you say things like that?" I ask her, exasperated. Then, before she can answer, I muster up all my courage and blurt out, "Mom, it's time for you to go. I want to unpack and rest. I start a whole new school year tomorrow and I need time to think."

She looks at me for a few seconds and then moves towards the door, sighing like it is all too much. "Okay, Miss Independence," she says dramatically. "I'm leaving."

She switches to her *wounded to the soul* look. Tears form in her eyes and she concludes, "It's hard to let my baby go. But I know

I must. I'll call you tomorrow and see if you need anything." She looks at me, and smiles through her tears.

I feel guilty – again.

"I'll be fine, Mom, and thanks, and goodbye." I move towards her and hug her small warm body. I love my mother – but in her presence I always feel either totally inadequate or terribly guilty.

"Goodbye," she whispers, back in her dramatic role. Halfway out the door, she stops and turns, all mother for an instant. "You be good, you hear?" Then, her *pathetic little me* voice takes over. "I only want you to be a good girl. I only want you to make your mother proud."

As she steps into the hallway, I move towards the door and close it behind her firmly. I feel the need to shut out everything.

I look at my new home. Yes, this will do just fine. I pick up the largest of my suitcases and plunk it on the bottom bunk. Time to unpack and make myself at home.

I feel free – free and excited about what is to come. I am enrolled in the Liberal Arts Program with a major in political science. The university advised me that this is the route into law school for proper young ladies. I first dreamed of becoming a lawyer when I was thirteen. A year later, I read my first in a long line of Perry Mason stories written by the attorney, Earle Stanley Gardner.

When I told my father I wanted to be a lawyer, he encouraged me. He told me he and his father both wanted to be lawyers. His father got close by spending most of his working life as the Wisconsin State Law Librarian. My father, however, just never got around to studying law.

I can see that happening with my father. He was too busy traveling and working internationally as a logistics expert with the Department of the Army. For my entire life, my mother and I followed him all over the world. His last tour overseas was in Ankara, Turkey and lasted three years. Before that we lived in Manila, Philippines; Yokahama, Japan; Washington D.C.; Lancaster, Pennsylvania; Arlington, Virginia; Salt Lake City, Utah, and Susanville, California. His tours were usually about three years in length, some shorter, a few longer. For me, it meant a different school nearly every year since I was six.

Right now, my father is under contract to an army base called Ft. Huachuca where, in his words, he is idling away his last three years until retirement. "It's my attempt at a normal life and it will give you a chance to settle down," I remember him telling me on the day he accepted the position. What my father doesn't understand is that I don't know how to settle down in one place.

I look around my new home at the university. I wonder if I will make it for four years. Four years is a really long time.

 Julia's Promise

Julia usually only comes to our room when it is time for her to get some sleep. One night, several weeks later, as I put on my pajamas and climb into bed, Julia arrives. The instant she closes the door, she strips down to her underpants. My mother is right about one thing: Julia does indeed have the biggest breasts I have ever seen. I try not to look. But, she catches me gawking at her.

She laughs and gives each breast an affectionate little pat. "Yeah, I know. They're lovely, aren't they? Jack always tells me I don't need a gun when I already have such a great pair of 44s." She throws back her head and laughs that down in the soul laugh I noticed when we first met. She turns and admires herself in the full-length mirror.

I smile, too embarrassed to say anything. I really don't see the humor in what she says. The next day, when Julia is in class, I sneak a look at one of her bras: Size 44D. I get the joke.

I am obsessed with Julia. She is everything I want to be. Attractive. Popular. Confident. I study her whenever I have a chance. I envy her slender hips and long tanned legs. She spends hours on her makeup, curling her long lashes with a funny little eyelash curler, and then loading each lash with many coats of mascara. Her large nose is the only imperfection I can find on an otherwise beautiful face. She looks best when she smiles.

Julia has beautiful clothes. She shakes her head from side to side and clucks disparagingly as I leave for class wearing the same thing every day, a shapeless shirt that hangs over my jeans. She reminds me of my mother, especially when she asks, "Are you wearing THAT to class?" I never know what to say. So, I pretend I don't hear her and close the door.

I am an only child, used to my own space, and I am uncomfortable having anyone see me naked. I can't stand to see Julia roll over and watch me get dressed, her arm tucked under her pillow and her eyes frankly appraising my body. For the first two weeks, I dress in the bathroom, which is at the opposite end of the hallway from our room, past the two rooms where Julia's friends live across from each other. Usually their doors are open and often the girls go back and forth between them, sometimes wearing only their bras and panties – their underclothes, my mother would say.

Hauling a full set of clothes down the hall and into the bathroom is complicated and dressing in the bathroom is awkward. I never have enough hooks for my clothes in the toilet stall and I always forget some essential article of clothing, like my bra or panties. Then, I have to redress in my dirty clothes and make the run down the hall to retrieve the forgotten item. I usually find Julia still in bed.

Julia seems oblivious to my efforts at modesty. After two weeks, I give up. I get dressed in our room. I keep my body turned away from Julia and hurry into my clothes, hunched over my bed.

I go to bed early most nights because I have early morning classes, but when Julia returns after a date, usually minutes before the ten o'clock curfew, she always flips on the lights. Sometimes, she turns the radio up to full volume. I push my annoyance back down in my throat and wish I were more like her.

Shortly after her joke about having such a great pair of 44s, Julia begins to come directly to our room every night, instead of stopping off to chat with her friends. I make sure I am in my pajamas by the time she gets in. After the first few nights, I anticipate her arrival, listening for the clump of her shoes.

As soon as she enters the room, she plunks herself down on the end of my bed and lights up a cigarette. I sit up in bed and light one as well. Then, Julia tells me about her evening with Jack. In the beginning, she only talks about where they go. Sometimes, they go to a drive-in movie or dancing. Other times, with a bunch of friends, they race down Speedway Boulevard to see whose car is the fastest. When she runs out of things to tell me about places she goes with Jack, she starts to tell me about what she does with

Jack. As she talks, we puff away on one cigarette after another. Just like friends would do.

These more intimate stories start one night when she staggers into our room with a less than steady gait. She opens the door, and stands there for a minute, hanging onto the doorjamb for support. Then, she propels herself onto my bed in one mighty thrust. The pungent boozy smell she brings with her is too familiar. It is the smell of my father.

Julia's deep laugh rolls over me as she tells me how she and Jack went up to Mt. Lemmon to park and look at the stars. "We saw stars alright," she tells me. "It was magnishifant." She tries again. "I mean magnifishant... Whatever... You knowsh what I mean," she slurs, still laughing.

I can't help but laugh with her, even though I don't really know what she means. I revel in the thought of two friends sharing tales of their dates, but I know that really I am the audience and Julia is the performer. I smile and laugh at what I guess are the appropriate places. Julia pauses sometimes and looks at me, but then she goes on with her story, watching me closely until she gets caught up again in the details of what she and Jack did.

To me, Julia is the expert on university life. She knows everyone in the dorm, at least the girls who hang out in the rooms where there is always laughter and music floating out through the half-open doors. She knows about Louie's, the cafe in the basement of the Student Union Building, where the cool people hang out drinking coffee, and maybe more than coffee.

She knows how to juggle her classes, attending often enough so that she doesn't get called into the Dean's office, but not letting them cut into her social life. She hates early mornings. She doesn't believe in getting up for her first-period class if she has been out late the night before. When she is supposed to be studying, she wanders around our room like a caged animal, smoking one cigarette after another and mumbling to herself.

One night, while she is telling me a story, she interrupts herself. "Do you get what I mean?" she asks in her *I know everything* tone.

"I – I think so," I stammer.

She makes me explain the story to her. When I get it wrong, she goes into gales of uncontrollable laughter. I laugh along with her, a willing accomplice to making fun of my lack of sexual knowledge and experience. I decide right then that I will always say I don't understand. That way, she will have to explain it to me, but I won't feel the discomfort of her laughter. I can't help it. I am fascinated with her body, and by her almost unbelievable erotic accounts of her time with Jack. I am okay with being the novice with Julia, as long as I can persuade myself that she is letting me in on what she knows about life, not just enjoying herself at my expense. Once though, when I trundle past her friends' room by the bathroom, my robe tied tight around the waist and my arms juggling my towel, shampoo, and soap, I think I hear my name mentioned, followed by loud giggling.

Julia really has two major goals in her life. The first is to spend as much time with Jack as is humanly possible, and still go to classes. The second is to be pledged to a sorority. I know about sororities. My mother made it clear that, only girls with lots of money, and only those from the top social status, are ever pledged to become part of that highly desirable in-crowd. My initial excitement about the fact that Julia and I smoke the same brand has disappeared. It seems that smoking is the only thing we have in common.

I have always used the mirror as quickly as possible, and only to make sure my hair is not standing on end. But, as a result of all these nights of Julia talking, and me listening and imagining, I take to looking at my reflection. One afternoon, when the dorm is quiet and I am sure no one is around, I muster up enough courage to examine myself naked. I strip off all my clothes and walk back and forth in front of my reflection. Immediately, I hate what I see. However, I am determined to examine all the little details of my body.

First, I note that my breasts are not nearly as large as Julia's and they hang much lower than I think they should. When I hold each one of them up in front of the mirror I feel a funny sensation passing from the breast itself down my belly to between my legs. I linger with the feeling for a few moments and then let it go.

Next, I let my eyes drop and I twist around to get a look at my bottom. It is too big and too ugly. I stare straight ahead for a moment. Is there any part of me that I like at all?

I look at my face. It is too bad about my skin. No matter what I eat or don't eat, it breaks out once a month in more than enough pimples to make my life miserable. My mother took me to a skin doctor last year, but he wanted two hundred dollars a treatment to zap each little zit with some kind of electricity. My mother decided it was too expensive and told me that the pimples would eventually go away on their own. I hope they do. In the meantime, I am stuck with them.

My other nemesis is my weight. Even when I was only five or six, my mother's friends always said I was *such a big girl* for my age. I am five-foot-six, but my dumpy stature belies my height. I sigh and hear my mother's voice. *You need to diet,* it says. She put me on a diet at the age of nine – but I got even with her! I bought cookies from the school cafeteria and smiled to myself when she couldn't figure out why I wasn't losing weight on her strict regimen. Except that now I am the one who has to contend with my weight.

My hair is thick and naturally wavy. My eyes dance over it. Reddish brown that shines more red than brown in the light. Strawberry blonde, maybe. It hangs down past my shoulders. My hair is my best feature, I decide.

I also like my eyes. My grandmother once told me they are hazel. They look gold or green to me, depending on the light. Sometimes, a deep brown.

I have my mother's long slender fingers – but I bite my nails to the quick. My father yells at me when he sees me chewing my nails, especially at the dinner table. When he yells, I run crying to my room, my mother's words following, "Oh, Frank, leave her alone, for heaven's sake!"

I have a gold front tooth, from when I fell on the slippery gym floor at school when I was nine. The dentist won't fix it until I am nineteen. He says I have to get to my full growth. I never want to smile.

I get dressed again, and go back to my books.

Julia arrives a short time later. As she enters our room, she scrunches up her nose. "Yuk, it stinks in here." She coughs suddenly, one of those exaggerated heaving sounds supposed to sound like gagging and coughing at the same time. "How the hell much do you smoke anyway?"

"I – I don't know," I stammer, surprised. "A – a lot, I guess."

"Yeah, I guess so, too!" she snaps. "You should cut back. Yuk! It stinks in here," she repeats.

"You smoke, too!" I lash back, surprised at myself for standing up to her. But, friends should be able to disagree with one another. Besides, smoking is one of the things we have in common.

Julia frowns, "Yeah, I do – but not as much as you do."

My resistance is short-lived. "I'm – sorry," I offer. "I guess I do smoke more than I should." I look for her reaction. I get nothing but a blank stare. I am confused. What did I do to make her mad at me? We have always both smoked while she tells me about her dates, and now my smoking is not okay, but hers is. She is being unpredictable – just like my mother.

I continue, "I guess smoking gives me something to do. My mom gave me a pack of cigarettes when I was twelve. We always had a conspiracy around smoking. She used to say to me, *It will help you control your weight, dear. But, don't tell anyone you smoke or we'll both be in trouble.*" I try to imitate my mother's voice. "I've always wondered who we'd be in trouble with," I laugh, trying to cajole a response out of Julia.

She looks surprised by my intimate outburst. But, still she says nothing.

I continue, again trying to elicit a response – trying to involve her as some kind of accomplice to my smoking. "Maybe, the more I smoke, the more weight I'll lose. What do you think?"

Her eyes run over me from head to toe. "If that were true, you would be the skinniest thing in the world." She laughs, not her deep-down-in-her-soul laugh that includes me, but a short cruel burst that lingers in the silence that follows it. She tosses her hair and climbs up into her bunk.

Shortly after this encounter, I awake several mornings in a row to find that she is not in her bed. Every time I come in from class, I see her unmade bed, the blankets bunched up at the back where she last threw them off, and one corner of the sheet hanging down over the edge like a promise that she means to come back. I ask around, but no one admits to seeing her. Then, I bump into her on my way to have a shower, my arms full of towels, shampoo and fresh clothes. She is doing her makeup and looks at me through the mascara that she is applying.

"Oh, I wondered where you've been," I venture. "I was getting worried about you."

Julia glances at me in the mirror with nearly blank eyes, as if she barely recognizes who I am. "What?" she mumbles. "Oh, yeah. Marsha's roommate left, so I'm moving in with her. I'll get my stuff one of these days." She turns back to her makeup.

"Oh, I – I didn't know," I mumble back. I stare at her for a few seconds and then go back to my room, my plan to have a shower forgotten. I throw myself on my bed, sobbing. My tears soak into my pillow as I cry my heartache into it. Out of the corner of one eye I see the corner of the sheet hanging over the edge of the upper bunk. It seems to be mocking me. Julia moved out on me. She didn't even tell me she was leaving – and I thought that she was my friend. I thought we shared things, like the stories about her dates she was so keen to tell me. I thought we were friends. That was the worst part. I thought we were friends – and she didn't care enough about me even to tell me she was moving out.

I try to reason my way out of my misery. My classes are interesting, I tell myself. I am doing well in them. It doesn't work. My brain can work overtime trying to convince me all is well, but my heart is broken. I hate my life. I have no friends. I hate how I am.

Somewhere between feeling miserable and hating myself, I hear a knock on the door. A girl enters and, looking at me with concern, inquires, "Are you okay?"

"Yes," I lie. "I'm fine."

"O-kay," she says, tentatively. Clearly, she doesn't believe me, but she doesn't know what else to say. "There's a phone call for you."

"Thanks," I mumble. I wipe my eyes on my sleeve and make my way to the residence phone. It is my mother – again. She calls me every day. I try not to take her calls, but she manages to track me down at least once a week. If I hadn't been so miserable, I would have guessed it was her and ignored the summons, or walked down to the phone and quietly hung up as if the call was disconnected.

"Hello, how are you doing, dear?" she sings.

"I'm okay," I lie.

She pauses. "You don't sound okay. What's wrong?"

"Nothing," I lie again.

I hear her *all American mother* tone. "You wouldn't lie to your dear old mom now. Would you, honey? You can tell me anything, you know."

No, I can't. However, against my better judgment, I blurt out the truth, trying to make it sound trivial and of no real consequence. "It's nothing serious. It's just that Julia moved out and went to live down the hall."

It is no good. My voice breaks and I say, "I feel like I have no friends. What's wrong with me, Mom?" It is a rhetorical question, but, as soon as I say it, I know she is going to give me an answer.

At first, there is silence on the line. I can almost hear her thinking. She finally answers me. "Oh, honey. You just need to fix yourself up a bit – lose a few pounds – and the boys will fall all over themselves for a date with you."

I wince, glad that she can't see me. "Mom, I'm not thinking about dates or boys. I'm talking about girlfriends. Right now, I just need a girlfriend."

"You'll be fine," she answers. "Just be a bit more outgoing. You can't sit in your room and study all the time. Go join in with the other girls. They won't come knocking on your door if you don't make the effort."

I hang up on her. My mother is a dork. I stop at the candy bar machine and grab a giant Eat More and go to the communal refrigerator for a large chocolate milk on my way back to my room.

I exist through October and into November. I get up at seven o'clock, find my way to the cafeteria, eat and go to class. Then, I head back to my books and study. Julia passes in and out of my room, picking up her things. Every time I see her, she is surrounded by her friends from the other end of the hall. They all keep their distance. I am stunned by her abandonment and still not sure what I did to cause it.

One day in late November, I notice the only thing left of her is an ashtray overflowing with her cigarette butts, dried and shriveled, like an old sadness. I grab the ashtray and heave it and its contents into the garbage can under my desk. "Goodbye, my so-called friend," I announce to the empty space. "Goodbye forever and ever. And good rid–"

My words are interrupted by a thud on the door. It flies open, and Julia stumbles in, arms overloaded with books. I blink, speechless.

"Oh," she spits grumpily. "I didn't know you were here. I'm looking for a quiet place to study." She heaves herself across the room and drops her load of books onto my desk.

"Julia," I say, hesitantly. "Are you all right?"

"Actually," she explodes, her words coming out in tight clipped sounds. "I'm not all right. I'm furious at my stupid parents. Seems they got notified by this stupid university that I'm about to flunk out – and, if I do, my parents said they'll cut off my allowance. I'll have to either go live with them or work or something."

"I'm sorry." I don't know why I say I am sorry. I am not responsible for her marks. Yet somehow, I feel guilty. I flounder, "I didn't know." At the same time, I am shocked. The way Julia talked, I always thought she did well in her studies.

"Frankly," she continues, "I don't really care much about this school thing. I only want to spend time with Jack – but now I have to study. Jack isn't going to like this new arrangement. He likes me at his beck and call." She stops and stares at me, as if she has just realized that it is me she is talking to.

"Anyway –" she mutters, "I don't know why I am going on about this with you." Then she stops and looks at me, really seeing me for the first time since she entered the room. "On second thought," she says, "You're a brain. Maybe you can help me."

"Help you what?" I stammer, reeling from having her barging in, from finding out that she is failing, and now from her sudden acknowledgement of me having some value.

"Help me study. You know, you could tutor me – or something." Her next words are spoken softly, almost as if she is talking to herself. "Yeah," she mutters. "That might work."

Julia turns toward me, her face creasing into a friendly smile. "Hey," she says. "Since you're here anyway, how about we go to Louie's and have supper together? My treat. We can talk about an arrangement. How about it, huh? You must be hungry."

Tutor her. Go to Louie's together. Her treat. Julia has never invited me anywhere, much less to Louie's. Maybe, we can be friends after all. If I help her study and she brings her marks up, she will see that I am a good friend – someone she can count on.

I can hardly believe my good fortune. "Go to Louie's?"

"Oh, come on," she says, impatiently. "Have you never been there?"

"No."

"Well, come on. You'll like it," she encourages me. "Who knows?" she laughs. "You might meet some tall, dark and handsome guy in Louie's – and fall in love and get married." She laughs her laugh again, and then we both laugh.

I shelve my misgivings, convincing myself in that instant that everything will be okay between us, and already imagining myself as one of her inner circle. "Okay," I say, jokingly. "I'll go if you promise me that will really happen."

"Of course, it will," she answers. "What Julia wants to happen, always happens. It's a fact of life."

 The Meeting

Louie's. I say the name to myself as Julia and I walk across the campus. I can't believe I am going to Louie's - with Julia. It is like a dream - one too good to be true. How many times has Julia told me about how she and Jack eat at Louie's, hang out at Louie's, meet their friends at Louie's? And now, she is taking me to Louie's with her. I have heard the girls in the dorm talk about how it is a good place to meet guys looking for a good time and how there is a bar in the basement. I am not sure I believe what they say about the bar - the university is so strict about things like that.

We cross the campus, silent. My mind is racing, trying to figure out how to fit into this new role in Julia's life. How can I possibly tutor her? Not only are we in totally different classes, but also we are in totally different programs. Julia probably has some idea - after all, she is the one who suggested the tutoring. Whatever her plan is, I am glad we are going to talk about it at Louie's - that's where friends go to talk about things.

We enter the Student Union Building. Austere and cold, I think, glancing up at the façade as Julia holds the door open. Just inside, a sign announces LOUIE'S - OPEN with an arrow blinking on and off, and pointing down the stairs. I stop dead. In my mind, the arrow flashes naughtiness.

Julia moves past me, oblivious to my reaction. She holds the door open, impatiently waiting for me to go through.

The noise from inside spills out, loud and insistent. The Beatles are screaming *Help, I Need Somebody*.

I enter tentatively. The room is dark and cool - air-conditioned. Momentarily blind, I stop. Julia quickly disappears. I stumble after her.

"Watch out!" A waitress with a tray of drinks barks at me as she maneuvers through the crowded tables.

"Sorry," I mumble, my face reddening.

"Yeah, you should be!" the waitress snaps.

Where is Julia? How will I ever find her in here? The room is filled with square tables of every size, and it is crowded to near capacity with boisterous students yelling at each other over the music that blares from large loudspeakers on every side. *Help, I need somebody.* I look around, trying to figure out where Julia has gone.

Then, I hear her voice above the din. "Hey, Susie, over here."

I look in the direction of her voice, and there she is – at a small table by the far wall. I thread in and out around the chairs, stumbling over bags and feet. I finally reach hers. "God, I thought I lost you," I say.

"Well, you just about did," Julia mutters. Then, louder, she continues, "We'll have to sit here and I'm not too happy about it."

I look at the table and around at the noisy crowd. The table looks no different from all of the others. "Uh – what's wrong with this table?" I ask.

"Yeah," she replies. "You have a lot to learn about Louie's." Her tone tells me that I don't know anything about anything. "You see, there are certain areas for certain people down here. This table is really in the brown area."

"Brown area?" I repeat. "What does that mean?"

"Oh jeez," she answers, " – if you were any dumb – " She stops herself. "Sorry – I didn't really mean that – but anyway – just so you know – " Her voice slows as if she has to explain carefully so she is sure I understand. "We are sitting in the area for the brown boys."

I look around, totally puzzled. What brown boys? Why is Julia so annoyed with me? For a moment, she reminds me of my mother, the same tone in her voice, the same exaggerated slowness that suggests I have to have something explained that I should already know.

I hear my mother's voice in my head insisting that we *don't as-*

sociate with those people. Even as a young child, I was aware of how my mom and dad were happy to have servants of all colours and races, yet still insisted that I not make friends with them.

Abruptly, Julia's voice changes, and she continues, "I'm going to get us something to eat. You stay here and watch the table. Burgers okay?"

I nod.

She gets up to leave, and then, abruptly turns back to me. Her voice now sounds like my mother in her *I know better than you do* role. Julia leans toward me and says, "Take my advice, honey. While I'm gone, ignore those brown boys. If they talk to you – ignore them. They are bad news. Bad. News," she repeats.

She leaves, and I stare after her, still confused about her reference to brown boys. I look around at the crowded room, where everywhere people are talking and laughing in the smoke-filled darkness. Two tables away, I see four dark-skinned men. I squint at them, trying to make out their features in the darkness.

As I stare, I notice they are all smiling in my direction. Are they the brown boys she's talking about? I look away. Then, I look again and just as I do, one of the smiling men stands up, staring directly at me. In two strides, he is at my table.

Oh, oh. I am in trouble now. I stare down at the tabletop and try to ignore him. He stands beside my chair. I can't just sit here, I think, so I venture a look up – into his face.

"Allo," he says, smiling broadly, his accent pouring out like thick sweet honey. "My name Moe and I am shy." His voice is deep, the perfect voice for singing *Old Man River.* The sound of his voice cuts through all the noise in the room. I hear what he says perfectly.

I stammer. "Hel – hello, I'm Susie," I manage. Susie? What a stupid name. It is what my mother and father call me. A baby's name. Why didn't I say Susan or Sue or something more sophisticated? My mind races.

Then, I hear, "Hi, Seewzi."

Ah, Seewzi, much better than Susie. His enchanting accent gives my name some sophistication – and gives me some sense of hope. What I might be hoping for, I don't know. I stare at his face.

After the voice, it is the eyes that get me. His large round dark brown eyes. I have never seen such long lush lashes. They are the first eyes I have ever seen that actually twinkle. I can't help myself. I smile at him. He smiles at me again. I smile back.

His lips are large and voluptuous. He smiles, showing his beautiful, nearly perfect white teeth. His nose is small – small with a funny bump on its bridge – like there wasn't enough cartilage inside to make a real nose so it ends too soon. It doesn't really seem to fit his face. Above his nose, a deep cut that starts in the middle of his forehead and continues down to just between his eyes catches my attention. It is a cut, but not a cut – a strange blue line at the bottom of a slight indentation. I look closely. It is more like a tattoo. Whatever it is doesn't detract from his richly classic features. When I know him better, I will have to ask him what it is and why it is there.

He is brown, but – what a delicious brown! Like very light creamy chocolate with a hint of olive. His skin, even in the darkness of Louie's, has the glint of buffed metal. I want to reach out and touch it to see if it is as smooth as it is shiny.

He has thick coarse black hair curled into the tightest tiniest ringlets I have ever seen. Here and there, a smattering of gray pokes through, like small pieces of shiny pewter in a sea of black grass. I wonder – if I put my fingers into his hair, would they get tangled up and forever lost?

He is wearing a white dress shirt with the sleeves rolled up so I can't help but notice his wide shoulders with muscles that ripple down his arms like ropes of brown taffy. He is watching me stare at him. I feel light headed. My face is hot and I know it must be red. I lower my eyes. He pulls out a chair and sits down beside me.

Julia is wrong about one thing – he may be brown – but he is definitely not a boy. My heart feels like it will jump out of my chest. My hands are shaking and I put them together in my lap.

I laugh nervously. "Nice to meet you," I venture.

He nods. "Yes, yes, I sa-ay so," he says slowly. "Sorry, English very bad."

I can't help but laugh. "Okay," I say.

He smiles and repeats after me, "Okay." We stare at each other. We smile at each other. We stare at each other some more.

All of a sudden, Julia is back, carrying burgers, iced tea and fries. "Hey" she snaps at me, "I thought I told you to stay away from the brown boys." Her voice is loud, annoyed.

She flicks her head at Moe disdainfully and tells him, "Get lost, brown boy. We don't need you around here."

"W-w-wait a minute," I stammer. "H-he – " But, before I can say anything more Moe gets up, glares hard at Julia, and returns to the table where his friends are.

Julia slams the food down on the table. "Look, I told you to stay away from those guys. They are bad news. They're just looking to get in your pants – if you even know what *that* means."

I blush. Of course, I know what that means – but how could she mean that about Moe? "I thought he was nice," I tell her, disappointed that she doesn't see what I see in him.

"Yeah, he's nice all right." She glares at the table where Moe is sitting, and flips her hand through the air to take them all in. "Those guys will play around with any girl they can and then they run back to their own country never to be seen again. You mark my word, friend of mine – they are bad news."

"Well," I offer, anxious to placate her. "He was just being friendly anyway. He wasn't really interested in me." Nobody is ever really interested in me, I finish in my head.

"Yeah," Julia turns her stare on me, and with it a *you really are hopeless* look. "Well, I saw the way he looked at you – and he was interested in something."

My face reddens again. Why does Julia have to be so crude?

I feel Moe's eyes watching me from his table. Again, my heart pounds in my chest. I resist looking at him.

Julia and I eat in silence. I keep waiting for her to talk about the help she wants with her studies, but she doesn't bring it up. She pokes each of her fries into the ketchup on her paper plate and chews as if that is all she has to think about in the world. Her eyes rove restlessly around the room.

I am so aware of Moe's presence two tables away I can hardly manage to eat. I nibble at my burger and sip at my iced tea.

Suddenly, Julia's constantly roving eyes pick out a group of her friends at a table part way across the room. They spot her at the same time, and one calls out to her, "Hey Julia, come on over here and join us."

I see the smile of relief as she turns to me, "Gee, Susie Q, hope you don't mind if I join my friends." She is halfway out of her chair, gathering her plate and drink as she stands up. "I'm not so comfortable sitting in the brown section anyway." Already moving away, she throws over her shoulder, "Let's talk about a study plan later."

I watch her leave, feeling my tears well up. I push them back down, blinking furiously. Never again, I think, as if I was the one who had made the choice to come to this place – never again will I come to Louie's with you.

I glance over at Moe's table. It is now empty. Too disappointed to finish eating, I stand up, push my chair back and head for the door. I hear laughter behind me – and I am sure it comes from Julia and her table of friends.

The dorm is unusually quiet when I return. My entire floor is empty. The silence wraps around me like a heavy black cloak and draws me into a moody dark place. Though it is much too early, I get ready for bed and lay down in the darkness, my mind reeling back and forth between the despair of Julia and the excitement of my beautiful dark Moe.

Julia didn't really want to spend any time with me, I wail inside. She just wanted to get me to help her so she doesn't flunk out – and then she didn't even want that – once she saw her friends.

Then I think of Moe. I run his name over my tongue. How funny it sounds. He doesn't look like a Moe. Not that I really know what a Moe looks like. To me, Moe would be a funny weird little dumpy person. No, Moe doesn't fit my idea of Moe. I wonder if Moe is his real name and I wonder what he meant when he said he was shy. I smile in the darkness. He didn't seem shy to me. He just didn't speak English very well.

Before I fall asleep at two in the morning, I have made two decisions about what I have to do when I get up. One is to tell Julia she can find another tutor and the other is to see Moe again.

The next day when my classes are over, I return to my room, intending to study. I sit down at my desk and stare at my open book – but all I think about is Moe. I shake my head and try to return to my notes.

Suddenly, I am hungry. I decide to go to the cafeteria. I leave the dorm, and that is when I realize that I am headed, not for the cafeteria, but for Louie's. He probably won't be there anyway, I tell myself, but somehow I know the chances are pretty good that he will be. My heart starts to pound and I feel dizzy.

Tentatively, I enter Louie's. It isn't nearly as full as it was the first time. I walk straight to the table where Julia and I sat the night before. The table where the men sat is empty. I relax a little, but I feel more than disappointed. After a minute, I decide I may as well get something to eat. I join the short lineup, my eyes staring at the display of food choices. My mind is picturing me having dinner with Moe in some intimate little cafe far from here, just the two of us.

My romantic fantasy is interrupted by a breath in my ear, and a thick, but familiar accent softly saying, "Sewzi."

"Hello, Sewzi," it says again.

That voice, that wonderful deep lovely voice. I turn to look up into his face and I smile. "Moe. Hello, Moe," I whisper.

"You eat now?" he asks.

I nod my head stupidly. "Yes, I eat now," It is difficult to get the words out. I have lost my English – I am copying his accent. My face goes red.

He laughs. "Okay," he says, "You – me – we eat some other place. Okay?"

I am unsure what he means and he reads the question in my eyes.

"Sorry, English very bad." He moves to stand right in front

of me as if that will make his English better. He reaches out and takes my hand.

"You – me. We go eat – not here." He slowly explains. He starts to pull me out of the line. "You – me – go to other place."

I try to pull my hand away, but he is holding on tight. He wants me to go with him to eat somewhere else. Julia's words run through my head, *Those boys are bad news*. I shake my head vigorously.

"No. No. I can't," I yank my hand away from his.

He lets go. His face melts into shock. Then, crestfallen and horror-struck, he blurts out, "Sorry. Sorry to bother you," He backs away quickly, visibly shaken.

I am also stunned. Oh darn. Now I have hurt his feelings. I run after him and try to explain. "No, no," I babble. "It's okay – just – maybe – we can eat here?"

He looks at me, trying to understand.

A moment passes, and he suddenly understands what I want. "Ah," he says, "Okay, me – you eat here. Okay. Okay."

He smiles. I smile. We get back into the food line.

We choose our food. At the cashier, Moe pulls a wad of bills out of his pocket and hands them to the lady behind the counter, saying, "Two dinners."

"No, no," I insist. "I'll pay for my own." I grab the money from the cashier's hand and thrust it back at Moe.

"Some other time," I tell him. "Some other time."

He repeats, "Some other time?"

He pays for his own meal and I pay for mine.

I follow him to a table along the back wall.

We watch each other eat and we smile – a lot. Near the end of the meal he says, "You help me do English. Okay?"

"Okay," I nod. "Yes, I can do that."

I smile. He smiles. We keep smiling at each other.

I need to break the silence. "Moe," I ask, "Where do you come from?"

"New York," he replies.

"New York?" I question. "You're not from New York. Country, Moe, what country?"

"America," he replies, his face unreadable.

"No, no," I say, looking for some other way to approach the question. "Where were you born?"

"Oh," he laughs, "I born in *Algerie*. You say Algeria. Far away," he stumbles. "Africa," he offers, "Nord Africa." He says Nord with a *d* and Africa like *a-freek-a*.

Rhymes with paprika, I add, silently. How sweet he is.

Still anxious to know what New York has to do with my original question, I ask, "New York?"

He looks at me with more questions in his eyes and ventures, "New York, yes. New York University. I go there, one year. Learn English."

I nod and smile. They don't do a very good job of teaching English at New York University.

He smiles back.

We both sit smiling.

It is getting late. "Moe," I say, hoping he will understand. "I help you with English. Okay?"

"Oh, yes, very good," he replies, smiling broadly.

"Okay. I will come here," I point to the table. "Tomorrow, five o'clock. Okay?"

"Five? Oh, yes. Good. Tomorrow. Five o'clock," He looks at his watch. He points to five. "I know *five*," he says.

"Good. Goodbye for now, Moe." I stand up to go.

"Bye, bye," he says, waving.

"*A demain*," he adds in French.

"*A demain*" he whispers, again.

Later, I look up *a demain* in my French-English Dictionary and discover it means *until tomorrow*.

 Girlfriend

For the next two weeks, I meet Moe in Louie's every day to work on his English. I have to keep asking him to re-explain or to find a different word to use. Eventually, I piece together whatever he is trying to tell me. The noisy music and smoky atmosphere in Louie's fade into the background, as do the crowded tables around us. If Julia is there, I don't see her.

The first week, I learn that Moe stands for Mohamed and he is 24 years old. He is an Algerian Arab and speaks fluent Arabic and a little French. He was a student at the Koranic school in his village of Mascara. There, he learned Classical Arabic by reading the Koran (the Moslem Holy Book) and studied to be a Moslem holy man. Because of the fighting in his country, he never finished his training. He adds that since coming to America he is not a very good Moslem. I want to know more about that, but I'll have to wait until his English improves.

His country, Algeria, is fighting for independence from France. Because of the war, he hasn't heard from his family in seven years. He has seven brothers and six sisters. He doesn't know if they are still alive. His mother died in childbirth when he was fourteen. His father's name is Abdullah and his stepmother is Aisha.

He tells me about the strange blue line on his forehead. "It is custom," he says, adding, "it small crosses. You see?" He puts his head close to my face and tells me to look closely. He is right. I can barely see the crossing lines, but they are there.

"My mother always say, I special. When I am at six years, I sit with her, and she cut my head with razor. It hurt very much. She put ashes in it and it turn blue. My mother say the cut make bad things go away – what you call *evil eye*."

We talk more about tattoos. In his country, women get tattoos, but not men. Sometimes, women get henna tattoos all over their hands and faces, usually before they marry. Sometimes, fertility symbols are carved on a woman's face to make her more desirable to her husband. Moe explains that his people believe tattoos will make women get pregnant as soon as they are married. When Moe tells me this, he blushes, and mutters something about his people not being educated.

In the second week, I find out that he first lived in New York. He attended New York University to learn English, but spent most of his time in a hospital. I am not sure what happened to him in the hospital because he doesn't have enough English words to explain it. I only know that it had something to do with an allergy to penicillin, and that he nearly died.

I find out that he is supported by the International Students Association, a U.S. government-funded association that provides money so students from war-torn countries can study in America. These students are encouraged to learn skills that will help their home countries get back on their feet once peace is re-established. Moe is enrolled in the General Agriculture Program. I learn that he dreams of going home when the war is over and he has graduated.

No matter how early I arrive for the study sessions with Moe, he is already there. After two weeks of eating dinner at Louie's, we progress to ending our study sessions with a walk around campus.

"What is this? What is that?' Moe asks, pointing to a tree, or a bush, or a hedge, or a cactus or any of the other dozens of objects that he doesn't have names for.

One day, we walk by a women's shoe store on the edge of campus. He stops and peers in the window. Turning to me, he says, "We go in." I already recognize his forceful voice – the one that he uses when he wants his way about something.

Okay, I think as I follow him inside, we can practice the words for different kinds of shoes. Instead, using sign language to get the clerk to understand what he wants, Moe insists that I try on every pair of high heels in the store. He inspects each pair like a man obsessed, running his hands over the smooth leather, and either smiling and setting a pair aside, or rejecting it outright.

I am caught up in his enthusiasm, and I go along with whatever game he is playing. I have never been very interested in shoes. When I need some, I buy flats in brown, white or black. Sometimes, I buy patent leather if I have a special dress or some special event to attend, but, overall, I don't really care about shoes.

Eventually, Moe chooses a pair of tawny cream, three-inch heels decorated with tiny quilt squares of colored leather across the toes. They have straps and the toes of the shoes are open. They are the most beautiful shoes I have ever seen. They are also very expensive. Moe bends down, takes the shoes lovingly out of their box, and fits them gently on my feet for the second time.

"Walk." he instructs me. "Walk there." He points to the carpet that runs along the floor in front of the mirror.

I walk. My feet are uncomfortable in such high heels and I feel precarious. But I want to please Moe, so I concentrate on looking as dignified as possible as I parade in front of the mirror.

"Ah," he says. "You like? Pretty, no?"

"Pretty – yes," I assure him. I nod in agreement as I wobble back and forth along the length of carpet. My ankle suddenly twists and I nearly fall.

Moe catches me by the shoulders. He holds me for a moment, his eyes meeting mine. "You okay?" he asks. He bends down to check my ankle, still looking up at me.

"I'm okay," I reply.

We both laugh nervously as he stands up.

"You have shoes," he announces, pointing to the pair on my feet.

I laugh, "Oh no, Moe. I can't afford shoes like these."

"No?" he asks, not understanding. "Why no?"

"Moe, I don't have the money." I slow down my words to make him understand. "I – have – no – money – for – shoes – like – these."

"Oh," he laughs. "No. No. No. I pay."

"Pardon?" I say. "Why you pay?" I ask, copying his broken English. "Why you pay?"

He smiles. "My present. My present to you. You help me learn English. I buy present."

I try to say no again, but he shakes his head and says forcefully, "I buy. You wear."

I hear that commanding tone in his voice again. I give in. "Okay, Moe. You win. Whatever you say."

He bends down and picks up my old shoes and throws them into the garbage can by the cash register. "You have beautiful shoes," he says. He reaches into his pocket, pulls out a large roll of money, and peels off the bills one by one. My eyes follow his hand from his roll of money to the clerk's outstretched hand and back again.

Before we leave the store, I retrieve my old flats from the garbage. Moe watches me, but says nothing. He takes my arm and we walk out of the store, me teetering to get my balance on the unfamiliar heels, and Moe, smiling happily. Barely a block down the street, my feet begin to hurt. I stumble around on the sidewalk as if I am drunk. Moe finds my wobbling very funny. "You learn," he says several times. "I learn English. You learn walking."

We laugh together. I notice that we have graduated from smiling at each other to laughing with each other. I feel very warm and – it has nothing to do with the Arizona sun.

The English lessons, the dinners in Louie's and the nightly walks continue into the first week of December. Moe's English gets better. I now understand nearly everything he tries to say. I tell him he is a fast learner.

One night we finish dinner in Louie's and, as we leave for our walk, Moe takes my hand. The place where our hands meet feels electric. He smiles at me and I smile back. We walk, holding hands, but not talking, until we reach my dorm. For once, Moe doesn't ask me to identify everything he sees along the way.

As I am about to say good night, he turns towards me and smiles nervously. "Sewzi," he says. "You be my girl friend?" The words rush out of him. I hear both a question and a demand.

But, the tone of entitlement doesn't matter to me. I know my answer even before he finishes. "Oh, yes. Yes, Moe," I gush. "I be your girlfriend."

He grins at me.

I grin back at him. "You be my boyfriend, okay?"

"Okay," he laughs. He pulls me close and kisses me on both cheeks.

I am in a dream.

"See you tomorrow. Same time. Same place," he says. "You my girlfriend now." He turns and walks down the sidewalk.

"Same time. Same place," I promise.

I watch him walk away. Then, I make my way inside, smiling. Instantly, the dorm is no longer a lonely place. I can join in the conversations of the other girls who talk about their boyfriends. I have a boyfriend. I am eighteen and I have my first boyfriend – a wonderful brown boy – no, a brown man – I correct myself – a wonderful brown-skinned Algerian man has asked me to be his girlfriend.

The next day I decide to surprise Moe by wearing the shoes he took so much pride in buying me. I dress in a cream-coloured long-sleeved silk blouse and a mid-calf blue cotton A-line skirt, both conservative enough even for my mother, and I slip the shoes onto my feet. They still hurt, but I decide to wear them anyway. I teeter out into the hall and pull the door closed behind me.

I turn and nearly crash into my mother who is rushing down the hall towards me. What the heck is she doing here?

"Oh, honey," she gushes.

Even as I struggle to stay on my feet, I think, oh-oh, she is in her proud mother role. I wonder what she has planned.

"I am so glad I caught you," she says. She hugs me, careful not to mess up her freshly applied makeup and fancy hairdo. "I have your father and grandmother in the car and we've come to take you out for dinner. Go – get dressed up. I'll wait."

I am devastated. What about Moe? My mother won't take no for an answer. And I have no way to tell Moe I can't meet him. What will he think when I don't show up? What can I tell my mother? That I have a date? That I am the girlfriend of a brown boy? God, she would just die if she knew that.

I hesitate.

"Well, go on," she's annoyed now. "Go and get ready. We can't wait forever."

I don't move. "I – I'm supposed to meet a friend." I stammer. "I – I promised."

"Well, unpromise. Your friend will have to wait to see you." Her disapproving eyes look me up and down and she turns up her nose like she has seen something utterly distasteful. "Go on. Get ready before I make you come looking like that."

"What? What's wrong with how I look?" I ask, not really wanting to know. I am angry. She is criticizing Moe – and she doesn't even know he exists.

Her eyes start at my head again, and when she gets to my feet, she stops cold. "Where in the world did you get those shoes? Since when did you start wearing high heels? They are so – well – so –"

"So what?" I interrupt, vehemently. "My new shoes are beautiful. I like them and I don't care what you say." By the time I get that far, I am shouting.

Slipping into her *I'm the sensible one here* mode, she asks calmly. "What's wrong with you?"

Then, her voice falls to the whisper of the *poor me* mother I know so well, "I just thought we'd surprise you and take you out for a nice dinner. I didn't come here to fight with you." She looks dejected, and immediately, I feel guilty.

"Okay, Mom," I give in. "Just don't tell me my shoes are ugly."

She looks at me again, and then she looks down at my shoes. "Okay, honey." She sounds like she has totally capitulated, but I know better. "I won't say another word about your shoes." "Just wear something else – and come on."

After dinner, my mother insists that we tour around the city. We drive by the house she and my father own, and are renting out. Then, we drive around the university and she makes me point out where all my classes are, and tell how they are going. All of the time I am thinking about Moe. I want to jump out of the car, rush back to the dorm and try to find him. However, they drop me off just a few minutes before my 10 o'clock curfew.

My mother calls to me from the car as I walk up the steps. "You be a good girl, you hear? You be good."

"Yes mother," I call back to her. But, her admonition comes too late. It is too late for me to be the good girl she wants me to be. My mother is going to kill me when she finds out about Moe. I smile.

The girl on duty at the front desk inside the dorm calls out to me. "Susie. Hey, Susie. Come here, I have a message for you."

"For me?" I ask, surprised.

"Yeah. Some dark guy came in a few minutes ago and asked for you. I tried your room, but you weren't there. He left this message." She hands me a neatly hand-printed note that I know immediately is from Moe.

"Oh," I say, and my face turns red. The girl looks at me curiously and then turns to answer her ringing phone. I clutch the note in my hand until I am safely inside my room. Then, I sit down and sigh out loud. Moe is probably so mad at me. I smooth out the crumpled paper and read:

Mon Chere SEWZIE

I wait for 3 hours. I am thinking you are sick. I can no longer sit in my seat so I come to your dorm house. The lady in the desk tells me you go with mother. I happy to hear it is mother and not a new boyfriend. I hope to meet you tomorrow at the Louies at 5. Boyfriend Moe

I fall into bed, happy.

The next morning, I wake up late. I am happy that I will see Moe later, and I hurry down the cold hallway to the bathroom. "They still have the air conditioning on," complains one of the girls, shivering in her pajamas. "They were supposed to turn it off the first of November and here it is December already and it's still on. We're all going to be sick for the Christmas holiday."

Christmas. Only two weeks to Christmas. Next week, I will be going home for the holidays. What about Moe? How will I endure three weeks away from my sweet boyfriend? Belatedly, I realize that I haven't done any shopping or anything to get ready for Christmas – or for exams. My attention has been totally focused on Moe. "I am as bad as Julia," I think fleetingly, knowing that that isn't really true, but relishing the naughtiness of the idea.

When I meet Moe in Louie's, it feels like we have been apart for two years, not just for two days. His eyes are sad as he takes my hand. "I miss you," he says.

"I miss you, too," I whisper, forgetting that I should be telling him that he should have said *missed* in the past tense. He smiles. I smile.

With his head still partially bowed and his eyes looking at the floor, he suddenly announces, "You come my house to eat now. Okay? You meet my friends, okay?"

"Uh, okay," I say tentatively, surprised at this sudden turn of events. "I'm happy to meet your friends." Never before has Moe suggested I meet his friends.

The English lesson is forgotten. Moe stands up and reaches for my hand. We walk down Tyndall Avenue to a little old red brick house partway down the block. "Here," he says, "I live here." He unlocks the door. The smell of exotic spice mixed with roasting meat greets us as we enter.

"Ah, Ahmed cooking. This is good," Mohamed, says smiling widely. I look up. A tall dark slender man with his hand reaching out comes from the kitchen. As soon as he is close enough, he takes my hand in his. I look into eyes that are similar to Moe's, except that Ahmed's are accentuated by long dark lashes and lovely laugh lines just at their edges. The other wrinkles on his face tell me that Ahmed is older than Moe by at least ten years. Unlike Moe, however, he speaks nearly perfect English.

"Allo," he says, "I am Ahmed. I am the chef." I smile. He slowly lets my hand drop and he looks away.

"The food is ready if you want to sit down," he says to Moe in English. Moe answers him in Arabic, and then turns to me.

"Ahmed is long time my friend. He is my – how you say – roommate?"

I laugh, "That's a new word for you, Moe. Who taught you *roommate*?"

"Ahmed did," he replies. "Ahmed very good at English."

I am led to a large table in the kitchen. As we are about to sit down, the doorbell rings and Ahmed goes to answer it.

As soon as he is gone, Moe turns to me and says in a whisper, "When you meet my friends, not look to their faces. Put your eyes down. It is against my customs for woman to look at man's eyes."

I look at Moe. "That's a funny custom," I say.

"No, not funny," he says in his authoritative voice. "It is my way. You do. Okay?"

"Okay," I reply, "Whatever you say, Moe."

Moe smiles, "Yes. What I say, girl. What I say."

Ahmed returns, followed by two Arab men and a young American woman who walks over to the chair next to me at the table and sits down. She introduces herself as Sandy. She then pats the chair next to her, "Ali, sit here," she says gently. As the young Arab man sits down, she introduces him to me as her husband. Despite Mohammed's order that I not look at the men's faces, I can't help but stare at Ali, though I don't meet his eyes. He is incredibly short with dark curly hair. He is clean-shaven and has a deeply furrowed brow that makes him look squinty-eyed and sinister. His face is overshadowed by a very long nose with a hook that turns under like the beak of some carnivorous bird. I can't help but think he is ugly, and, with that thought, I can't help but stare at Sandy. She is stunningly beautiful. Blue eyes. Long honey-blond hair. Skin like a china doll. A dainty little thing, only about five feet tall. Yet, even at that height, she is taller than Ali. She is wearing a skirt partially covered by a long loose blouse. How could someone as beautiful as Sandy possibly marry such an ugly man?

Sandy looks at me, smiling. "I heard Moe had a girlfriend. Welcome to the other side of the world."

I am not sure what she means.

Despite having such an ugly husband, she seems quite happy and I want to know more about her. As she settles into her chair, she suddenly whispers to me, "I'm having a baby soon."

"Oh, that's nice," I respond, surprised that she told me something so intimate right after meeting me. I have never known anyone who is going to have a baby. My mother's friends are all old. None of my girlfriends have been pregnant.

The last guest to arrive at the table is introduced as Quereshi, who says hello and tells me he is from India. He is tall with very dark chocolate brown skin, short straight black hair and a smooth face that looks like he has never had to shave. His eyes are round and his smile dances. He is totally fluent in English, and talks very fast. I love his accent, which is very different from the accents of the Arab men around the table. I try to keep my eyes lowered, but I have to glance up at him now and then, just because he is so interesting, and I am not used to avoiding anyone's eyes.

I ask him where he learned English and he laughs. "I learned English in India. Nearly everyone in India speaks English as a first language." I look away, embarrassed at my ignorance.

There is little table talk as we eat. The first course is served on a round plate, at least twenty inches in diameter, which is covered with a bed of lettuce and topped with a heaping mound of tuna fish mashed up with bits of lemon and sweet onion. The tuna fish mixture is surrounded by three kinds of stuffed black olives, intermingled with sprigs of hot peppers, green onions, slices of radish and tiny little sardines peeking out from under pieces of salty white goat cheese. This first course is served with a home-made bread that tastes like rye bread to my unknowing palate. My host simply calls it North African bread. The men at the table find this label amusing, but offer no explanation of how it is made or where it really comes from.

As Ahmed is taking away the dishes from the first course, Moe talks about his home in Algeria. At the end of his story he adds, "My friend, Ahmed the chef, is from Morocco, next to Algeria. We eat same food. Algeria, Morocco – same food." He finishes by saying, "When you come to Algeria – you eat same food."

At that moment, Quereshi leans forward and says in a loud voice clearly intended to be heard by all, "Oh, Mohamed must really be in love if he is offering to take you to Algeria." The men all laugh, except for Moe.

I don't fully understand Quereshi's statement because I am thinking about how the food is the same in the two countries. I look at Moe. He isn't happy about Quereshi's remark. He frowns at Quereshi and mumbles to me not to pay any attention to him. I see Quereshi's eyes meet Moe's and Quereshi smiles – a secretive smile. Undeterred by Moe's comments and frowns, he pushes ahead with what he wants to say to me. His voice comes out in clear staccato words, "You are very young, very beautiful girl. You must be careful of these Arab men. They are very dangerous people." The men laugh again – all but Moe.

Nervously, I look at Quereshi. His statement confuses me, both the words and the underlying tone.

Then, as if to erase what he has just said, Quereshi laughs uproariously and adds, "But more importantly, if you are brave enough to eat North African food, you will never be able to escape their charm." Everyone nods, laughing, and the next course arrives.

For the second course, we are served a thick red soup called *shorba*. Moe explains that the redness comes from tomatoes and the spices used in cooking. The soup is full of chickpeas, lentils and bits of roasted lamb. I eat all that I am served.

Moe leans over and whispers in my ear. "Don't eat too much." He fumbles for his words, "Not too much for each time."

I look at him, confused.

Quereshi interjects, smiling, "He means you shouldn't eat too much of each dish because there are seven more courses."

I nod, understanding. Ahmed goes back and forth to the kitchen and, as soon as one dish is emptied, another appears. One course after another. Roast lamb, stuffed grape leaves, couscous, *breck*, a small triangular pastry filled with rice and ground beef, and vegetables of every size and shape. Each item comes with an explanation. The taste of each new spice in each new morsel makes my tongue tingle and cry out for more, and the aromas tantalize my nose as much as the taste teases my tongue. After more than two hours of eating, I have to agree with Quereshi. Eating this food and keeping this company may mean that, I not only can never escape, but that I may never want to. I feel the spices settle into my soul.

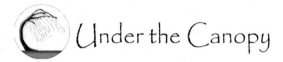 Under the Canopy

"Why would Sandy marry someone like Ali? He is so ugly."
We are walking home after dinner, my arm in Moe's. The question has been burning in my mind all evening. I have to ask it.

In reply, Moe bursts out laughing.

"Why are you laughing?" I ask, stopping to study Moe's reaction. His laughter is more than puzzling.

"Woman not like man for how he look. She like man for his money." Moe continues walking, pulling me along with him. His voice is matter-of-fact, as if the information he is sharing is common knowledge to everyone – everyone, but me.

"Money? You mean Ali has money?" I ask, stopping again. "I had no idea – you mean, Sandy married Ali because he's rich – "

"Yes," Moe drags me forward and my feet move to keep up with him. "Ali belong to – what you call – royal family of Kuwait. His father is king of Kuwait."

I stumble over my footing as my mind stumbles over what he has just said. "King? Kuwait has a king? Wow! I never knew that." I am distracted by a piece of political information that has never crossed my mind before. First, that Kuwait, that tiny nation somewhere in the Middle East, has a king. I didn't know any countries had kings any more, except for England, of course. Second, that I had just had dinner sitting at the same table as a prince. Third, that Moe has friends who are royalty and he has never told me about them, didn't even mention it when he introduced Ali and Sandy tonight. Fourth, that my mother would sit up and take notice if she knew I was hobnobbing with royalty. She would say, "It's a big step up."

"Yes, Kuwait have king." He pauses to look at me, his face hard to read.

I feel like a small child who hasn't learned her lessons thoroughly. My mother always looks at me that way when she discovers that I don't know something she thought I should already know or when she thinks I am not mature enough to understand what she is telling me.

Moe walks on, his pace now driven by his thoughts. He is pulling me along so quickly that I have to hurry to stay beside him. "But I feel sorry for this girl. She will go to Kuwait – but his family not be happy to have foreign wife for a prince. She not able to go outside without relatives, and never without veil. She not drive – or do anything like she do in America. She has money – but it *his* money. I think it is boring life. She have someone to take care of baby, so she not see baby very much." Moe lifts his hands in a *what can I do* gesture and my hand follows his through the air as if it is part of his body, not mine. "I think it is trouble for her, but he not tell her these things. I not like Ali very much."

We continue walking. I think about what Moe has just told me and wonder if I should talk to Sandy about it. Surely, she would want to know what her life would be like in Kuwait. Of course, maybe she knows. She would have thought of that before she married Ali. The incongruity of her with Ali remains in my mind. How could she have committed herself to someone so different from her – in looks, in culture, in language? Could being rich solve all the problems those differences might bring?

Suddenly, Moe turns to me and blurts out, "Never want see you in Louie's!"

I am barely able to believe what I have just heard him say. We weren't even talking about Louie's. "What's wrong with going to Louie's?"

"Louie's is place of bad girls," he says quietly. "You are a good girl, no?"

I say nothing but I think of my mother and her last words as she dropped me off at the dorm a few days earlier. How could Moe and my mother use the same words? How could they have the same thoughts?

"So," he repeats, stopping to face me on the sidewalk, his hand moving to take hold of my arm just above the wrist. I can't read the impassiveness of his face. "You are good girl, no?" He waits for my answer.

"I – I guess so," I hesitate, still uncertain what he means, still wondering where this is all leading, and where it all came from. I met him at Louie's. He and I have eaten at Louie's almost every night for the past couple of months. Does that make me a bad girl? What could going to Louie's have to do with being a bad girl? What does he mean by a 'bad girl'? Is it the same thing my mother means? Because I don't understand what she means, either.

"Good girls no go to Louie's," Moe announces, authoritatively. He turns and strides down the sidewalk, his hand still holding my arm so I am forced to turn and move with him.

I nod my compliance like a child who understands she has strayed out of bounds but doesn't know why it is such a big deal.

He pauses and looks at me again. "Ever," he finishes, even more forcefully, and waits for me to speak.

"Whatever you say," I answer. At this moment, I only want to placate him, to reassure him that he has nothing to be concerned about.

"Yes. What I say," Moe repeats my response.

I think of my mother – again.

Abruptly, Moe changes the topic. "My roommates and me go to mountains for your holidays – this – Christmas – " he says, brokenly. "My host family invite us."

Moe has talked about his host family before. They are an older brother and sister that are part of a university volunteer program to make foreign students feel welcome in America. They have taken him on trips and invited him for all the big holidays. He seems genuinely fond of them.

Christmas – I have hardly thought of the upcoming holiday at all. I haven't told Moe that I leave tomorrow to spend the next three weeks at home.

Moe continues, not noticing my silence. "You go home to Mommy and Daddy and I go to mountains with host family."

Once more, we stop on the sidewalk as he turns to face me. His eyes ask me if I understand and I do.

But 'Mommy and Daddy' strikes me as strange. Where did he get these words? That phrase makes it sound as though I am a small child who has to be passed from the care of one adult to the care of another. The help-Moe-learn-English part of me wants to laugh and explain to Moe that 'Mom and Dad' or 'your parents' would be more appropriate phrases to use, but the be-Moe's-girlfriend part notices that he seems unconcerned about us being separated for three weeks. I know that it will be good to have a break, to get away from school and studying, even to have some time away from Moe. But, I can't help but want to cling to him and cry.

We fall silent until we reach the south end of campus where the sprawling red brick library is surrounded by lovely old trees whose branches are knitted together overhead so they form a thick canopy along the front and to the side of the building. The canopy provides shelter from the heat for students who prefer to study in the warmth of the Arizona evening rather than in the icy chill of the air-conditioned interior of the building. Wooden benches and stone chairs are placed strategically throughout the space under the canopy, offering privacy for reading and studying, and for those couples who want to make out unobserved.

Moe is now holding my hand and as we reach the entrance to the canopy he leads me off the main sidewalk and onto the path that leads into the leafy coolness. "We go here." His voice is gentle, but firm. "We talk."

I feel his hand tighten on mine and I follow him. We pass a few benches occupied by kissing couples and I try not to look at them. It is cool and dark under the canopy. In fact, it seems to be getting even darker the farther we go. We pass some empty stone chairs set in a small group. Moe chooses to sit on a long park bench at the very end of the enclosure. I realize that he must have come here before to know it was here. I move to sit next to him, but he motions for me to sit on his lap. When I hesitate, he pulls me down, and I find myself in a place I have never been.

He puts his arms around me and kisses me – long, slow, hot

kisses that take my breath away and make me want him in a way I have never wanted anyone before. His hands wander as if he is unaware of where they are going. When I cannot stand it anymore, he stops. "Not now," he says, abruptly. He takes me by my shoulders and gently pushes me off his lap and onto the bench next to him. "This is not the place."

I move away from him reluctantly. I am totally confused. So much has happened this evening that I don't really understand. It reminds me of Julia and her stories, except that I don't think that Moe will explain like Julia did when she saw that I didn't understand, trading my lack of knowledge for her enjoyment of the telling.

The questions from the evening run through my head, piling one on top of another with no answers in sight. Why did Sandy marry Ali? Why would she want to have money if she won't be able to have the freedom to enjoy it – with someone she loves? Why is Moe so adamant that I not go to Louie's all of a sudden? Why does he treat me as if I am some kind of a child – going home to 'Mommy and Daddy' for Christmas? Why doesn't he seem concerned about us spending three weeks apart when I am so sure I will miss him terribly? Why did he bring me to the canopy? What does *This is not the place* mean?

Moe straightens his clothes. I straighten mine. He looks at his watch. He sticks his arm in front of my face and points to the watch on his wrist.

"Half hour," he says, "We talk English now for half hour."

"Half an hour," I automatically say by way of correction. I don't want to talk English. I don't want to talk anything.

But he begins anyway. In that half hour, he talks to me about his homeland and his family, and about the dreams he has for his new country. When he talks about his family, he begins to cry. "I not know if they are all dead. I cannot go back until I know. My life is nothing without family. Maybe, when we meet after Christmas, I tell you about them?"

I nod, a little taken aback by his emotion. I love my country and my family, too, but I don't cry when I talk about them.

Besides, I can't understand the abrupt change from making out to talking about family.

We reach the dorm just at ten o'clock. He smiles and says, "I see you in three weeks." Then, he turns and walks away. He doesn't look back.

Somehow I manage to keep my secret boyfriend a secret through most of the Christmas holiday. Two days before returning to school, I am in my bedroom listening to "Somewhere A Place for Us" from the musical *West Side Story*. I sing the lyrics over and over to myself.

Half in dreamland, I don't hear my mother, until she flings open my door. "Phone," she shouts, though I am just a few feet away from her.

"Okay, Mom," I say.

I walk downstairs and pick up the receiver, noticing that my mother is standing rather close to me. "What's the matter with you?" I ask, irritated.

"It's a guy," she whispers. "A guy who talks funny."

I roll my eyes at her and turn away. But I still can feel her glaring at my back. "Hello," I say into the phone, as softly as I can.

"Hello," says a familiar, wonderful, deep voice.

"Oh, hello," I say, making my voice as neutral as I can. "H-H-How are you?" I fall over my words, anxious to talk with Moe, yet conscious of my mother behind me.

"I am missing you," Moe says. "I am missing you too much."

"Me, too," I whisper. "Me, too."

Silence.

After what seems a very long time, Moe continues, "I see you in two - three days, no?"

"Yes," I respond. "Goodbye."

"Your mother, she is listening?"

"Yes," I speak normally this time, glancing at my mother.

"Goodbye, my girlfriend. I see you in two - three days."

"Goodbye," I answer, and the conversation is over.

"Well, who the hell was that?" My mother demands as I hang up.

Wincing, I say, as casually as I can. "Just a friend. Just a friend I met at school."

I turn to go back upstairs.

"So, what's his name?" she continues, like a freight train at full speed.

Without thinking, I answer, "Moe."

"Moe?" She questions, a disbelieving look in her eyes. "Moe? What kind of a name is Moe?"

"It's just a name, Mom – and he's just a friend – so get off my back!"

Our conversation falls into a long-established pattern. It is much like a boxing match.

Round one. As quickly as the conversation starts, it ends.

My mother recoils in shock. "I wasn't aware I was on your back," she retorts. "I just want to know who your friends are. That's all. So – shoot me for caring about you." She turns and goes back to her work in the kitchen, muttering to herself.

I stare after her, feel guilty, and follow her.

"Sorry, Mom," I make my voice soft, anxious to make her feel better. "He is just a friend," I lie. "Next time you come to Tucson, I'll introduce you. I'm sure you'll like him." I know she'll hate him.

My mother turns on me. She has won the first round, and comes out fighting mad. "Oh god, you are such a baby. Why haven't you talked about this person before? Why is he calling you here if he is 'just a friend' as you claim? He talks funny. Who is this person? I want to know."

Round two. Broadsided by my mother's demanding questions, I flee. My guilt melts into rage, bubbling like a cauldron of hot oil. I have to get away from here, from her.

I take the stairs two at a time, calling back over my shoulder, "He's nobody – just nobody."

Round three. We go to our corners. I slam my bedroom door as hard as I can and throw myself on the bed. My mother is such a stupid dork. I refuse to come down for dinner and stay in my room, crying and playing the same record over and over again.

My mother ignores me and I eventually fall asleep sometime after midnight.

It is all tied to the moving – the traipsing back and forth across the world that my father's job orchestrated during my childhood and adolescence. Sometimes the move meant, not only one school a year, but one country a year. At each posting, I was carefully taught to stay away from the locals. *Stick with your own kind* was what my father's voice told me, whether he was in the room or out of earshot a continent away. When I was eleven and wanted to play with the little girl down the street, he told me I couldn't, because she *isn't like us*. It took me two years to figure out that she *wasn't like us* because she was black. When I asked my father why he didn't like black people, he said something had happened in Atlanta, Georgia, where he had lived for five years in his late twenties. He never told me what had happened, but by the time I turned eighteen, I was aware that he felt anger towards anyone without white skin.

Round four. The fight is declared a draw.

The next day, all seems forgotten and forgiven. My mother and I are our usual selves again. I let her do my laundry and pack my things to return to school. I am happy when the time comes to leave, and much happier when I learn that my father will be the one driving me back to the dorm. At least, with him, I don't have to talk about anything important.

He listens to the radio and I get lost in my own thoughts. I daydream about a life with Moe – away from the prying eyes of parents. I imagine little scenarios of what my life with Moe would be like. I like living in my mind. It feels like I belong.

Time passes quickly, and suddenly we are pulling into the dorm parking lot. "Well, here we are, pumpkin." That's my father's pet name for me. "Can you manage the suitcase by yourself?" he asks, as he gets out of the car and opens the trunk.

"Yeah, I think so," I answer. I reach up and kiss his cheek. "Thanks, Dad."

"Yeah, you're welcome," he says.

Just before I turn to go up the steps, he looks at me with his *sorry to say this* look and grudgingly announces, "By the way –

your mother wants to meet this new beau of yours the next time she comes to town. You know your mother. She never takes no for an answer."

"Yeah, okay, Dad, but he's just a guy."

"Yeah, I know, but you know your mother." He sighs.

I smile at him. In this, we are co-conspirators. We both know my mother. "Yeah, I know my mother. Bye, Dad."

"Bye, pumpkin." He stands looking at me. I get the feeling he wants to say something more, but he doesn't. After a minute, he smiles half-heartedly, and returns to the car.

I drag my huge suitcase up to my room, unpack my clothes and fall into bed. I am so tired. All the drama and excitement of the past few days has exhausted me. I awake the next morning with barely enough time to get to my first class. As I race out of the dorm, I run smack into Moe dashing up the stairs.

"Hey, you are here. Why you not call poor Moe?" he asks, sounding pathetic. "I wait all the night and you no call." His pathetic look changes to anger as he struggles, reaching for words he doesn't know.

At first, I smile when I see him. But, when he blathers on, I get concerned. He is so angry. When I can get a word in, I try to explain. "I'm sorry Moe. I was very tired last night. I got in late and I went straight to bed." I intend to go on to tell him that I have to get to my class, and we can talk about all of this when we get together later.

But, he grabs my wrist and yanks me around to face him. "No. No. No," he repeats loudly. "You call me. Why you no call me?"

"Moe, I have to –" I try to explain I have to get to my class, but he doesn't let me speak. "Why you no call?" he asks, louder.

Moe and I are standing right in front of the dorm. Other students on their way to classes turn to look at us as they walk by.

"Moe," I break in, speaking quickly and raising my voice slightly. "I have to go to class, Moe. Let go of my arm. People are looking."

As if I have uttered a magic word, he drops my arm, and his voice. He steps closer to me and whispers. "Sorry. I worry, I think you in accident."

My concern melts. "Oh, thank you for worrying about me." I kiss him, hard and full, on the mouth. He looks stunned.

"See you later," I call to him as I head for class, leaving him standing on the sidewalk, confused and speechless.

At lunchtime, I find him waiting for me outside my classroom door.

He greets me by saying, "We eat lunch now."

I go with him. I don't see any of the anger from the morning. We go to the cafeteria and he buys my lunch. When we finish eating, we walk. In time, we find ourselves at the library canopy again, but I turn away when he tries to pull me inside. "Moe, I have to go to class – and I have to study. You have to study. We will both flunk out if this continues."

He laughs out loud at this. I am not sure he understands a word I am saying. "Yes, we study," he repeats after me. "We study – and then we go to seat. Okay?"

"Okay," I agree.

In the evening, we have our usual dinner and walk to our place under the canopy. But, instead of insisting that I sit on his lap, Moe motions for me to sit next to him. I am surprised – usually he can't wait to get his hands up my skirt.

"We talk," he smiles, as if nothing has changed. "I tell you about my family. Tonight, I tell you story of my mother."

He reaches into his pocket and pulls out several folded sheets of paper and a pen. He thrusts it at me and declares, "You take notes. When I finish this story, you go home and write it. You write it in good English. You understand?"

I nod. I understand what he is saying, but I don't understand why he wants me to write the story down. "Okay," I agree again.

I take the pen and get ready to write. He begins by telling me that his mother's name is Zohra. My hand races across the page, trying to catch every detail, trying not to be drawn away from my writing by the story content. Word by word, sentence by sentence, I write as Moe tells the story of his mother's young life, her first marriage, her rescue by his father, and then of her death in childbirth.

By the end, I am unable to speak. Gently, I kiss him and he

kisses me. Then, I leave him, sitting under the canopy, sitting alone, with tears running down his face. I go back to my dorm to write up the story as he instructed me to do.

 Valley Fever

Time flies. January turns into February and midterms. Moe and I establish a pattern to our time together. We go for lunch and a walk every day and we part only for class. At night, we have dinner in the cafeteria and then walk to the canopy. Here, we play at love making until one or both of us can barely breathe. Always, just on the brink, he pushes me away gently, straightens his clothing and either takes me back to the dorm or tells me stories about his family.

Since Christmas, my mother insists that I come home every weekend. She picks me up at my dorm on Friday nights promptly at six, and greets me with "You promised to introduce me to your new boyfriend. So, where is he?"

I always counter with "He's not my boyfriend," but I know she doesn't believe me. I know I will have to follow through on my promise to introduce her to Moe soon.

University class work is becoming more and more difficult. At home on the weekends, I tell my mother that I have homework and she leaves me alone. I spend most of my time in my room and I try to study, but I mostly think about Moe and our life under the canopy. Every week I bring home notes about the latest stories Moe has told me about his family and I work on getting them written out. I read the story of Moe's mother over and over again. I decide that when all the stories have been told and written, I will bind them into a book as a special present for him.

Weekends when my parents travel or have social gatherings of their own, I stay on campus. Then, Moe invites me to his house for dinner with his friends. The men fall into casual conversation, mostly in Arabic. When there are no women to talk to, I eat and try to understand pieces of what is said. Later, I ask Moe if I understood the subject. I am generally wrong. When Ali brings Sandy or when someone else brings their American wife or girl-friend, the women talk about recipes and babies. I have little in common with these women other than the fact that we are with foreign men.

The first glimmer that something is physically wrong with me comes in early March when Moe gets upset with me. "Sewzi, what's wrong with you? You not remember to come to lunch to-day. Yesterday, you not remember to go to your afternoon class. This not like you."

"Moe," I reach out for his hand. He seems to be a great dis-tance away, though he is sitting right across the table from me. "Moe – I don't know. I'm so tired all of the time. It seems so hard to remember anything."

By the next day, I have developed a rasping cough and aching limbs. I feel as if a giant weight is sitting on my chest. I am discon-nected from my body and hear an echoing in my head. I am in a different world. I hear people talk to me, but I can't respond to what they say – I am just too tired. My face feels red hot. School no longer matters to me. I only want to stay in my room and stare off into space or sleep – especially sleep.

Then, I wake up to find my mother shaking me gently. "Honey, what's wrong? Are you sick? What's wrong?" she says.

I can't answer her. I open my eyes and try to sit up, but it is too much for me. I fall back on my pillow. I just want to sleep. My mother pulls me by my arm to a sitting position. She holds up my clothes and tells me I have to get dressed. "We are going to see the doctor," she says gently. "You look terrible."

I see my mother and my room as if I am in a long dark tunnel. The way back from the other world looks impossible. I can't figure out why my mother is in my room, why she is trying to pull me to my feet and get me dressed. Nothing makes any sense. Eventually, I let her get me into my clothes and she half carries, half drags, me to the car.

A blood test and an X-ray confirm the diagnosis to be Valley Fever, a common disease of the Arizona desert, caused by breathing in contaminated fungal material that is sometimes carried on the wind. The doctor tells my mother that I have to have three months of complete bed rest. I don't need any medication, just a very long period of bed rest. I hear the conversation, but I don't care what they are saying. I just want to sleep.

My mother drives back to the university. I stay in the car, sprawled across the front seat, asleep. When I wake up, the back seat is filled with my belongings, and my mother is trying to make me sit up, so she can get into the driver's seat. I notice only that it is dark outside. "That was quite a job, gathering all of your things," she says, patting my cheek as I struggle to sit up. "You will have to do the school business stuff when you feel better," my mother says matter-of-factly. "Got to get my honey home and to bed."

Even though I am sick, I can sense my mother is happy. She pats my face and arm all the way home, muttering something about what a blessing it is to have me back.

A week later, I become aware of my surroundings when my mother tries to feed me. Her face is determined and as I come out of wherever I have been, I can tell she is worried. She has a bottle of some dark liquid with a straw in it and is pushing it towards me, trying to direct the straw into my mouth. Whatever it is, it stinks. "Drink a little," she coaxes.

"What is that?" I croak.

She is surprised. "Oh, I'm so glad you're back among the living. You haven't said a word nor eaten a thing for days. You're scaring me to death."

I feel awful – tired and disconnected. I need to sleep again.

"Whoa," my mother says. "Whoa, you just woke up. You can't go back to sleep again."

"Why not?" I manage.

"Because you have to eat or drink something."

"Okay," I mutter, and then I say the first word that comes into my mind. "Milkshake."

"That's a bit extreme, don't you think?" She thrusts a glass of water at me. "Here, have some water."

I struggle to swallow a few sips of water. The coolness of it going down my throat holds me in the real world for a few minutes, and I hear my mother's voice continue.

"Oh, by the way," she says, "I met your boyfriend – Moe. Well, I didn't really meet him face to face or anything but he called me last week and said he was your friend. I didn't know what to think at first. Then, he said he thought you might be sick and I should come right away."

She takes the glass from my hand as it wanders away from my mouth.

"He was right. I can't figure out why the dorm people wouldn't have called me instead of this boy having to do it. I guess that is something I will have to look into."

My eyes close as I feel her get up off the bed and leave the room.

After two weeks of nearly constant sleep, I start to feel better. I no longer need to sleep all the time and my power to think returns for short periods. During one of my lucid periods, my mother comes into my room and asks me if I feel up to coming to the phone. She explains that this Moe friend of mine has been calling every day, but she has been telling him that I am too sick to talk. I struggle to get up and stumble down the stairs to the phone.

My mother brings a chair for me to sit down. The receiver feels heavy and Moe's voice sounds stiff and business like. "Allo, Sewzie. How are you?"

"Fine," I answer. It is just too much effort to explain how I feel. Besides, I don't want him to worry about me.

"When you come back?" he asks.

"I have to stay in bed for the rest of the semester. I won't be back this year." It is an effort to put sentences together. I can't believe how much work it is to talk.

"Okay. I will call every week." I hear the disappointment in his voice. "Please feel better. I will write you some letters and practice my English. Okay?"

"Okay," I answer.

"Your mother – she listens, no?"

"I don't think so, Moe." I glance around but I don't see her.

"We only have one phone and she isn't here in the room so there's no way for her to listen in."

I hear a soft, "I love you, Sewzie." Then, I hear him put down the receiver.

My heart begins to beat faster at his final words. I must be getting better. I stumble back up to bed. I am exhausted, but I feel much less like sleeping.

The weeks go by and I start to recuperate. I begin to feel restless and get out of bed to wander around the house, sitting in different rooms, looking at magazines, trying to read a few pages of a novel. True to his word, Moe phones once a week. My mother always picks up the phone and always calls out to me. "It's your boyfriend on the phone."

I always answer, "He's not my boyfriend."

But, there is no rancour in either of our voices. I don't have the energy to fight with her, and she is strangely content with things as they are. I figure that she is happy to have me home, happy to have me in her care again, happy to have me compliant – even if it is because I am not well enough to disagree with her.

Moe writes to me. Every day I get a letter, some days I get more than one. Some letters are filled with poetry, painstakingly translated from Arabic. These poems are beautiful and filled with dramatic words of passion – just as his family stories were. Sometimes, he uses the wrong words and the lines come out funny.

In other letters, he tells me that he is having trouble with one of his courses because he doesn't understand English well and the professor doesn't want to help him. His friends have always helped him by taking notes that he can copy and usually the professor will give him an oral test for his exam so he doesn't have to write anything. Now, this one professor is refusing to give him an oral test and insists that he write the exam with all the other students. He writes how angry he is and how now he will fail the class and be sent home in a *disgrace*.

I try to make him feel better by telling him that I doubt they will send him back for one failure. He assures me they will.

Even though we have been separated for a few weeks, and we haven't had our daily language practice, Moe's English has continued to improve. I realize, that in all the time I have known him, I have never asked him how his schoolwork is going. I never thought about how he manages in the classroom until he mentions his problems in his letters. He sounds very worried. We write back and forth about this and then in one of his letters he says that now all his friends are going to different classes in summer school and for the first time he will be alone in a class with no help. I AM IN BIG TROUBLE NOW he writes all in capitals.

Shortly after this exchange, he phones. He is frantic. "I will have to leave America," he shouts into the phone. "I will be laughed on by everybody."

I am well enough to stand leaning against the wall while I talk to him. I smile to myself and try to be sympathetic. "Moe, calm down. It will be okay. We will find a way. Nobody will laugh on you."

"Find a way? How you can find a way? It is not possible. I am going to put my head in pillow and shoot it off."

The picture of Moe with his head in a pillow trying to *shoot it off* is too dramatic. I can't help but laugh out loud. He does not see the humour in my mental images. "You hate me!" he lashes out, even more dramatically. "You hate me."

"No, Moe, I don't hate you." I notice that I can respond to his feelings without it taking all of my effort any more. Another sign that I am getting better. "It's just that sometimes you say funny things when you don't mean to. I'm sorry. I didn't mean to make you angry. It really will be all right."

He sighs and seems to calm down. "Okay, you make it all right. How you make it all right?"

"I will call you back tomorrow, Moe. We will make a plan."

"A plan?" he asks, sounding confused. "What you mean, a plan?"

"Look it up in the dictionary," I tell him. "Look it up in the dictionary and I will call tomorrow." Without giving him any chance to respond, I hang up, wondering, "What is this plan that I just promised to come up with?"

The plan comes together in that strange space between being awake and falling asleep. If Moe had a tape recorder, he might be able to talk the professors into letting him record their lectures. Then, he could bring the tapes home, listen to them again and take notes. That might solve his problem for summer school.

Thinking about Moe and his classes brings my own classes back to my mind. It occurs to me that I have received *Incompletes* for a whole semester of work. And – even more importantly, because it signals to me that I have fully regained my thinking abilities – and – if I went back to university for summer school, I could make up all the work that I missed – and I could help Moe. That night, in my dreamland, I am with Moe under the canopy doing more than talking. It is time for me to return to school.

I am up early the next morning, ready to face my mother, ready to convince her that I have to go to summer school to finish the courses I missed while I was sick. I lay out my plan, and after breakfast, while she is still sipping her morning coffee and seems in a good mood, I approach the subject.

"I'm feeling good these days. I think I'm over this dumb disease." I stand across the table from where she is sitting.

My mother's lip immediately starts to curl under. "Well, you may think you are," she snarls, "but the doctor said three months and then you have to get retested. It has only been two months."

My fingers tighten on the back of the chair. I am determined to talk this out calmly and reasonably. "I'm sure I'm fine. Mom, I'm worried about my grades and my class work. I've been thinking, if I could go to the last session of summer school, I could make up all the course work I missed and be ready for the fall."

"Don't even think about it. You have to get over this, and then, we'll talk. I'm not even sure you are going back in the fall, let alone for summer school. You're still sick and you need to just rest and get better." She puts her coffee cup down in a gesture of finality.

"I said I am fine, and I am going to summer school." I feel my face turn red. I can't believe my mother will make me stay home for the whole summer.

"Oh really? Says who? I guess you have the money to go to school?" She leans forward, thrusting her face at me.

"No." My voice falters. I realize that I don't have money to do anything. "But – you don't understand!" Now I am yelling at her, my plan to be calm and reasonable gone in the face of her threat to keep me at home by refusing to pay for my schooling. "I have to go to summer school!"

She pauses for a moment and then in her booming authoritative *I am god voice,* she announces, "I know why you want to go to summer school. It's not to finish your classes. It's to see that boy, isn't it?"

I look at her, and in my most defiant voice, I scream, "No, it isn't! I just want to finish my classes!"

"Well, let me tell you something, young lady," The gloves are off. My mother is going to tell me what she really thinks, what she hasn't said during all of the weeks that I was sick in bed. "That boy is too old for you. I can tell by his voice he's too old. And I can tell by his accent that he's not our kind." In a no-holds barred finale, she slams her fist down on the table, making her coffee cup jump in its saucer. "If it is the last act of my life, I will not allow you to see him again. If I have to keep you out of university, I will. You need to stay away from the likes of him. Do you understand?"

What I understand is that, if she gets her way, I may never see Moe again. "I hate you," I scream louder. "You are the meanest, rottenest, worst mother in the whole world and I'm never talking to you again. I hate you."

"That's probably a good thing," she coolly responds as she calmly and confidently picks up her coffee cup and gets up to put it into the sink. "That's a very good thing. One day, you will thank me."

I scream, "I hate you!" one more time before I run up the stairs. I throw myself on the bed and sob. I vow to never say another word to my mother as long as I live.

The next day, my mother behaves as though nothing of any significance has occurred between us. Even when I walk by her to make my own breakfast, ignoring the one she has already prepared, she smiles and tries to chat me up. I refuse to acknowledge her. I eat in stony silence. Later, when she goes out to run errands, I grab the phone and call Moe. I tell him what has happened.

He tells me gently not to fight with my parents. He offers to come to my house to reason with them.

"Oh, please don't do that, Moe. They will be more mad than ever." The thought of him being *not of our kind* is bad enough. If they were to see him, they would be infuriated.

I tell him I will figure it out and call him when I do.

I also tell him about the plan I conjured up in my dreams last night about the tape recorder for his class. He likes the idea and says he will work on getting one. At least, we have done one thing that is productive.

I continue my stony silence routine for the entire week. Then abruptly, the hostilities end. My mother walks into my bedroom and announces that she and my father have discussed the idea of summer school and have agreed that I can go. However, she makes me promise not to see *that boy* again.

"I just don't know what I would do if anything happened between the two of you," she says in a low, sad, voice. "I don't know what I would do," she repeats.

I am overjoyed to hear that she has relented. I don't care about the terms. I will agree to anything, if only I can go back to where Moe is. I push the last of her words out of my mind even as I hear them. Everything is a catastrophe to my mother!

I leap to my feet and hug her hard. "Yeah!" I squeal. "Yeah. Thanks, Mom. Thanks," I blather. "I will make you proud."

"I don't want to be proud," she ventures slowly. "I just want you to promise me you won't see *that boy* again."

"Of course not, Mom. I promise." I lie, blatantly. What she asks is too ridiculous – too impossible.

When my mother goes for groceries later that day, I sneak another phone call to Moe.

"I'm coming. I'm coming – I'm coming back next week," I scream into his ear.

The excitement in his voice matches mine. "You come next week?" he asks, incredulously.

"Yes, next Monday."

"I meet you at our place by library at six o'clock?" he asks.

"Yes, Moe, by the library at six o'clock." Then I tell him what my mother said about never seeing him again, and I tell him I lied to her. I want him to know that nothing she says can keep me from being with him.

To my surprise, I hear him sigh and pause. "It is very bad to lie to your mother," he says in a quiet voice. "I am sorry that you lie to your mother. It is a bad thing."

 An Adobe Surprise

For the summer session, I have been assigned to live in Manzanita Hall. Getting settled this term is very different from my trip with my mother last September. My dad drives me to the campus, drops me and my bag off in front of the dorm, and says, "Looks nice, pumpkin. Have fun – and," he hesitates, "as your mother would say – *Be a good girl.*"

The minute I walk into Manzanita Hall, I know I will love it. It is a five-storey red brick building just around the corner from the canopy. How convenient is that? And – on the weekends, it has a midnight curfew. I sign in and proceed to my third floor room. I am next to the elevator so I don't have to lug my bags very far. I peek into the room. Comfortable looking twin beds sit up against each of the bright, slightly peachy walls on either side of the room. Matching desks sit like old friends, snuggled up against each other across the back wall. The matching closets are large and nearly walk-in size. The whole room looks newly painted and smells fresh.

I throw my bags on the bed to the right and plunk myself down beside them, breathing hard and realizing that the enforced bed rest of the past few months has taken its toll on my stamina. I am worn out. My roommate comes in. She is a sandy-blonde, cheery-looking, slender, young woman named Elaine. She is wearing jeans and a t-shirt.

Just as I am about to ask her *where are you from?* and *what classes are you in?* another young woman pokes her head in the door and asks in a very businesslike voice, "Which one of you is Susie?"

"I am," I answer.

"You have a gentleman caller downstairs," she mutters in a disgruntled voice. "He says he is going to wait at the desk until you come down. I told him he'd have to wait outside. Doesn't he know that no men are allowed in the dorm at this hour of the day? He's not very happy with me – but those are the rules."

"Oh, sorry about that," I reply. "He doesn't understand English very well and sometimes he gets confused."

"I figured that out – but he seems rather pushy," she adds. She turns and disappears.I turn to Elaine. "Guess that would be my boyfriend. Talk to you later. I better get downstairs or he'll be coming up here."

I find Moe pacing up and down at the front entrance. When he sees me, his whole body seems to come forward in greeting. Expecting a hug and a kiss, I walk toward him. Instead, he grabs my hand and starts to walk as fast as he can go, pulling me along behind him.

"Wait a minute!" I yell. "Where are you taking me?"

"I have surprise for you. Come on. Walk faster."

"I'm walking as fast as I can," I sputter. Running out of breath trying to keep up, I start to cough. "What's the rush?" I yank my hand out of his and stop. I take in deep breaths, grateful that I can do that, after the months of lying in bed too exhausted even to fill my lungs with air.

"I have surprise." He repeats, moving forward the minute he finishes speaking.

"You said that." I plant my feet firmly. "I am not going another inch until you tell me what is going on."

"I have surprise," he says once more. I look into his eyes and they are smiling.

"Okay, Moe, but for heaven's sake, slow down. I can't go that fast."

"Moe sorry. Just happy to see you and want you see surprise." Suddenly, he kisses me. Then, he pulls away and resumes walking, still holding my hand and pulling me along, a little more slowly this time, but still insistently.

At the edge of the campus where the university buildings give way to residences, Moe stops and tells me we have arrived. He

leads me to the door of a little white adobe house that is surrounded by other little white adobe houses that look exactly the
same. A sign on the lawn spells out in bold black and silver letters,
Catalina Apartments.

"This my surprise for you," he says, obviously delighted with
himself. "When you are gone," he hesitates, "I get my own house.
Come in. I show you."

I am stunned. I can only stammer, "Oh Moe, this must be
very expensive."

"Yes," he echoes, "Very expensive." Slowly, and with great
ceremony, he pulls out a key and unlocks the door and leads me
inside. The house has the musty smell that comes from being
closed up for a long time.

"Moe, did you rent this? There's no furniture."

"Moe know that," he says. "Mr. Landlord say he bring furniture in few days. There is bed. That is all I need right now." He
blushes.

He grabs me by the waist and pushes me through a small
arched doorway and into another room, obviously meant to be
the bedroom. The double bed, the only furniture in the house, is
covered with an incredibly beautiful, exotic-looking quilt made of
shiny red sateen intricately embroidered with delicate white and
yellow flowers and tiny birds intermingled with white Moorish
buildings.

"You like my bed cover?" Moe asks, reading my mind.

I nod. "It's very pretty." Then, I add. "Where did you get it?"

His eyes suddenly fill with tears. "It from my mother," he explains. "She made it when she young girl."

Not knowing what to say, I reach for his hand. He takes a
white handkerchief out of his pocket and wipes his eyes. After a
moment, he moves on to the next part of the tour.

"Look here." He rolls back a door to reveal a small kitchen.
Immediately, the whole counter top moves as cockroaches scurry
to get out of the sudden shaft of light coming through the open
door.

I hear Moe choke when he sees the bugs. "Oh, I not like that
bug. I not know it here."

He is so wretched, so disappointed. "Oh, no. I have bugs in this house," he mutters, unbelieving.

"Moe," I reassure him. "Every house in Arizona has bugs, some more than others. Tomorrow, we'll call the exterminator and get some good cleaning stuff. It'll be okay."

"No," Moe says, firmly, "My friends come to fix this house. They make promise." I glance at his face, wondering what he means, but I say nothing. I know he prefers to make the decisions.

Next, we look in the bathroom. It is dirtier than the kitchen, and reeks of urine and cats. No one has cleaned this little white adobe house for a very long time. Moe tells me again that his friends will fix it. I stay silent.

As we leave, Moe takes my hand, and looks at me, his other hand gently moving a strand of hair back from my face. He says sadly. "I want to make nice place for us."

My heart wells up. I can't help it. I lean toward him and give him a hug. "It's okay. It will all work out, Moe." I do my best to sound reassuring.

"Yes," he smiles and nods. "I tell you truth now, Sewzie. I no like lies, so I tell you truth. My friends rent this house for me. I only see one time before. My friends tell me they fix it for me. I think it be good surprise for you."

Why would Moe's friends rent a house for him? Maybe, they think it is better for him to have a place of his own where he can study. The more I think about it, the more I find it strange. At the same time, I imagine how it might be fun to have a private little place for us to come to. But, then I hear Julia's voice in my head, "Be careful of the brown boys." I look at Moe, with his eyes shining as he tells me how he wanted it to be a good surprise, and I decide I don't care if it seems strange. Moe is so protective of me. What could happen?

We have dinner at the cafeteria and then walk back to the canopy. I have missed him so much. I just want to touch him again.

Moe, however, is disconnected, and after a few attempts on

my part to be passionate with him, he sighs as if he is bored, and says, "You sit beside me this night. I tell you story of my father."

Bewildered and frustrated, I move to the opposite end of the bench. This is another surprise – and not a good one.

Before Moe begins the story, he pulls out a bundle of rolled up paper, spreads it out, and hands me a pencil.

"You listen and take notes," he orders. "Same like last time."

Moe walks me to the dorm in time for my midnight curfew. "Moe, I love your stories about your family." The stories aren't what I want to talk about, but I know that Moe doesn't like me to question his actions. He won't want to talk about why he pushed me away, why, after all the time we were apart, he doesn't want to have me close to him. "Thank you for sharing them. They are very special,"

Moe only nods and looks at the ground. "There are many more," he says. "I want to tell all my stories. We find time someday." He kisses me on the cheek, pats my hair and turns away.

I watch him disappear into the darkness at the end of the street before I turn and go into my dorm, wondering why our reunion has turned out to be nothing like my fantasies.

My days are spent finishing up last year's courses and studying the new material for this term. Moe and I continue to have dinner together, but he is distant and inattentive. He doesn't talk very much. I chalk it up to the heat. He complains about the hot Arizona sun every time we get together. When I ask him if he is worried about his classes, his answers are vague and short. I fall into silence, lest I upset him and he tells me *women not need to know everything,*

He doesn't mention his little adobe house, and when I ask him about it, all he says is that his friends *fix* it, and that he is living at Ahmed's until they do. He doesn't want to talk about that, either. Mostly, we walk around campus naming objects along the way or talking about his family and his country. He always kisses me when we get to my dorm, but they are not the kisses of passion that I love so much. In my heart, I feel something is very wrong.

Finally, one night, when we are sitting under the canopy and he has once again gently pushed me away from him to sit on the other end of the bench, I can't stand it any longer. I ask him straight out what is going on.

He looks at me as if from a far distance, as if he has just noticed that I am there with him. "I have trouble," he whispers. "I think I soon go away."

So, there it is. He is leaving. I stare at him, blind-sided. Tears slide down my cheeks. I make no attempt to hide them or to brush them away.

He looks at me, confused. "Why you cry? What I do?" he asks. "You have pain? You sick? What?"

I stare at him, wide-eyed, teary – and suddenly, I am angry that he doesn't get it. "What do you mean? Am I in pain? Am I sick? Of course, I am in pain! Of course, I am sick!" I blubber. "You are leaving. You are going away. You don't love me anymore."

"Oh no," he says frowning. "Not cry. Oh, I sorry you not understand me." He takes me in his arms and holds me.

I can't stop crying.

After a few minutes, he pushes me a little bit away from him. "I never see woman cry so much. In my country, women never cry except someone die. Oh, I so sorry. I not mean to make you so sad." He pats my head, he kisses my eyes and my tears, and I realize he is also crying.

"Come," he says, "Come home with me. We sit, we talk. I try to explain."

I wipe away my tears. To my surprise, he takes me to the little white adobe house. I expect the musty rank smell from before. When we enter, I am surprised. Gone is the musty smell, and when he turns on the light, I see that the little house has been transformed. The walls have been freshly painted and a large overstuffed chair and ottoman sit in the corner of the living room. There are pictures on the walls and a small TV on a little silver metallic stand sits in the corner. Books are stacked on the coffee table. A fuzzy white rug on the floor under the chair lends a cozy air to the room.

"You like?" he asks, smiling broadly.

"It's very nice," I sputter. "Wow. Did you do this by yourself, Moe?"

"No," he answers. "I tell you, friends *fix*."

"Oh," I repeat. "Friends *fix*. You have very nice friends."

"Yes, more than friends. We are brothers. In my culture, Arab brothers help each other. When I am in bad time, they help me. When they in bad time, I help them. It is our way."

I am beginning to understand how deep relationships between *friends* run in Moe's world. I know that I couldn't - wouldn't - ever expect that my friends would rent me a house and clean it thoroughly and furnish it for me. I vaguely wonder what the house has to do with the *bad time* that Moe is talking about. Clearly, there is a lot going on in Moe's life that I don't understand. Could things have changed while I was sick for two months at home? Or am I just more aware of things between us, and between him and his friends, now that we have had some time apart? Or – even worse – does his *bad time* have something to do with me and he just doesn't know how to tell me?

"Why did you tell me that you were living at Ahmed's?"

"I do live with Ahmed these days. I want to surprise you with house in few days –" He shrugs, "but now we here."

I turn back to examining the little house. The kitchen is now clean and has been painted. I can detect just the slightest lingering smell of pesticide in the air. The bathroom has been scrubbed till it is spotless. The beautiful exotic quilt is still on the bed, looking even more beautiful in its newly scrubbed surroundings. "It's beautiful," I gush. "Beautiful and clean," I reach out to touch the quilt, my fingers brushing the embroidery.

Moe smiles. He takes me by the hand and leads me into the living room. "Come and sit with me," he says. "Sit with me not crying. I not like woman to cry. I love you. Not cry."

He seats himself in the overstuffed chair and then pulls me down on his lap and I curl up like a puppy with his arms around me. I just know we will talk about why he is talking about leaving and we will sort it all out. Everything will be fine.

However, I soon find that Moe has no intention of talking. He kisses me hard and full on the mouth. His hands reach for my body. I feel his breath come harder.

I push at him to make him move away a little. "I'm afraid,"

I whisper. The words slip out of me, unbidden, but true. "I – I – What's going on?" I ask him, whispering, not wanting to trigger the anger that often lies hidden just below his surface.

His hands stop, and he opens his eyes to look into mine. "Why you are afraid? I not hurt you." His voice is soft, but has a determination that tells me he is not about to turn back from what he has in mind.

"I – I don't know," I whisper back, my eyes searching his for some reassurance that everything will really be okay. "I – I thought we were going to talk about why you're going away," I falter.

"We talk later," he says, firmly. He kisses me again and again until I cannot get my breath.

"Come to my bed," he whispers. "It comfortable there."

I let him lead me to the bedroom. As I am about to sit down on the edge of the bed, he reaches past me and pulls back the beautiful exotic quilt, tossing it to the floor. I glance down at the bed and staring back at me is a filthy mattress, stained red and black from countless years of other people's body fluids. I gasp.

"I can't," I sputter. "Please, Moe. Stop. I can't – I can't." The words tumble out one over another as I push against him. I don't want to have any contact with that soiled mattress.

As if he doesn't hear me, he holds me tightly and moves me closer to the bed. Something hard presses against my belly. I try to move away, to look down to see, but he is holding me too tightly. I hear his breathing in my ear.

"What are you doing?" I cry out. I try to wriggle free from his grip, but I can't move.

His breath is coming faster now. "It okay. I not hurt you," he moans. "It be okay."

Abruptly, with one quick movement, he grabs my shoulders and pushes me down onto the mattress. Down onto the dirty red and black stains. At first, I struggle to keep my body, even my clothing from touching them. But then, Moe lowers himself on top of me, forcing me to lay back on the bed. I try to push away from him.

"No, please, Moe, don't. I can't. I'm scared. Please stop." I am crying again. "Please stop."

"I not hurt you – I promise," he murmurs, his breath now coming in short gasps. "I promise." He pushes against me again and as he does, he reaches under my skirt, grabs my underpants and rips them away from my body. Roughly, he pushes my skirt up around my waist, then stops, unbuttons and unzips it and yanks it down past my knees and over my feet. He reaches for my blouse and in one movement pulls it over my head. Holding me with his body, he reaches behind me and undoes my bra. Skirt, blouse and bra land on the floor next to the quilt.

I gasp, and sob loudly. "No, Moe. No. No."

He forces his legs between mine and pushes my legs apart. He is breathing as if he is working hard, and he seems unaware that I am crying, that I am struggling, that I am even there. He fiddles with his hand down there and then pushes his body hard against mine. I feel the hard thing, the thing I felt earlier against my belly, enter my body, suddenly and sharply. I hear Moe moan, and then hear myself cry out as the pain of something tearing reaches my senses. The rush of something warm and heavy enters my body. Then, beyond all of the feelings of weight and pain, I hear, disconnected from me, as if it comes from a long ways away, the sound of someone screaming.

I hear Moe's authoritative voice. "Stop screaming," he says. "The neighbours hear you. They think I kill you. You want trouble?"

The screaming stops. He rolls his body off mine. My body begins to shake.

The authoritative voice says, "Get up and clean yourself. You make mattress dirty. Moe be in trouble with Mr. Landlord. He see this big mess. How I clean this? Why you not tell me you in your blood time?" Moe covers himself with his clothing, and standing next to the bed, points to where fresh new blood stands out against the faded dark stains on the mattress.

"What? Blood time? Oh my god, are you stupid? I'm not in my blood time," My voice is shaky. I struggle to make sense of what he is saying. "You made me bleed."

My teeth chatter and my body shakes uncontrollably. "You

said you wouldn't hurt me." I say this over and over again, unable to believe that my gentle Moe could have done any of this.

Then, briefly, anger takes over and I lash out at him. "Are you happy now? You got what you wanted." That spent, I slip back into the devastating shock. I pull my legs up against my chest, shaking so hard I can hear my teeth chatter, and sob hysterically.

I feel Moe sit down beside me on the bed. He has put his pants back on and the fabric brushes against my feet. I pull them closer so that I don't have to touch him. I try to stop my crying to look into his face.

Moe stares at me in stunned silence. "Oh, Allah," he says. "You are virgin. No, it cannot be. No, no," he keeps saying. "My friends tell me there are no American girl virgins at this age. You are virgin. Oh, Allah. What have I done?" he repeats.

"What do you mean your friends tell you there are no American girl virgins?" I scream at him. "You have stupid friends." I push him away and wrap my arms around my knees. "You don't love me. You just wanted to do that to me. My friends are right. You are bad, all you brown boys are bad – horrible!" I cry some more.

"No, no, please, not cry. I not bad man. I so sorry. I thought you have other boyfriends before me. Moe is biggest fool. Moe, poor Moe, now he in big trouble." Moe turns toward me and then away from me, unsure about whether he should stay or flee.

I slowly work my way to the edge of the bed and stand up. I am still shaking. Moe brings me a towel and, taking my arm, gently leads me to the bathroom. I close the door in his face and hobble over to sit on the edge of the tub. My body aches all over. What my mother always calls *down there* feels raw and battered. I am afraid to stand up, afraid to move.

I hear a quiet knock.

"What do you want, Moe?" I snarl.

"I have clothes," he answers in a tiny voice.

I open the door, take my clothes and close the door. After a long while, I gingerly pat myself *down there* with a facecloth. Then, slowly, carefully, I dress myself, fumbling with clasps and zippers as if my clothes don't belong to me.

When I open the bathroom door, I find Moe standing there,

staring. He takes me in his arms and rocks me back and forth like a baby. I have no strength, no will to protest. The emptiness is complete. It has taken over my body. It doesn't matter what happens now to the shell that is left.

"I so sorry," Moe repeats, again and again. "I not know. I thought you want to. I not believe you are virgin."

"Well," I choke out. "I'm not a virgin anymore." My voice is flat.

"No, you not virgin now," he says. "Moe did bad thing. I love you. I not leave you. I promise."

Void of feelings or thoughts, I look at him. He is a stranger. The gentle Moe that I thought I knew so well is gone.

For a long time, I sit in the overstuffed chair, crying intermittently, and Moe paces the length of the living room. Neither of us speak. We have no words that can bridge the chasm between us. I wrap my arms around my body and clench my jaws together to stop the shivering that has invaded me. But, I can't. After a while, I see that darkness has fallen, and eventually I stand up and move toward the door. Moe opens it for me to go out. He turns off the light and closes the door. The little white adobe house disappears behind us in the dark as we walk down the sidewalk.

In silence, we walk side by side across the quiet campus, past the canopy, to the dorm.

"I see you tomorrow, okay?" he asks gently.

"I guess so," I sigh. "I guess so." I have no idea if I will see him tomorrow or not. I simply say what seems to be required of me. I have nothing left inside.

I turn away from Moe and go in. I take the stairs to my room, pulling myself up each step. My body aches. I feel like a broken doll. What have I done? Julia's words haunt me, "Those brown boys are bad news. They will go back to their own country, never to be seen or heard from again." Moe promised he wouldn't leave me. But, Moe's promises don't offer me any comfort or assurance at all.

I feel torn. Not just physically. But torn out of my life, torn apart in my emotions, torn up about what to feel or think about Moe. I spend the night curled up in a foetal position, with my head under the blankets so Elaine won't hear me. I cry on and off till early morning, not wrenching sobbing, just tears that flow unbidden and beyond my control. My thoughts and emotions bounce back and forth. One minute, I am afraid that Moe will not like me anymore. The next minute, I relive how I kept telling him no and how I struggled and pushed against him, but he just overpowered me entirely. I remember the shock and the pain and I feel so undone, so frail.

The next day Moe, unkempt and wrinkled, is at my dorm at the usual time to take me to dinner. "I not sleep last night," he says. "Moe not know what to say."

I don't know what to say either. Julia and my mother take over my mind. "Those brown boys are bad news. Bad. News." and "If you allow boys to touch you, before you get married, they won't want to marry you." I now understand what my mother meant by *touch* and I have a clear idea of what *bad news* Julia was talking about.

Moe stands in front of me, waiting for me to speak or move. I start to walk and he falls in beside me, not touching me, not hurrying me. Following our long-established pattern, our feet take us to the cafeteria and we make our way down the food line, putting dishes onto our trays, but not paying any attention to what we have selected. I pay for my own dinner. Moe pays for his and sits down opposite me at a table near the back. We don't see any of the other students who are there. We eat, but we do not talk. When I push back my chair and stand up to leave, Moe does the same.

As we arrive back at my dorm, he puts his hand gently on my arm, leans forward and says, "Please not tell what I do. Moe get in big trouble if the government find out. Please." He looks so sad, so wretched. None of the authoritarian Moe is there.

I sigh. "Okay, Moe, I won't tell anyone." It doesn't matter anyway. The government can't fix what has happened. No one can change things back to the way they were. I turn to walk away, wondering why the government would care.

He pulls me back to face him.

I let him. It doesn't matter anymore what happens to me. I can't be hurt or frightened any worse than I am.

Moe holds my hand tightly for a moment and looks into my eyes. He gently kisses me on the cheek. "We are so different," he whispers. "We are so different. If I take you to my country – you must bend like willow tree – or you break. Maybe, someday, if you learn to be like willow, I take you there."

He leaves me. I stand there, looking after him as he walks quietly away into the night. What does *bend like willow tree* mean? Where did he get the word *willow*? It is not one I taught him. I glance at the sky. It is about to rain, unusual for Arizona at this time of year. I am about to cry.

Over the next few days we meet, as we did before anything happened between us. We meet for dinner and a walk. Conversation slowly starts up again. I teach Moe a few more words. He learns them, seriously, as if that will mend things between us. We don't go to the canopy. We don't return to the little white adobe house. When I ask him if he lives in the little adobe house, he tells me no. He has decided to stay with Ahmed.

A few more days, and we return to the canopy, but now it is reserved for a few gentle kisses and the rest of the stories that Moe wants to tell me. No matter what happens between us, I will always have his stories.

 Moe's Most Best Day

It is the last day of summer school, classes are over and I wait for Moe to pick me up for our final supper together before I move back home for the semester break. I stand at the top of the dorm staircase and look out over the campus.

Suddenly, there he is. His gait and the confident way he is holding himself tells me he is happy and has something positive on his mind. He is smiling as he approaches the bottom of the stairs. I look at him and hope that his good mood will rub off on me.

Since our episode in the adobe house, both of us struggle to re-establish some kind of communication. Moe is afraid to even hold my hand. I feel both sadness and relief at his distance. The physical pain of that afternoon has subsided, but I am no longer sure where I fit in his life. Over and over, I hear a voice in my head asking, "What if he isn't here when I return for fall classes?" I can't bear the thought of him leaving me.

Moe leaps up the stairs in one bound, startling me out of my thoughts.

"I think you are thinking big thoughts," he whispers affectionately in my ear.

"Oh, yes. I guess I am thinking big thoughts, Moe. You look really good today, and happy. What's happening?"

"I have surprise for you," he answers, smiling, somehow not noticing that he uses the same words as he did when we went to the adobe house.

I wince inwardly and choose to focus on what Moe is saying now, refusing to acknowledge the images that crowd the edges of my thoughts.

"We go to fancy restaurant," he continues. "You order what you want and we have big celebration."

"Celebration? For what?" I ask, surprised that Moe wants to eat in an expensive restaurant. He doesn't have money to spend. He always goes to great lengths to find the cheapest food in the cafeteria and often belabours the fact that he sometimes has to pay more than ten cents for a cup of coffee.

"Today, it is my most best day," he says proudly. "I am happy man."

Again, I choose to focus on this day and not on whether his *most best day* might mean that he is going back to Algeria and leaving me behind. We have never talked about his dire announcement that he was leaving – the announcement we were supposed to talk about in the adobe house – before – before everything happened.

"What?" I ask again. "It's clear you're happy. Tell me what makes you so happy."

"Oh, I tell you," he says, "but Moe so happy he cannot talk right now. We go for supper. I tell you then. Oh, and you wear shoes I give you. Your beautiful shoes. Moe like that. Okay?"

He says *okay* as if he is asking – but I know that he means for me to do as he says.

"Go now and put on nice pretty dress. We have celebration." He shoos me off.

I leave him smiling on the steps, winking at me like a child with a new secret.

I change into the prettiest dress I have and stuff my feet into the beautiful tan shoes, hoping his celebration doesn't involve walking very far. I look in the mirror and run a comb through my hair.

I could use some makeup, but Moe hates it. "Make-up is for whore women," he always tells me. "Do you want to be whore woman?"

"No, of course I don't want to be *whore woman*." Ever since he told me this, I hear his question in my head every time I see my girl-friends wearing make-up. I want to shake my head self-righteously and point my finger at them while slowly asking, "Do you want to be whore woman?" Moe will never know, but I always laugh inside when he says *whore woman*.

As quickly as I can in my heels, I run down to meet him. A taxi pulls up and out of it steps Ahmed. "Hello," he calls, a grin covering his entire face. "Your chariot awaits." He bows, indicating that we should get into the taxi.

"What in the world is going on?" I ask, shocked by the extravagance of a taxi. "Are *you* going to tell me what's happening, Ahmed?"

"Ah no, Susie, I am not. This is Mohamed's party and I will let him tell you. I can say, however, it is very, very exciting and important for Mohamed."

Moe smiles, nods and puts one finger over his lips. "Secret," he whispers, as he ushers me into the back seat of the taxi. Ahmed jumps into the front and we are on our way.

After a twenty minute taxi ride, we arrive at the restaurant. Moe and Ahmed have outdone themselves. It is one of the best eating places in Tucson – and the most expensive. I feel like an escorted princess in my fancy shoes and pretty dress. The *maitre d'* seats us at a lovely table by a large window where the chairs have thick plush padding and the tables are covered with beautiful beige linen cloths adorned with crystal glasses and china plates, all in perfect symmetry, reminding me of the tables my mother sets when entertaining for my father.

Moe seats himself across the table from me and smiles. The waiter asks what we would like to drink.

"Ice tea for everyone," Moe says, without asking what anyone would like. "Ice tea, please," he repeats.

Ahmed nods his approval. "Yes, ice tea is good."

I have had enough of the mystery. "Okay, Moe, what is going on? I can't wait any more. Please tell me what is happening."

Tears form in Moe's dark eyes. He gathers in his breath and then blurts out, "I have found my family. After seven years, I receive letter from my cousin in Tunisia. He went inside Mascara, the town of my birthday, few weeks ago and talks to them all. Now, he back outside Algeria and he sends me letter. They are all okay, except for Tahar, my first brother. The FLN (how you say –

National Liberation Front) cut his throat and leave him to die, but French find him and fix him. He is alive. My cousin tells me war is over and everyone goes home. He says my father will send me letter soon." As Moe speaks and tears stream down his cheeks, he smiles a smile larger than I have ever seen.

I reach across the table and take his hand. "I am so happy for you, Moe. This is truly a day of celebration for you."

"There is more. Tomorrow, we make a parade down the streets of Tucson. It is parade to celebrate the end of war in Algeria. I not believe that it will happen even here in this American city but my African friends have permit to drive down streets and carry Algerian flag. We all go in it. It is wonderful thing." He pauses suddenly and then asks, "You will come with me, no?"

"Me?" I ask. I haven't quite taken in all of the information yet.

"Yes, Sewzi. You. I want you to go with me inside the parade. It is a good day for us."

The waiter is waiting to take our order. Before I can say anything, Moe orders swordfish and potatoes. He doesn't ask if it is what I want, he just gives the order. I say nothing. It is his special day.

Moe and Ahmed spend the time eating and talking. Mostly, they speak in Arabic. I am glad because I feel light-headed, and I have trouble eating the swordfish. As lovely as it is, the smell is overwhelming. Early in the meal, it smells like normal fish, but, later in the meal, it smells like fish gone bad. The farther into the meal we go, the more rancid the smell.

Suddenly, I stand up, looking around wildly for the restroom. I see the signs at the back of the restaurant and head in that direction as quickly as I can. Thank goodness it is empty. I lose what supper I have eaten, and splash my face with cool water. I start to feel better. I hope the fish isn't bad. I hope I don't have the flu. Either of those would ruin Moe's parade.

When I return to the table, Moe frowns at me and blurts out in his authoritative voice, "Are you sick? You not eat your expensive meal. You waste." His voice is very loud and a few people turn and look at us. Ahmed murmurs something to him in Arabic. Moe lowers his voice and says, "You don't like the fish?"

"It's fine," I lie. It is his celebration and I don't want to ruin it. "I am not very hungry," I say, hoping he will accept my explanation. I usually like fish, but today it just doesn't taste right. Moe frowns again, but says nothing. He resumes his conversation with Ahmed while I sit, trying to ignore the rancid smell from the fish left on my plate. The waiter appears and removes my plate. I silently thank god. Moe orders dessert for himself and Ahmed. He doesn't ask me if I want any and he doesn't talk to me again. I assume that he and Ahmed are making plans for tomorrow's parade.

It feels like a long time before we are again in the taxi and on our way back to the campus. In the dark I sit silently watching the lights pass by. I really don't feel well. We pull up to my dorm, and Moe jumps out and opens the door for me. He tells Ahmed to go home and he will come later. He takes my hand.

"Are you still being sick?" he asks, gently.

"I'm okay," I lie again. "I just feel funny, that's all. Probably, just a bug of some sort."

"We go to canopy?" he asks.

"Moe, no. I really need to sleep," I say, feeling truly sorry.

"That okay," he says. "Moe tired, too."

He kisses me lightly on the cheek and walks away. I climb wearily up the stairs. The nausea is starting to subside. I lie down and think back over the evening. Moe has a difficult time when I don't feel well. He frowns and sometimes he gets angry. I fall asleep wondering if this irritation of his is another cultural thing.

The next morning I don't want to get out of bed. I wake up, but I just turn over and pull the covers up over my head to shut out the light. By the time I look at the clock again, it is already ten o'clock. I remember the plans for the parade. Moe is picking me up at 10:30 to celebrate the end of the French Algerian war. Along with the other Arab students, Moe and I are going to motor down the streets of Tucson waving Algerian flags and honking horns. Later, my mother is picking me up and moving my stuff back home until the semester starts in September.

I swing my feet over the side of my bed and stand up, only to feel suddenly dizzy and sick to my stomach. I breathe in, hold my breath, and run for the washroom. Oh no, I think, that fish is still bothering me. Yuck.

After vomiting, I wash my face in cold water and get in the shower, letting the water run full force over my body. When I step out onto the cool tiles, I am feeling better and I make my way back to my room.

I am ready to meet Moe exactly at 10:30. He arrives in a rented white 1960 Chevrolet convertible with the top down. Ahmed is driving and they are both grinning from ear to ear. Ahmed smiles at me.

"Nice car," I tell him.

"Yes," nods Ahmed. "Nice car."

Moe chimes in, "If this my car, I not be shy anymore."

I look at him, remembering that he told me he was shy when we first met. "What do you mean by *not shy anymore?*" I ask, as he opens the door and I slip into the rich-looking, but fake, leather seats.

"You know. If I had this car, I not be *shy.*"

"Moe I don't know what you are talking about. What does a car have to do with being shy?"

Moe clearly doesn't understand what I am saying. Ahmed looks away from me and says something to Moe in Arabic. Moe responds in the same language and suddenly Ahmed bursts out laughing. He laughs so hard that he has to stop the car to catch his breath.

"What?" Moe and I ask at the same time.

It takes Ahmed a few minutes to stop laughing and settle down enough to explain. Slowly, he gets himself together and begins. "This is a very funny story." He goes into spasms of laughter again. "A long time ago when Mohamed first came to live with us in our house, we would laugh at him because his English was so bad. We liked to play jokes on him all the time and tell him that certain English words mean different things than they really do. We did it just to tease him. Pretty soon we realized that he believed us all the time and we decided we shouldn't do that anymore. He still thinks that being *shy* means *he doesn't have a car.*" Ahmed bursts into laughter again.

"Well," I tell Moe. "That answers one question for me. I always wondered what you meant when you first talked to me. The first thing you said was *Hi, I'm Moe and I'm shy.* You didn't mean you were *shy* at all. You meant you didn't have a car."

Moe looks at both of us. "My friends are very bad to me. They tell me American girls only like boys with cars."

"You really should stop listening to your friends, Moe. They get you into too much trouble." I sigh, trying to block out just how much trouble.

We drive off and spend the next few hours waving to the people of Tucson who really have no idea who we are or what we are doing. We honk and smile and they wave back at us. If the size of his smile is any indication, it all makes Moe very happy.

Finally, at two in the afternoon, Ahmed pulls into the parking lot of the dorm. I climb out, hungry, tired and not feeling at all ready to move my belongings out of the dorm. But my mother will arrive in an hour to take me home for the rest of the summer. Moe tumbles out of the back seat after me and we stand looking into each other's eyes for a moment.

"I have to go and pack now, Moe. I'll be back in a couple of weeks to start school. What are you going to do while I'm away?" I ask, curious.

"I go with my host family to Grand Canyon," he answers, smugly. "I think it will be good time." He pulls me close and kisses me on each cheek. "Good bye, Sewsi, I will see you someday."

"Someday?" I ask. The panic begins to rise inside. Moe is going to leave me, after all. He just hasn't told me.

"Yes," he answers, "Someday – in two weeks."

Relieved, I laugh. Will Moe ever get the language right?

The weeks at home in Ft. Huachuca are uneventful. Out of habit, I avoid my parents as much as possible. They seem too busy to worry about me anyway, my father involved in his work and my mother in her Red Cross volunteering.

I am tired most of the time. I go to bed early and I sleep in every morning till just before noon. The day before school starts,

I pack my things and carry them downstairs. As I come down the stairs to leave, my mother looks up at me, and says in her concerned voice, "You look like you don't feel well."

"I'm okay," I lie, as much out of habit as anything. "I'm just a little tired."

When I reach the bottom step, she reaches out and touches my face gently. "You don't seem to have a fever," she announces. "You don't feel particularly hot."

I brush by her quickly and pick up my packed bags. "I'm fine, Mom. I'm fine."

"You look funny," she adds. "I hope you're not getting that Valley Fever thing again."

I take my bags to the car and she follows. Surprisingly, the drive back to school is nearly silent. I am able to put my head back on the seat and close my eyes. My thoughts echo my mother's words. I hope it isn't the Valley Fever thing again.

Before I know it, we arrive at my dorm. Manzanita, the same one I had for the summer. I am glad. I like it here. My mother says good-bye at the car and drives off.

I am surprised that she isn't trying to interfere in my life, but I also feel a tinge of sadness at being abandoned. Oh well. Maybe, she understands that I am grown up now.

I check into the dorm and make my way to my new room, this time on the fourth floor. I spend some time unpacking and hanging up clothes.

Just as I finish, I hear my name called over the loud speaker. "Phone call for Susan Glasier. Susan Glasier, please pick up the yellow phone by the elevator."

I find the phone and pick it up.

"Hello, Sewzi," booms a familiar voice. "How are you?"

"Fine," I whisper. I feel like the whole campus can hear him.

"I come to get you now, okay?"

"I am really tired, Moe, and I don't feel very well."

"It's okay, Sewzi. You feel fine when you see Moe. Okay?"

"Okay," I concede, though I am really more interested in sleep than in Moe right now.

He arrives in the dorm waiting room smiling and relaxed. He

takes my hand and leads me out into the evening air and away from the building. He turns and faces me and takes me in his arms. Several students walking by stare at us, but I don't care.

"You miss me?" he asks, gently lifting my chin so I am looking into his eyes.

"Of course," I say, "I just haven't felt well lately." We turn and walk to our spot under the canopy. We sit down side by side and Moe turns toward me.

"Maybe you are still having your fever?" he offers. His eyes search my face for some sign of what might be wrong.

"Maybe." I drop my arms from his shoulders. They are just too heavy to hold up.

He says nothing for a few minutes and then he coughs, nervously. "I ask you question?"

"What is it, Moe?" I ask. I shift so I can see his face. His eyebrows are drawn together and he looks down at me sternly. He is worried.

"Does your mother tell you about women's things?" The words come out softly, as if he is speaking about a forbidden subject.

Not sure that I hear him correctly, I repeat what he says. "Does my mother tell me about what *women's things?*"

"Women's things. You know," he stumbles on. "Does she talk to you about bleeding, about babies? You know, about woman's things."

"Uh, I guess so. Why?" I can't think why he is bringing up that subject.

"I not understand American ways," Moe continues. "You people have movies about sex. You let young girls go by themselves with any man they see." He shakes his head. "But, I don't think your mother did very good job warning you, telling you the big dangers of men. In my country, all mothers tell their daughters not to talk to man of any age because every man have penis." He is still shaking his head.

I am shocked to hear him actually say the word *penis*. I doubt I have ever heard anyone use that word out loud before. "What? What are you trying to say?"

Moe continues as if I hadn't spoken. "In my country, mother

pick son's wife. Mothers know if girl is good girl or bad. Mother look at her teeth, at her body and make sure she is good for having child, and that she is nice and gentle woman that will obey her husband. Then mother tell son about girl and he will say yes or no to marry her. Then, man meet girl's father and talk. It is good way."

"But Moe," I interrupt. "What about love?"

"Love come later. Doesn't matter." Moe shrugs his shoulders.

My tiredness and the strangeness of this conversation push against one another inside me. "What do you mean, *it doesn't matter?* I love you. Are you saying it doesn't matter?"

Moe shrugs his shoulders, "I not know. I am sometimes sorry I come here. I don't understand anything about these customs. I not know about love."

In the darkness of the canopy, sadness comes over me. Tears well up and trickle down my face. I have no words. I sit there crying, not even moving to wipe away the tears.

Moe tries to wipe them away with his fingers. "Oh, I sorry, Sewsi, I am one confused Moe. I not believe how much you cry. I am bad man to make you cry."

I realize that I am confusing Moe with my tears, and I make an effort to stop them. "No, you are not a bad man, Moe." I fall back on my old excuse of fatigue. "I'm not feeling well. Maybe it's because I haven't had my period since the middle of August."

"Period? What is this period?" Moe asks, taking me by the shoulders and looking hard at me.

"You know period, Moe. You once called it my blood time, remember?" I fall into the teach-Moe-English mode, doing my best to help him learn a new word.

Even in the darkness of the canopy and even with the darkness of his skin, I can see his face turn a deep red. Moe's mouth slowly opens and then slowly closes. "Oh my god," he whispers, "Moe now dead for sure."

"What do you mean?" I ask, caught off guard by his reaction. What is he thinking? Is he mad that I told him I haven't had a period for two and a half months? Why is he so upset?

"Oh god," he keeps saying over and over again, talking as if I am not even there next to him. Finally, he is quiet and turns to look at me, his eyes blazing. He asks angrily, "Oh girl, are you so stupid?"

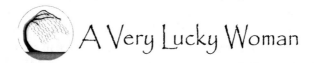 A Very Lucky Woman

"You need to go to doctor." Moe's voice is hard and cold.

"Why? I'm not that sick." My voice comes out defensive and confused.

Moe shakes his head back and forth. Even in the darkness, I can see his eyes flash. "You are stupid, stupid, stupid girl. You are pregnant," he shouts. "You have baby. You have baby and Moe have death. Moe in big trouble now."

My world stops and then begins to spin. It cannot be. Being pregnant has never crossed my mind. We haven't done anything – nothing but that night in the adobe house. Oh, no. Was that enough to make me pregnant? My mind reels. I suddenly realize what my mother meant when she told me to be a *good girl*. Getting pregnant is something that doesn't happen to *good girls*. Moe thinks *he* is in big trouble. What about *me*? My parents will kill me!

"You go to doctor soon," he says in his authoritative voice. "Tomorrow."

"But – but – I don't know any doctors," I stammer, tears spilling out again. "I don't know any doctors."

"You find," he commands. "Soon. It important."

I am scared. I can't understand why Moe is so angry at me. He has become a stranger again. I start to sob.

"Please not cry," he says in a gentler voice. "Crying is for babies, not for woman. You are woman now. Tomorrow you find doctor. I go with you."

Moe looks at his watch. "It time to go back to dorm," he says.

We walk in silence back to the dorm. Moe doesn't kiss me, doesn't touch me. He just turns and leaves me at the door.

I toss and turn all night. The next morning, I am nauseated and light headed – and terrified. I stumble out of bed, throw on a t-shirt and some sweat pants and go down the hall to the telephone. I look through the phone book. ...Gynaecologists.... I read the list of names and one pops out. Dr. Bryson. It sounds familiar. I think he is the doctor my mother had for her hysterectomy a few years ago. Do gynaecologists know about babies? Moe is right. I am so stupid, stupid, stupid. I look around to see if anyone is within listening range and then I dial the number in the book.

A cheerful woman's voice answers, "Good morning, Dr. Bryson, Mason and Young's Office. How may I help you?"

I stumble on my words, trying to ask for an appointment.

"I'm sorry, Miss," the voice interrupts, "but you have to have a referral from your family doctor to see Dr. Bryson."

"Oh, I see. I – I don't have a family doctor." I start to cry. I can't help it. Nothing is going right. I feel sick. The thought of going to see any doctor is overwhelming. I sob into the phone.

"Honey," the nice voice on the other end of the line says. "What's your situation? You tell me all about it and I'll tell you who to see. Okay?"

I pour out my whole story. The nurse listens sympathetically and makes an appointment for me on Thursday.

I hang up the phone, go back to my room and cry myself to sleep. Later in the afternoon, I awake to my roommate shaking me. "Hey, Susie, you've got a visitor down stairs in the waiting room. Are you okay?"

"Yeah, just tired," I tell her. That lie seems to cover everything. I pull myself out of bed, change my clothes and go downstairs. As the elevator doors open, I see Moe standing there waiting. I can clearly see that he is very angry. Moe's voice is cold and hard and the words slam into me as he demands to know why I didn't go to class or meet him as usual.

I explain that I spent the day in bed and add that I made an appointment to see a doctor.

Moe looks surprised, and then relieved. "Oh, Moe very

happy." He puts his arm around me and guides me out onto the sidewalk. "We go for walk and have dinner." The anger seems to have disappeared.

We head toward the cafeteria.

On Thursday, Moe and I arrive at the doctor's office a few minutes before 9:00. Moe pays the taxi driver and we walk down a pathway that winds through a forest of saguaro.

"I like cactus," says Moe. "I mean I like word *cactus*. It a funny word. Another funny word you have in English is *zip*. In Arabic, *zippy* means *penis*." He laughs.

I am on my way to find out if I am pregnant and Moe is making jokes, jokes about *penises*. "Moe, I don't think that's very funny."

"Why?" he asks. "English very funny language. You should laugh more."

"I don't want to laugh more, Moe. I want to cry."

"No, no, please no cry, Sewsi. It hurts my heart to see you cry. We fix this –" he pauses, "this – this thing."

I look at him. I don't know him. One minute I love him and the next, I don't understand who he is. What does he mean *we will fix this thing*? It is not a *thing*. Oh god, please don't let there be a *thing*.

We arrive at the office door. We enter to find ourselves in front of a high, dark mahogany counter. The nurse behind it looks up. "Uh, you are –?" she asks in a no-nonsense voice.

"Susan Glasier," I whisper.

"Oh," her voice changes to the gentle one I remember from the phone. "Yes," she adds, "Just have a seat and the doctor will be with you right away."

She looks at Moe and frowns. "Are you with her?" she nods in my direction.

"Yes," Moe answers.

"Oh," she says, "just sit over there. You will have to wait for her here. The doctor doesn't like anyone but the patient in the office with him. Do you understand?" I notice that her voice is crisp and impatient, not the gentle one she used with me.

"I understand," Moe responds as he pulls his thick brows together in a nasty frown.

We sit down on thick comfortable cushiony seats and I look around at the richness of the office. Magazines like *Time* and *National Geographic* and the *Saturday Evening Post* lie side by side on real wooden tables. Dr. Bryson obviously caters to a rich clientele. It is a place my mother would like.

"I not like that nurse," Moe whispers as he moves closer to me on the fancy sofa.

"It's okay. I don't like anything about any of this either."

The nurse appears. "You can come with me now, Miss Glasier. This way, please." She winds her way down the hall. "Take off all your clothes," she says in the examining room. Then, she points to a pile of blue cotton sitting neatly folded on the examining table. "Put a robe on and climb up on the table. The doctor will be in shortly."

I do as I am told, finding the blue cotton robe is made for a person three sizes smaller than my generous frame. As I sit myself on the table, I hear the door open behind me and I turn to come face to face with a good-looking, tall, suntanned, graying older man. He smiles and takes a seat on the little swivel stool at the end of the table.

"Well, honey. My nurse tells me we have a situation here. What's the story?"

I pull the thin cotton robe down over my knees as far as I can. Pulling it down in front causes the opening in the back to widen. I feel a cold wetness form on my back as I sit there, scared to death that I might be pregnant, and overwhelmed by a man that I have never seen before who wants to know everything. Before the image of the adobe house can even fully form, I push it out of my mind. I think about telling him about how gentle and caring Moe can be, but I know he won't understand. He will only see that Moe is responsible for what has happened to me. I can't find any words. I don't know what to say. I sit there looking at him, and the tears run down my cheeks and make dark wet spots on the thin blue gown. I don't even move to wipe them away.

The doctor says nothing, but he looks at me as though he has all the time in the world. Finally, he reaches for a box of tissues. He holds them out to me and offers, "I see by the notes from my nurse that your mother is a patient of mine. Is that why you are here?"

I nod. "Yes – I mean no. I'm here because I might be – might be –"

"Pregnant?" he offers.

I nod. I take tissue after tissue and wipe my eyes. They are so small that they pretty well disintegrate when they touch the wetness of my face. I try to blow my nose discreetly. I wad up the used tissues and hold them in my hand.

"Well, did you have sex?" he asks directly.

"I – think so," I respond, shaken by his question. Images of Moe and the adobe house fill my head.

"You think so? Does that mean you don't know if you had sex?" His voice is low and matter-of-fact. He doesn't seem surprised by my response. He has had this sort of conversation before.

"I – I – don't know." I stammer. "I think I did, but only once."

He laughs, a short harsh laugh. "Well, honey, don't ya know that it only takes once?" With that, he stands up from the stool and moves toward me. In a business-like tone, he says, "Let's see what we can find out. Lay down on the table and put your feet in the stirrups."

I sit frozen. I try to move, but I can't. The tears take over again, and I reach for the tissue box that I have set down on the examining table beside me. I pull out a handful and try to stop the flow.

"Have you never had an internal before?" He looks at me kindly.

"N – no," I stammer, my voice shaking. The skin on the back of my legs has stuck to the plastic of the examining table. I want to run away, but I am glued in place.

"Okay," he sighs. He turns toward the door, and over his shoulder he tells me he is going to get his nurse to help me.

He walks out, and I burst into fresh tears. Chilled to the bone in the thin blue gown, I want to die. Nobody told me about this. Nobody told me anything.

The door opens and a young woman in a white uniform enters. "Honey, it's okay. So, this is a new experience for you. Don't worry. It doesn't hurt and it will all be over in a minute. I'll stay right here with you and you'll be fine." Her voice is soothing and she moves easily about the room, taking the tissue box from my hand, giving me fresh ones, and holding out the small white trash can so I can deposit the soggy mess I have in my other hand.

She shows me where to put my feet and legs and how to lie on the cold hard table. She stands beside me and holds my hands for a minute. Her hands are warm and they gently massage my fingers. My stomach muscles loosen a little. When she sees that I have stopped crying, and have some degree of control, she asks, "Now, are you ready to get this over with?"

I nod slowly.

She pushes a button, and in a few seconds the doctor enters. She returns to stand at my side, smiling at me, and holding my hands on my stomach. Dr. Bryson pulls back the sheet and tells me to drop my knees and relax. I start to cry again. I hate what is happening to me.

In a few minutes, it is all over and the doctor pats my hand, "Well, honey, that's all. Now you just get dressed and we'll have a little talk, okay?"

The nurse helps me off the table and hands me my clothes. She leaves the room. Tears slide down my face. I dress as quickly as I can and stand in the middle of the room unable to bring myself to sit down anywhere. I want to get out of here.

The nurse returns and leads me to the office where the doctor is writing on my chart. I sit for several minutes before he looks up.

"Well," he begins, "as far as I can tell you are most likely pregnant. The uterus is a bit swollen and there are other signs." He glances down at his notes. "But," he continues, "we can't be positive until we take a urine test and wait a few days. It's called a rabbit test. We don't actually use rabbits but that's another story. So that information will be forthcoming. I think you can be pretty confident that you are going to have a baby." He drops his pen onto the paper and turns to fully face me. "Now, I understand you don't have a husband. Is that correct?"

I nod.

The doctor ploughs on. I am not sure if he even really noticed my response. "So – what about the baby's father? Will he help you out – or are you on your own?"

The baby's father – I can't get used to the idea that there is – that there will be – a baby. "I don't know," I mumble. "I – I have a boyfriend." I remember when Moe asked me to be his girl-friend, and how pleased he was when I agreed. I wonder if he ever thought he would be in this situation. I wonder if I am a *whore woman* now. Irrationally, I think – wearing makeup or not wear-ing makeup had nothing to do with it.

I focus on Dr. Bryson's voice again. He is saying, "Well, I sug-gest you talk to him about what he plans to do about this. Does he have a job?"

"No, he's a student." What does it matter whether he has a job or not?

"How do you expect to pay for the delivery?" Dr. Bryson picks up his pen and idly plays with it as he speaks.

I stare, stunned, "Pay for the delivery?" I ask incredulously. I have no money. My parents pay for everything.

"Yes. I charge $1,500.00 for the delivery. That includes all your prenatal care. You will also have to pay for the hospital. It's usually five or six days in the hospital depending what kind of delivery you have. Could be up to $3,000 – unless you have some kind of insurance."

"Insurance? I don't know anything about insurance." I didn't know that there was any kind of insurance except for life insur-ance and car insurance.

"Well, then – I think you should tell your parents about this as soon as possible." He drops the pen onto the paper again.

"I – I can't," I stumble. "They will kill me." I feel the tears again.

"Well, I doubt they will do that. I know your mother. She's a fine woman and I am sure she will help you." The words come easily out of his mouth. He has probably said them many times before. "So, under the circumstances – with no insurance and everything, I will give you ten days to tell her yourself. Then, I will phone her and tell her. Do you understand?"

My life is over. I sit there, numb with fear.

He continues, "Phone my nurse in a few days and she will tell you the final test results. But I am more than certain you are pregnant." He smiles at me, stands to open the door, and I walk zombie-like out of his office.

I walk right by Moe and towards the outside door. He hurries after me. The nurse behind the desk calls out to us, "That'll be twenty dollars for your first visit and you need to make an appointment for your next visit."

I return to the inner office. I look around at all the other pregnant woman sitting in chairs along the walls. They all smile at me like this is some happy occasion. I see their bellies. I see their joy. I push back more tears. I drop my voice and tell the nurse I have to pay next time. I have no money.

She clicks her tongue at me, but agrees and makes me an appointment for the end of October.

Moe takes my hand as we walk out of the clinic. We walk down the street, not knowing where to go or what to say. We walk and walk and walk. The silence between us stretches and stretches and stretches. Hours later, we arrive back at the campus, too tired to do anything. Moe stops holding my hand as we approach the dorm and I watch him walk off, wordless, in the direction of his house.

I stumble to my room, undress and fall on my bed. Before I can close my eyes, I hear the loudspeaker in the hallway announce, *Phone call for Susie Glasier*. Now what? I drag myself into my robe and down the hall to the phone.

"Hi, honey." It's my mother.

"Hi." I try to put some life in my voice, just so she won't ask any questions, as she is sure to do if I don't sound lively and interested.

But, this time, she has her own news and it bubbles out of her and into my ear. "I have a surprise for you. I'm coming into

Tucson tomorrow to the Junior League rummage sale. You remember – the one I go to every year where we get such great deals
on clothes. I thought I'd pick you up and we would make a day
of it. In fact, I am planning to stay overnight at a hotel. You are
welcome to join me. What do you think?"

I think I would rather die – but my better judgment kicks in.
This is my opportunity to tell my mother my secret. She can kill
me in peace and quiet and away from the world.

"If you're too busy, honey, it's okay." She cuts into my
thoughts. "I just thought you might like a chance to get away from
your studies for a day or so. It will be fun and we might find you
some neat stuff." She is in her reasonable mood.

The annual Tucson Junior League rummage sale is the biggest
occasion of my mother's entire year. It is the place where she buys
most of her and my dad's clothing. They both love pretending to
be rich and designer duds are all part of that facade. My mother
has never had a full-priced new dress in her whole life. She always buys the very best, but it is always on sale or second hand. I
give her credit. She has a stunning wardrobe and my father wears
$500.00 suits every day to the office and no one knows they come
from this rummage sale.

"Are you still there?" she cuts into my thoughts.

"I – I'm here, Mom," I stutter. "I was asleep when you called.
I'd love to come with you. What time can you pick me up?"

"Well, that's my girl," she sings out. "We'll have such a good
time."

Little does she know how not true that will be. I say nothing.

"I'll be there tomorrow evening about six. We'll get a room
and I'll take you out for dinner. The sale starts at eight the next
morning but I want to get to the fence by at least five. Otherwise,
we'll miss all the good stuff. Okay?"

I wonder if my mother will still be interested in all the *good
stuff* when I finish with her. Resigned to my fate, I tell her, "Sure,
Mom. That's great." I hang up the phone and head back to my
room. My roommate informs me that I have a visitor in the waiting room and she thinks it is my boyfriend.

Oh god, what is Moe doing here at this hour? I thought we

agreed to meet later for supper. I make him wait while I change clothes and wash up. When I reach the waiting room, Moe is pacing back and forth. The look on his face tells me he is mad. When he sees me come out of the elevator, he comes towards me, grabbing my arm roughly and pulling me toward the outside door.

"Moe wait and wait and wait. Where are you?" he looks at me menacingly as he talks. I notice he is spitting as he speaks; something he does when he is mad and can't find the right words.

I pull my arm out of his grip and stop walking. "Calm down, Moe, I'm here. What is so important that it can't wait till tonight?" He grabs my arm and starts pulling again.

"Stop pulling on my arm." I yank it away once more. "I hate it when you do that."

"Scut," he says in his guttural Arabic. *Scut* means *shush* or *shut up* in Arabic and is usually used for children. "Come with me. People are looking. You come with me," he repeats in his authoritative voice.

"Moe, I will come with you. Just stop trying to drag me around by my arm."

"Okay." He mutters and drops my arm. He walks by my side until we reach the steps leading down to the street. "Moe want to talk to you. I have very important thing to tell you."

"Okay, Moe," I tell him as calmly as I can. "Just stop trying to drag me everywhere. I will walk with you."

"You make me wait and I not like it," he blurts out. He stands in front of me, belligerent, and definitely ready for a fight.

I look at him, ready to argue, and then decide it is not worth it. "Okay, whatever you say, Moe, whatever you say."

"Yes," he agrees. "Whatever I say." He visibly relaxes, and takes my arm again, but more gently this time.

We find a place to sit near the bottom of the steps, out of the way of students going to and from the building. I don't feel like talking, but I can tell that Moe has something serious on his mind. I wait.

"We will have baby, no?" he asks, hesitantly.

"I think so, Moe," I answer. "It depends on what the tests say, but I think so."

"Okay," he says in his authoritative voice. "Moe think about this very much. I make you understand my position. I am poor student. U. S. government agency sends me here to do school. They pay me $200 a month for rent, for food, for school. I only stay here until I am graduated. Then I go back home to help my people. Right now they have no educated people. The French kill one million of my brothers and all the educated people. So, now the war is over, it very important I go back. Also, I find my missing family so I have family now. You understand?" He pauses. This has been a long speech for him.

He has explained all of this to me before. Why does he have to explain it all to me, all over again, right now? "Yes, Moe, I understand. Do you think they will make you leave if they find out?" If Moe leaves the country, I will be left with the baby on my own.

Moe puts his head in his hands and sits very still for a few minutes. "Moe made big decision." He raises his head and takes my hand. He holds it for a moment and then continues his speech. "You must understand. In my country, a man only marries when his mother find him a wife. You very lucky woman. My mother is dead and that mean I choose my own wife." He pauses again.

Very lucky woman. I am very likely pregnant. My parents will kill me when they find out. What does Moe mean by telling me I am a *very lucky woman?*

Moe continues. He has thought out what he wants to say. He doesn't stumble over any of the words and he speaks in full sentences, as best as he can. "Very important thing to tell you. If you marry me, I go to Algeria and you go with me." He glances at me to be sure I am listening. Then, his voice slows, and he speaks as if he is explaining a difficult concept to a small child. "Living in Algeria, you have to be like young tree—bending always, like willow. Remember? I tell you before. If you not bend, you snap like dry twig and have many heart attacks."

The heart attack part makes me want to laugh, but I try not to. I wonder where he got the word *snap.* I try to correct him. "Moe, I think you mean I will have my heart broken." My mind is racing. Moe has just said he will marry me.

He looks irritated at my attempt to correct his English. He looks at me, seriously, "Do you understand what it is I say?"

"Yes, Moe. I understand. If I marry you, we will go to Algeria to live and I will have to bend like the willow." A huge sense of relief floods through me. I ignore that it is not a romantic proposal. I ignore that he hasn't said he loves me. Moe has just said he will marry me and take me to Algeria with him. That is all I hear.

"Yes, I know I tell you before. But I want you know that you are very lucky that I marry you. I make decision to believe you are virgin – or I not marry you." He pronounces each of the words slowly and clearly so that he is sure I understand him.

I can't understand why the question of being a virgin has come up again. "Why wouldn't you believe me?"

Again, the images from the adobe house fill my mind. How could he have any doubt that I was a virgin? I sigh. Surely, he knows that I am/was a virgin. I can't understand why he keeps bringing it up.

Moe continues, "Some girls try to trick boys about this. Some very bad girls." He shakes his head from side to side. "I see you come from good family. They try to make you be good girl and so I say, okay, I respect them. It is my culture. In my country, only virgin girls marry."

"Whatever you say, Moe. Whatever you say." Agreeing with him is the best thing to do. "I am a very lucky woman. I am very lucky you will marry me."

Then, I change the topic to something much more important to me at the moment. "Just so you know, Moe. I'm going to go out with my mother tomorrow and I am going to tell her about the baby."

"Oh, *mon dieu*," flies out of Moe's mouth before he can stop it. "Do you think she will call police?"

"I hope not, Moe." I smile at the fear in his face. I can't help it. He has such an irrational fear of the police. He doesn't understand that they have way too much to do to be worrying about arresting men who get girls pregnant. "I think my mother will be okay if I tell her you will marry me."

Moe looks at me in surprise. "Really? If this happen in my country, they take you to whore house."

I can't believe some of the things that come out of his mouth. "Take me to the whore house?" I repeat. What happened to me certainly doesn't make me a whore. If I had had my way, it never would have happened. How could anyone think I am a whore?

"Yes, you know, house for bad women." Moe looks at me and explains. "In my country," he says emphatically, "if woman go with man who not her husband – and she have no family – then she has to go live in the town whore house. Sometimes – if she come from very conservative family – then brother or father kill her. I tell you this so you understand. We have different culture. You are lucky I agree to marry you."

"That's awful, Moe." A girl being killed because she *went with a man who is not her husband.* Surely, that must be a rare situation. I ask, "What if a boy and girl love each other?"

Moe shakes his head at me. "If parents agree, then they marry. But it not happen in my village. Boy never see girl before he marry her – so how can he love her before he marry her?"

He considers for a moment. "When you go to my country, we live in city. I think village too hard for you. In the village, you must cover yourself with veil when you go out and you can never go out by yourself."

"Never go out by myself? Moe, that's just plain silly." Where does he come up with all of these strange ideas? Surely, he can't mean never.

"Not silly. Woman in your country not exciting to man. Woman in my country very exciting because we cannot see her. Man look at woman in veil and wonder what she look like. Very exciting to man."

He continues. "When I first come to America, I cannot believe man and woman can walk together holding hands and kissing. I go to beach one day and I see man and woman in bathing suit and she is kissing his face and he is just lying on the beach and he is not excited. His penis not even stand up. Nothing. How can that happen? Beautiful girl on top of you and you do nothing? I not believe it."

I shake my head, embarrassed by his graphic description. "You are so funny, Moe."

"Funny? Moe not funny. Moe right. Why you think Moe funny?" He is angry again.

I hurry to explain. "It's just so strange to me how you think sometimes." I sigh. "I don't know if I can live the way your people live. I can only promise to be like the willow."

"Yes," Moe whispers, "You must promise. Moe help you and show you how."

We kiss and he walks away. "Good luck with Mother" is the last thing he says.

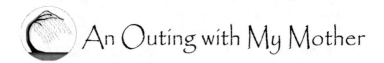

Precisely at six o'clock, my mother arrives at the dorm, bright-eyed and full of chatter about all the wonderful bargains we will soon lay our hands on. Under ordinary circumstances, I would be as wound up as she is, but this time, I know the day is not going to be one of our better ones. I throw my overnight bag onto the back seat and make myself comfortable in the familiar red and white Desoto. I smile at her and we drive away from the dorm.

"I'm going to check us in first," she informs me, "and then, how about we have a nice dinner in the hotel restaurant?"

"Sure," I nod. I feel a wave of nausea coming on and, with great determination, I try to push it down. I breathe in quickly, but not quickly enough to hide it from my mother.

She looks at me quizzically, with raised eyebrows. "What's wrong?" she asks. "You don't sound very happy. Are you okay?"

"Yeah, I'm fine, just a little queasy for some reason," I respond. "I think I ate something at lunch that didn't agree with me. I'll be all right." Why do I keep lying? How am I ever going to tell her the truth?

"Well, that's not so good. We have a big day ahead of us. You better get to feeling better or you'll be missing all the fun." She laughs and I smile at her. Sometimes my mother gets so much enjoyment out of the silliest things.

We pull up in front of the Days Inn. It is one of those high-end hotels that my mother loves so much. Its red brick facade supports beautiful bougainvillea vines that run across the entire front of the hotel. White and fuchsia flowers add to the lushness of the setting, making it appear more tropical than desert. The entry has white marble pillars that support a red tile roof. Through the large glass entry doors, fine Mexican leather furniture sits invitingly, waiting for the next visitor. The hotel sits next to the municipal golf course, which adds to its prestige.

The young parking attendant trots up to the car as my mother slowly winds her way between the marble pillars. He greets her as if he has known her all his life. "Welcome, Mrs. Glasier. Nice to have you back at the Days Inn."

She gets out and hands him the keys. "The bags are in the back seat, Jonathan. Bring them in, will you? My daughter and I are going to have supper."

"Yes ma'am," he answers. "Right away. Enjoy your stay."

She pushes a five-dollar bill into the boy's hand and we enter the hotel.

I like it here. I have been here a number of times. I always enjoy the luxury of the place – the marble-floored lobby, the wide thick-carpeted stairways, and the large rooms extravagantly furnished with brightly polished solid wood and leather furniture, the comfortable beds with heavy gilded bedspreads and ornate matching drapes – and a TV in every room.

My mother ushers me straight into the dining room. "Let's eat here. I know it's more expensive than the café, but I feel like having a real nice dinner with my grownup daughter." My mother is truly happy. She is enjoying the luxury of the hotel and she is enjoying sharing it with me. She sees herself as the adoring mother. At the moment, there is no tension between us. All of the disagreement over me going back to summer school, over Moe – all of it doesn't exist at this moment. "Honestly," she continues, "I feel like I never see you any more and I do miss you. I'm so happy you decided to join me for my little outing. I feel like we never have any fun anymore."

I smile weakly at her and nod as though I agree, which I do. Today, however, is not the day to get caught up in her joyous energy. I have to organize my thoughts. The time to tell my secret is drawing near and I need to figure out how and when I am going to do it.

The *maitre d'* approaches us and my mother requests a table by the window. He complies – after she passes him a couple of bills. We are shown to an intimate little table overlooking the pool and hotel gardens. The sun is setting and the red Arizona sky is beautiful. My mother chatters through the entire meal. At times, I listen to her, but mostly I concentrate on my food. Surprisingly, my nausea has subsided and I can enjoy what I am eating. "This is really good," I say as I finish up the chicken I ordered. It is so good to be able to eat without feeling sick.

"Yes, it is," she smiles in response, "and the only thing that will make it better is to have a big plate of rich gooey pastries. Let's share. How about it?"

Surprised, I look at my mother. "Aren't you afraid of gaining weight?" She always is so careful with her weight. I can't even remember the last time I saw her eat a dessert. It is hard to imagine her even saying *rich gooey pastries*. The only time I usually hear her talk about sweets is when she is telling me that I eat too many of them.

"Not today, honey." She looks at me with a sly smile on her face, "I feel like being totally wicked. What do you say?"

"I say okay." I grin back at her. It is a little strange, but nice, to see my mother relax. I think about how seldom I see her laugh, really laugh – and I feel guilty. Not the usual guilt I feel that comes from my responding to her moods and manipulations. No, this guilt comes from the knowledge that my little secret is going to destroy all of her enjoyment of the outing – her enjoyment of the rest of her life.

She calls the waiter over and orders. The waiter returns in a few minutes with four large, three-inch square, chocolate-covered, cream-filled pastries on a beautiful china plate, the edges squiggled with caramel and marshmallow sauce. I look at the plate and then at my mother. Her eyes see nothing but the pastries. She reaches out and snatches the one nearest to her. I have never seen my mother behave like this. Fascinated, I watch her down the succulent sweet in two gargantuan bites. I wonder if she tasted it at all. As she reaches for the second piece, she suddenly stops, realizing I am watching her.

"Oh, here, honey," she says, pushing one of the pastries towards me with her fingers. "I am such a pig when it comes to this stuff." Then, she reaches again for her second piece. "I am so bad," she mumbles into the flakey layers. "You better eat yours quick or I'll do it for you."

The second pastry disappears, and I watch her carefully pick up her napkin and wipe her lips. "God, that was good," she announces. She stops patting her lips with the cloth napkin and looks at me. "Well, aren't you going to eat yours?" I hear urgency in her voice.

"I don't think so," I murmur. "I think I've had enough." I would really like to eat my share of the creamy confections, but something urges me to say I don't want them – just to see what she will do.

As soon as the words are out of my mouth, she reaches for the last two pastries and piles them onto her plate. This time, she carefully cuts each pastry with her knife. We both watch the pudding-like whipped cream slowly ooze out of the flakey crusts. She pops the first piece into her mouth. This time, she slowly chews the soft sweet morsel, savouring every bite. She is intensely focused – so focused, in fact, that there is no room for conversation. It is as though time has stopped.

When all the pastries are gone and she has finished chewing, she uses a spoon to scrape every bit of the remaining sweet sauce from both her plate and the pastry plate. She drops her fork onto the plate with a loud clatter and sighs. "Well, that was fun!" she laughs. Then, with a quick glance at me, she adds, "Maybe, we'll go out for ice cream later?"

I laugh. I don't know what to say. My usually uptight, no-nonsense mother is behaving like a child caught with her hand in the cookie jar.

She laughs, "Let's go back to the room. It's getting late and we have to get up very early."

We pick up our key at the desk and go up to our room. It has two beds and, over by the window, a coffee table flanked by two plush chairs. My mother walks over to one of the chairs, sits down and slips off her heels. "Come," she says, "Come and sit down and tell your old mother what you have been up to. You hardly said anything during dinner." She leans back comfortably, closing her eyes.

I kick my shoes off and sit down in the other chair. She offers me a cigarette and I take one. We smoke together as we have done since I was twelve and she first taught me how to inhale. On the surface, the whole scene looks so relaxed. Fleetingly, I wish things were always this peaceful with my mother. If only we could always just sit down with each other and smoke without talking.

I take a deep breath, and a sigh escapes into the room. I barely recognize that it comes from me.

"Wow, that was a heavy sigh," my mother observes. "It seems to me you have something heavy on your heart. You want to tell me about it?"

I am surprised by the amount of interest and concern I feel in her voice. Something has changed in her. I feel close to her, closer to her than I have ever felt. Here is my mother, being the kind of mother I have always wished she could be – and I am about to tell her something that will totally destroy our relationship forever. What kind of a daughter am I?

I open my mouth. At that moment, to my amazement, I feel a fluttering in my belly. Involuntarily, I jump. "What?" I exclaim, and then add, "Wow!" half under my breath, as I realize that I have just felt my baby move inside me. Some little spirit is telling me to get on with telling my secret.

"Susie, you seem really different today," my mother continues. "Your face looks different and you seem very –" she pauses, searching for words, "– well – not quite yourself."

I look at my mother. I can't keep it from her one minute longer. Tears fill my eyes. "I am different, Mom." I start hesitantly, leaning a little toward her, silently imploring her to understand – and to forgive me. "I – I'm – I don't know how to tell you –" I hold my breath for an instant, and then I blurt it out, the words falling over one another as they tumble out, "Mom – I'm going to have a baby." My voice drops with the last word so that *baby* is barely audible, even to me. The words hang in the silence – and the warmth of the previous few moments dissolves instantly.

My mother looks as though she has been slapped across the

face. She sits frozen in her chair. I turn away from her, get up and lay down on one of the beds. The brocade is hard against my face. I want to cry, but I can't. I feel frozen, too.

I listen for a sound from my mother, but I hear nothing. I venture a look in my mother's direction and find her staring into space, rocking back and forth. I watch her and she continues to rock. I get up off the bed and walk towards her. I reach out and touch her arm, but she slaps my hand away.

"Don't touch me!" she snarls. She wraps her arms around her body and resumes her rocking. "God, how could you? I told you I would just die if anything happened with you and that boy." She spits out the words as if they are poison.

"Goddamn! Goddamn. Goddamn," She repeats over and over, the words first coming out with force and then losing their strength. For the second time in the same night, I see a part of my mother that I have never seen before. This is real shock – shock that is not tainted with any manipulation or any attempt to control me.

"Mom, please," I say to her when I can no longer stand another Goddamn. "Mommy, I am so sorry." This time the tears pour out, more because I am frightened by her reaction than I am by my fear of my situation. Tears continue to roll down my face. I reach for a tissue. "I'm so sorry," I repeat.

"Sorry? Do you know what you have done? You have ruined your life. How could you? Don't you understand what you have done?" My mother's face is so red that it almost matches the shade of lipstick she is wearing. "God, how could you?" she says over and over. "God, how could you? How could you do this to your mother? God, how could I be such a failure as a mother? God, you've ruined my life."

I sit on the bed again, feeling helpless. In some small part of myself, I had hoped that telling my mother would help. But, I see that that is not possible. It is as if the pregnancy has happened to my mother. She keeps talking about how her life is being ruined.

What about mine?

Suddenly, she stops *Goddamning* and turns to me. In a calm

and cool voice, she asks, "How do you know for sure that you are pregnant? Did you go to the doctor? Is it for sure?"

"I went to the doctor. He told me it was for sure." I wish I could say it wasn't.

At that, my mother cries harder. Every time she tries to say something she cries some more. I try to hug her, but she turns away.

At midnight, I undress, get into bed and try to sleep. All I can hear is my mother crying. All I can feel is the fluttering in my belly. I fall asleep.

Something wakes me at five o'clock. I roll over and realize it is the alarm clock my mother has set. She is in the bathroom and the shower is running. She must have sat up all night. The other bed hasn't been slept in. The shower stops, and after a few minutes, she comes out of the bathroom. She is dressed for the day in a light green sundress with matching purse and shoes. Under her makeup, her face is red and she looks exhausted. But she isn't crying anymore.

"Oh, you're awake," she says quietly, her voice tinged with fatigue. She walks over to the bed where I am sitting and sits down beside me. "What are you going to do about this?" she asks, her voice choked with tears. "Just what exactly are you going to do now?"

I shake my head. "I – I don't know."

She looks into my eyes. "How could this happen?" she asks again. "This boyfriend of yours is so old – why did he allow you to get pregnant? I don't understand it. How can I tell your father? What in God's name are the neighbours going to think?" She works herself up as the questions come out. Each one brings on the next, and each question reflects a worse possibility. "Don't you know what they say about unmarried mothers? You can't have a baby. You are a baby." At this, she reaches out to touch my hair, but her hand falls short, as if she can't reach me. "God, this man is so dark. Don't you know that you could have a black baby?" With that revelation, she starts to cry again.

"Please Mom, stop crying. Moe will marry me and it will be okay." I try to reassure her everything will be all right. That is such an irony – because in trying to reassure her, I am trying to make myself believe the same thing. Then, my brain suddenly registers the comment about the black baby. Why would my baby be black? Moe is not black. Who cares anyway? Why does she say such stupid things?

My mother's wailing changes, and she looks at me incredulously as her mind registers what I have been saying. "Marry you? Did he say he would marry you? Does he even know about the baby?"

"Of course he knows, Mom. He says he will marry me." I avoid looking at the thought that this isn't the way I had dreamed of my marriage happening.

"Well, under the circumstances, you have no other choice, do you?" She stands up as she says this, and I can see the shift happen in her thinking as her *I know better than you* self gets the upper hand. "I still think you have ruined your life – but then that's just what I think."

Then, reconsidering, she suddenly blurts out, "If – if you don't want to marry him, we could cope." She is looking directly at me, and, for a minute, I see that she has accepted that I am pregnant. I see that she will be on my side, that she will be there for me – as best as she can.

"Mom, I love him. Of course, I want to marry him." I ignore the things that come into my mind from my last conversation with Moe about *bending like a willow* and *never being able to go out on my own*. He couldn't really have meant that, anyway. He probably just wanted me to know that things are different in his culture – and I already know that. After all, I have known him and his friends for a year or so now. I don't tell my mother any of what I am thinking.

She turns, looks at herself in the mirror hanging on the back of the door, touches her hair, and smooths down the skirt of her outfit. Then, as if the world has turned right side up again, my mother throws the last of her clothes back into her suitcase, closes the lid, picks it up and announces. "Well, guess we'd better get going to the sale. We're already late."

I throw on my clothes – old jeans and an oversized shirt. My mother looks at me, but doesn't say anything. We leave the hotel, put the luggage into the trunk and my mother gets behind the wheel.

We arrive at the gate to the sale at 5:30 in the morning. Already, at least a hundred people are gathered there, forming a ragged line behind the fence. My mother isn't happy with her place in the crowd and complains out loud about how we should have got here earlier.

This sale is really the most important thing in my mother's life. We are lucky we got here at all. How is it possible that she heard the *worst news of her life* last night – and this morning, she is standing in line as if nothing happened? How is it possible that I told her my secret last night – and I am standing here next to her – as if nothing happened? The fluttering in my belly continues as it has through all of the talking and the anger and the crying, just a faint movement like butterfly wings against the skin that keeps reminding me that someone is in there, that that little someone is changing my life with every beat of its little heart, with every flutter that I feel.

Standing in the not very warm Arizona morning, I think about how really smart my mother is – how she takes care of my father and me all the time, how she has done that for all of the years since I was born. She has always handled the everyday household responsibilities, many times in cultures foreign to her. She has also done all the banking and all of the paper work, including what has been necessary because of our traipsing from country to country, passports and visas and tax forms. Besides that, she has always been the hostess for the entertaining my father's military career demands. My mother is known for the way she keeps her house, for the parties she gives and for her gracious style of making people feel welcome. Her career has consisted of making my father look good.

I remember listening in on a conversation she had with my father when I was younger. She was asking him if she could go to work for the Red Cross on the base where we lived at that time. In response, my father asked her if it would be for pay. She told him it would. I will never forget my father's voice. "No wife of mine will ever work for money. People will think I can't provide for you and my career would be over."

Suddenly, I see that my mother is a prisoner of her life. Sorrow touches my heart. In the next instant, I feel the flutter in my belly, and involuntarily, I shudder. Why would I shudder? My life with Moe couldn't possibly be like my mother's.

Suddenly, the crowd noises grow louder and there is a rattling at the gate. It slowly rumbles open and everyone runs toward the doors of the warehouse that have been opened to receive them. My mother grabs my arm protectively as we dash across the wide space to the tables heaped high with clothing and household goods.

The touch of her hand on my arm coincides with another gentle flutter in my belly. My mother will be a grandmother.

By noon, we are exhausted. Loaded down with bags and bags of clothes, we trek back to the car. My mother seems satisfied with her nearly new purchases. She chatters away about this item and that, reciting the brand name items she has been so lucky to rip from the grasps of other desperate buyers. It truly is my mother's favourite entertainment, this sale.

I am glad that the tears have stopped and that her old self is back. At the car, she sorts through the bags as she puts them into the trunk, pulling out a few things to show me, describing how they will fit into her wardrobe. She hands me a blouse and a skirt. "These will look good on you, Susie," she says.

She doesn't show me what is in one bag, but I already know. I watched her as she bought some booties and little shirts and sleeper things for a newborn, for my baby.

As we pull away from the parking lot, my mother tells me, "I'll go home and tell your father about the baby. We'll come back in a few days. We'll take you and Moe out to dinner. We must plan a wedding as quickly as possible. The sooner the better." She pauses as she checks for traffic before changing lanes. "You let him know we are not happy about this. We could get him thrown out of this country, you know. I'll talk to your father about that."

Seeing the expression on her face, I know she is serious.

"Mom, please, don't do that. I don't want to live if I have to live without him." My voice almost breaks.

"Don't talk like that," she fires back. "Of course you want to live. No man is worth dying over."

"He is," I whisper. "He is," I say again. Tears spill out.

"Oh, for Pete's sake," she sighs. "Quit crying. It's not good for the baby." She reaches out and pats my hand.

We are both silent the rest of our trip back to the dorm.

She is right. I have to think about my baby. I put one hand on my belly and feel the flutter, almost as if the little one is agreeing with my mother. I stop crying. But, I can't stop what is running through my mind. What if my parents want to get Moe sent back to Algeria? I can't tell him that. I just can't.

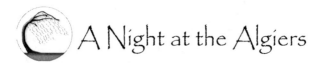# A Night at the Algiers

When Moe shows up to find out what has happened. I keep him waiting for a few minutes while I brush my hair and change my clothes. I am not sure what I should say to him.

As I come through the door of the dorm, he runs up the steps to meet me and grabs my hand. "How are you? What happen? Is mother going to kill me?"

His anxious words and tone strike a funny chord in me. I say, glibly, "Yes, Moe, my mother and my father are both going to kill you," and then I go on to embellish my little joke even more. "Actually," I tell him, "they have decided to kill me as well." As I finish, I look at him, only to see shock and horror take hold as he struggles to understand what I have said.

"Oh, *mon dieu*," he whispers, "They kill Moe?" Moe doesn't understand my attempt at humour. He believes me.

"Oh, Moe," I laugh. "They are mad. But they will get over it. I was making a joke."

Moe stares at me, horrified. "What you mean joke? This no joke. You think I am fool?" His face expresses more than his words. He is furious at my attempt to make a joke. He turns to leave. Then, halfway down the dorm steps, he stops, turns, and suddenly, strikes at my face with his fist.

Instinctively, I duck. His fist hits my shoulder. It hurts. "What's the matter with you?" I yell. "Why are you trying to hit me?"

"You try to make me like fool," he spits out at me. "You make joke. Joke not funny." His eyes are blazing with anger, and his hands, held stiffly at his sides, are still curled into fists.

My attempt at humour was a serious miscalculation. I say, "You are right, Moe. It's not funny - but I was trying to make it not so bad." I tentatively reach out to touch his shoulder. "I'm sorry if I upset you."

Moe abruptly swings around to face me. "Yes, you upset me." His eyes bore into mine. "No joke, you understand?"

"Yes, Moe, I understand."

He demands, "What your parents say?"

I decide not to mention anything about the possibility of him being sent out of the country. "They said we can get married," I look at him, anxious that he may have changed his mind, "and they will come next week to plan the wedding."

A deep frown furrows Moe's eyebrows. He glances sharply at me. "Your parents say you marry me?"

"Moe, we are having a baby," I explain patiently. "Of course, they say I can marry you. This is America."

Moe shakes his head in confusion. "America is very strange place." He is silent for a minute and then he continues, "Okay, I must tell government people this. They not be happy." He is silent again.

I touch my shoulder, which is still hurting from the force of his fist.

Abruptly, Moe announces, "I have only little money."

"Moe, do you want to marry me?" I ask.

Moe doesn't have the words or the disposition to be subtle or to be dishonest. He looks directly at me as he speaks and I read both confusion and resolve in his face. "Sometimes," he replies.

"Sometimes?" I ask, shocked. I am totally unprepared for that answer. "Do you love me?" I press him.

"Sometimes," he replies again and then adds, "I not know what this word *love* means. I – I do – what your parents want." He speaks firmly, with decision in his voice, but as if the words are coming from a faraway place. "You lucky I marry you. You remember important thing – I go back to my country." His voice drops, almost as if he is speaking to himself. "My family not be happy not to choose wife." He shakes his head, returning to the present. "But I tell them, I want you for my wife."

Suddenly, his eyes grow larger. He places his hands on my shoulders and looks earnestly into my face. "You must make to

Moe a big promise." As he speaks, he squeezes my shoulders. "You never tell any person we have baby before we marry. In my country, this is very, very bad." He shakes me, gently. "Do you understand?"

I frown back at him. Sometimes, he acts as if he thinks I am stupid. "Yes, Moe, I understand." Recalling my mother's reaction to the news, I say, "It is also very bad in my country."

"I not think so," he says, quietly. "It not bad like in my country." His eyes search mine again, looking for something. Then, he drops his hands and walks away. He leaves me standing at the bottom of the dorm stairway, without a kiss or a good-bye.

I watch him trudge off into the night with a resigned slouch to his shoulders and his eyes to the ground. Who is this man that I am going to marry? It used to be so exciting to hold his hand as we walked across the campus. I used to feel so at ease sitting beside him, listening to stories of his family, of life in his country. Memories of his actions in the little adobe house crowd into my mind, followed by the image of his explosive behaviour tonight when he misunderstood my attempt at humour. I rub my shoulder. I wonder if we can ever return to the times when we were happy just to be together, when walking across campus and sitting under the canopy were times to share, times to learn more about each other. I feel a flutter in my belly, reminding me of just how much has changed. I go back inside.

When I reach the coolness of my room, I see the notebook of Moe's stories sitting open on my desk. I leaf through the pages, remembering how I struggled to capture every word, how Moe cried when he told me about sad events, how the stories show his love for his family and his country. I know who Moe is through these stories.

A few days, later my mother phones to make good on her promise to show up with my father to plan the wedding. They will meet us at my dorm at six o'clock on the dot the following day to go out for dinner.

Moe arrives an hour before my parents do. Today, especially, I don't want to make him wait and I especially don't want to do anything to make him mad. I hurry to finish dressing and rush down to meet him.

He is dressed in his best suit and tie. His hands shake as he lights a cigarette. He looks up as I approach, and smiles awkwardly. "Hello, Sewzi," he says, trying to smile at me. "Moe is early today." He laughs a nervous little laugh. "I think Moe die today."

I can't help but laugh at his exaggerated worry. "No, Moe, I don't think you die today." I take his hand and stand close to him. "I love you, Moe. What can my parents say?" I brush my fingers across his face. "Don't worry. They want to get to know you. You are a good man and they will see that."

Moe is looking at me, but when he speaks, the words come out as if he is talking to himself. I think he is practicing for the meeting with my parents. "Yes. I am good man, and I tell them I take care of you and my baby. I marry you. I am good man. You be my wife. Yes, you be my wife."

He stops and turns to me, "You and mommy and daddy and baby are my new American family." He nods and smiles at me, as if suddenly understanding what everything means. His smile grows wider as he thinks about what he has said. "Yes," he adds, "a new family. I think this is good."

As Moe finishes this contemplation, my parents pull up in their blue Cadillac, my father's favourite vehicle. He only uses it for special occasions. I take it as a sign that he is not considering murdering Moe – or else he would have brought the Desoto. I laugh to myself. My father is being a bit ostentatious – to me, that is a good omen.

The car stops in front of us and I signal Moe to get in. He opens the door and then steps back to let me in ahead of him. I slide across the red velvet seat covers to the other side. Moe gets in and pulls the door shut. Abruptly, and without a word to announce his intention, he reaches over the seat to my father and offers his hand in greeting. "How you do. I am Moe Chaabane. Nice to meet you, Father Glasier."

Moe's words are followed by dead silence. I feel the urge to laugh hysterically at the 'Father Glasier,' but something holds me back. My father holds my future in his hands. I glance at him in the rear view mirror. I can see he, too, is having a hard time controlling his laughter.

"Oh, yeah," he finally says, chuckling softly, and offers Moe his hand in return. "Pleased to meetcha."

Moe smiles, shakes my father's hand up and down several times and then, as he lets it go, he turns to my mother. "I am with extreme gratitude to you, my mother," he says addressing her in a loud nervous voice. "You are most beautiful woman. You must be the sister of Sewzi, not the mother."

My mother looks at him, wide-eyed. She stutters before she can find her voice. "Uhhh, thank you, Mr. Chaabane," she manages, "I think." She looks at me and the points of her eyebrows come together in an *is-he-for-real?* look. She turns back to face the front. I hear her say in a soft voice, "He may turn out not to be so bad after all."

I smile at Moe as he sits back, reaches over and takes my hand. He is very pleased with his first encounter with my parents.

My parents have chosen a quiet little Mexican restaurant on Broadway Boulevard close to the university for our planning dinner. When we arrive, the place is nearly empty and we get a nice table in the center courtyard. We spend several minutes ordering drinks and *hors d'oeuvres* and chatting about the weather. When the drinks arrive, my father turns to both of us and says, "So, you want to get married?"

Moe and I look at each other. Then, Moe turns to look at my father and says, "Yes, I marry your daughter. I am man. I know it very sad for you. She is only one child. I promise I take care of her. I tell her we go to Algeria when I am graduate. It is hard, but I make a place."

"We'll talk about where you will live later. But, for now, we need to have a wedding." My father hesitates and my mother looks at him, disgusted.

"Oh, Frank," she interrupts. Then she turns to speak to Moe. "What Mr. Glasier means is that we have made arrangements for you and Susie to go to Las Vegas to get married on Saturday. We will drive you there, have a little ceremony, see a show, spend the night and come back on Sunday. That way you won't miss any school and everything will be fine. Susie, I will pick you up on Friday to take you shopping for some new clothes and a dress. In the meantime, I think I found a room near the university where you two can live. I've made arrangements for you to see it after dinner."

Moe looks at my mother as though he can't quite understand what she is saying. When she pauses, he says, "You are very nice mother. I think the government will send me back, if I marry."

"Moe, I can guarantee the government will send you back – but it will be if you don't marry," interjects my father in the authoritative military voice that he doesn't often use. "I think it is best you don't tell the government until it's over. What do you say?" He looks intently at Moe and adds, "Man to man." My father has worked with, and for the military, all his life. When it comes to negotiating deals, his peers have described him as the best. This final pronouncement of *man-to-man* means there is no going back where my father is concerned.

"Man to man," Moe repeats, his eyes big with understanding. "I know *man to man*. We have *man to man* in my culture."

Our part in the conversation over, Moe and I nod and let my parents do the talking and the rest of the planning. After dinner, we get back into the car and drive to a house a block from the dorm. It is an older house with a wide veranda out front. An older man answers the door when my mother knocks and immediately, he recognizes her.

"Ah, Mrs. Glasier, so this is the happy couple. I have the key for you." He hands the key to her and she leads us back down the veranda stairs and around the side of the house to a small door.

She puts the key in the lock, saying, "I think this little place is just perfect for you two." She pushes open the door and we follow her into a tiny bedroom, fully furnished with one large closet on the opposite wall, a double bed, and two nightstands. She walks across the bedroom and down a short hallway that has two doors opening off it. The first door hides a small bathroom with a tub, shower, toilet and sink, and the next door leads to a small kitchen with a stove, small fridge, small sink and a couple of cabinets. I open the door to one of the cabinets. It is full of dishes. Knowing my mother, the shelves will be stocked with everything we need.

"Wow, Mom, this is nice," I say. "How did you find this place?"

"We have connections," my mother answers curtly. "Just you make sure you are quiet here. Don't disturb Mr. and Mrs. Coring. They are pretty old and they need their sleep. I promised them you wouldn't be a bother. However, when the baby comes, you'll have to move. There's no room here for a baby. I figure you can live here till January and, then we'll look for something else. You'll have to quit school then, Susie, because you can't go to school and have a baby at the same time."

I look at my mother in disbelief. "What do you mean I have to quit school? I love school. I can't quit."

"Well, you'll have to for a while," my mother says, turning to Moe. "Having a baby and going to school don't mix, isn't that right, Moe?"

Moe looks at my mother and bats his long lashes at her, "Yes, my mother," he replies, "Baby is much work."

I am devastated. I haven't thought about what life will be like when the baby comes. I have enough trouble living through everything that is happening at the moment. "I love school," I repeat. My mouth forms into a pout, like when I didn't get my way as a child.

Moe takes my hand, "You not talk bad to your mother. She knows these things. You be quiet. She is good woman."

My mother is smiling. Moe has clearly won her over. I open my mouth to speak but nothing comes out.

On October 21, 1962, my parents pick us up in front of the dorm at 7:00 a.m. My mother greets me by yelling out the window. "Your grandmother is meeting us in Vegas at the hotel this evening. She decided to fly instead of riding. I think the car would be too crowded anyway."

I put my suitcase into the trunk of the Cadillac and Moe does the same. We slide in, Moe behind my mother who is driving and me behind my father. He hates to drive, especially with my mother in the passenger seat. I wonder what we will say to each other for six hours and forty minutes. My mother stops every two hours, either to fuel up the car with gas, or herself with coffee and smokes.

It feels like we will never get to our destination. Moe says almost nothing throughout the whole trip. He stares blankly out the window, only responding to what is asked of him, but adding nothing to further the conversation.

I am happy and confused at the same time. Yesterday my mother took me on an extended shopping trip to buy new clothes and underwear. She was especially adamant about buying new underwear, and she carefully picked out what she said were just the right pieces. She kept telling me which piece was too sleazy and which was just right and which was something my grand-mother would wear. Later, when we got back to the dorm, she stood next to me with a stack of my old underwear in her hands, methodically tossing each piece into the garbage. It was evident that new underwear was the most important item of clothing for a newly married woman.

She attempted to explain how important it is to stay clean and fresh *down there*. I couldn't really understand what she was trying to say. She was so red-faced about it. She brought out a rubber bag with a long hose and a long thin hard plastic nozzle ending attached to it. She called it a *douche bag*. She explained how I should use it. I didn't know what to say to her. I was glad when she put it back in its special little bag. I could not imagine ever using such a thing.

Her parting statement at the end of the day will always stay with me. "If you had gotten married the RIGHT way, we could have bought a lot more nice things. We could have had a nice shower for you and invited your friends. They would have bought you lovely things." Then she sighed, and I thought she might cry, but she didn't. She just said, "Oh well, under the circumstances, you will have to make do."

We pull into Las Vegas at three in the afternoon. Moe and I stare out the window as mother heads the Cadillac down The Strip. She tells us to look for the Stardust Hotel. Even though it is afternoon, the neon is shining in the sunlight. Moe is particularly wide-eyed at all the funny girlie signs. It takes my mother a lot longer than it should to get to the hotel. She takes great pleasure in driving slowly and showing off the Cadillac. We finally see the hotel and she parks. We all pile out, grateful this part of the journey is over.

My mother speaks as Moe reaches to pull our suitcases out of the trunk. She announces, "Your father and I will stay at this hotel. Bring your suitcases to our room for now and we will dress for the ceremony here. But, we have a special treat for you two. We got you a room at the Algiers. We thought that would be nice for your wedding night. You can go there when you are married. By the way, our wedding gift to you is this trip – and the wedding, of course.

My mother has more to say. "By the way, you might as well know that Mr. Glasier and I can't bear the thought of you two getting married in some sleazy Las Vegas chapel. We made a date with a real reverend to marry you in a church in Boulder City, Nevada. We told him the circumstances and he seems to be very understanding. We told him we would make a considerable donation to his church if he did us this favour." This first part of her explanation is directed at me. The second part is for Moe. She continues, "I hope you don't mind, Moe, but when you are in this country you have to do things our way."

Moe looks at my mother intently and is silent for a few moments. Finally, he answers, "It is for you to decide, my mother."

I am amazed at his reply. His religion is very important to him. Yet, here he is, giving in just like that. He must really love me. When I get the chance, I whisper to him how happy I am with what he is doing. Instead of smiling at me, as I expected he would, Moe, snaps, "It is of no matter to me. We all have same God. In my country, no one will ask if I marry in church. They don't know of such things."

It is thirty miles to Boulder City and Grace Community Church, the little church that my mother has picked. She says she chose it because it is an interdenominational protestant church and she figures it will be the least judgmental.

The reverend opens the door to his office and asks my parents to wait outside. He sits Moe and I down and takes a chair behind the desk. The first question out of his mouth is directed at Moe. "Do you believe in God?"

Moe looks at the reverend and in a strong voice answers, "Yes."

Then he looks at me and asks, "And do you believe in God?"

I answer, "Yes."

He looks at Moe again and says, "Do you believe in Jesus?" This question surprises me, but Moe's answer surprises me even more.

"Of course, I believe in Jesus," he answers, emotion starting to crackle in his voice.

The reverend turns to me and asks the same question. "Yes," I repeat quietly.

Then, he turns back to Moe and asks, "What religion will your child be?"

I watch Moe's face for signs that he is growing angry, but he is only giving a lot of thought to what the reverend asked. "I will grow child to believe in God and be good person. Religion not matter now."

The Reverend smiles, looks thoughtfully at Moe, and stands up. "Yes sir, you are right. Right now, it doesn't matter, does it? But, I have a feeling that it will matter – some day."

Turning to me, he states cheerily, "You should spend some time thinking about what religion you will use to raise your child. But for now, let's go get married."

He opens the door and indicates to my parents that we have passed his test. My parents look pleased. The ceremony is basic. I feel as though I am in a dream. I don't hear much of what is said until the reverend tells Moe he can kiss me. Moe does, a light little peck on the mouth. Moe and I sign something and then my mother hugs me.

"Well, my baby girl is a married woman." I see tears in her eyes. I look at my father and he turns away, taking a handkerchief and wiping his eyes. My grandmother is stoic. She shakes her head and frowns. We pile into the car again and head back to Las Vegas.

My mother pulls up to the Stardust again and we all get out and she drives off to find parking. We stand around inside the lobby.

When she returns, she says excitedly, "We are going to see the *Folies Bergere*."

My father smiles broadly.

Moe looks at her like she has lost her mind. "Mother," he says, "You like this *Folies Bergere*?"

"Oh yes," my mother answers. "Frank and I like it very much. Tonight's show includes dinner. We'll have so much fun!"

Moe smiles timidly.

"What is so special about this *Folies* thing?" I ask.

Moe looks at me, surprised. "You not know this?" he asks, incredulously.

My mother interrupts, "Of course, she knows the *Folies*." She turns to me. "Remember when you were fourteen and we took you to Paris? We saw this same show in Paris."

Suddenly, I remember. *Folies Bergere* is what I remember as the *naked* show. I can't believe my mother would choose such a show for our wedding day.

We find our way to the show venue and stand in line for an hour. My father grows impatient. He takes a handful of bills from his wallet, shows them to the *matre d'* and we are immediately led to a front row booth. Moe watches without saying a word.

Even before dinner is served, my father has refilled his own and Moe's wine glass three times. My mother drinks more slowly than the men but she enjoys it just as much. My grandmother and I have those fake drinks called Shirley Temples, which makes me feel like I am still a baby. Then, I remember that I am not a baby – I am having a baby – and I am married.

The show turns out nothing like I remembered. The dancers are wonderful athletes with beautiful bodies. Their naked breasts are definitely an attraction, but what I appreciate is their talented dancing. Moe doesn't stop smiling. He sips on his drink continually and his eyes never leave the stage.

After the show, my mother drives us to the Algiers Motel. She hands Moe the keys to Room 17. When we are halfway up the stairs, she yells out the car window at us, "Be packed and ready at exactly 10:00 a.m. We have to go back to Tucson and I don't want to have to bang on your door to wake you up."

"Yes, mother," Moe responds softly. I catch him rolling his eyes. We enter the lobby. It is decorated in gold from top to bottom and my first thought is *tacky*. Moe walks in and looks around, smiling. "Wow," he says, "this funny place. This not like Algiers in my country." He bursts out laughing.

We go down the hallway to our room and Moe unlocks the door. Thick ornate drapes cover the windows and a matching quilt covers the biggest bed I have ever seen.

"Well," says Moe, "We have much place to sleep, no?"

"Yes, Moe, much place to sleep."

I open my suitcase and discover a new pair of pyjamas. My mother's words ring in my head, "You must look nice for your wedding night." I take the pyjamas out of the suitcase and hold them up. Baby Dolls is what the sales ticket says. She must have wanted me to know she bought them new. The bottoms are tiny little shiny underpants and the top is like a lace-infused slip cut so low that I might as well be naked. God, what was my mother thinking?

I retreat to the bathroom to figure out what to do. I struggle to fit into this garish outfit but it is at least two sizes too small. It is so uncomfortable. It pulls in all the wrong places. I feel foolish. I look in the mirror and see a terrified fat girl in Baby Doll pyjamas that are too tight on her. I want to cry.

I open the door to the bathroom and peek out. Moe has turned out the lights. I tiptoe across the carpeted floor and slide into bed next to him. He reaches out for me and holds me close. I notice that he is naked. I feel embarrassed. He feels my growing stomach. Then, he abruptly orders me to take the pyjamas off. I don't know what to do so I start to cry.

"Why you cry?" he asks, exasperated. He throws back the covers, snaps on the nightstand light, and tells me to sit up. I do as I am told. He takes off my top and looks at me. "Lay down," he orders.

When I lie down, he runs his hands over my stomach again. "The baby grows. Can you feel him kick?" he asks softly.

"Sometimes," I reply, equally softly. "It feels like a fluttering butterfly."

"What is this butterfly?" he asks.

"It's a bug. It has wings. It is very beautiful."

"Oh, that funny." He laughs out loud.

"I didn't mean it to be funny. I meant it to be true."

"Oh," he repeats. "You think child is bug?"

I roll away from him. Sometimes, it is hard to keep explaining to Moe what things mean.

He follows me across the bed and pulls me back to face him. "You are strange woman. I not understand you – but I like you very much." With that, he puts himself between my legs, begins to breathe with quick, grunting noises and in a moment I feel a huge gush of thick liquid run down my leg and onto the bed. He rolls off me, "I like you enough," he whispers.

I am unsure of what I feel at that moment. I want to get up and clean myself, but he reaches over and wraps his arms around me, holding me firmly to the bed. "After you have baby, I will teach you to like my sex."

"I – I do like you," I whisper, not sure what he means.

He laughs, "No, no. I mean I make you like what I do for you. Now you are stupid, but Moe make you smart. Moe make you woman. I think you really are virgin, or you are good actress. I think girl a girl until she have baby. Then she is woman."

This must be another strange cultural thing. Does anyone really think that a girl is a girl until she has a baby? What if she never has a baby? It doesn't make sense to me.

I am about to ask him to explain what he means when he suddenly lets go of me, climbs out of bed, goes into the bathroom and turns on the shower. A few moments later, he comes out, reaches out for his clothes lying on the chair by the bed and gets dressed. He sits in the chair and slowly smokes a cigarette. I sit up in bed and reach for my own pack. I light up and we sit smoking. Not talking, just smoking. He blows smoke rings that float up the side of the drapes and disappear into oblivion. Then, abruptly, he stubs out his butt in the ashtray and stands up.

"You sleep. You take care of baby," he orders. "I go out."

"Out?" I blurt. "Out now?" I ask, shocked. "Where are you going? It's –it's our wedding night."

Moe matter-of-factly announces, "I come back later." He walks out and locks the door behind him.

I cry until I fall asleep, wondering what I did that drove him away.

Hours later, I hear the key in the door and feel his weight on the bed. Even in my sleep, I smell the astringent reek of scotch whiskey on his breath. I think of my father.

# Don't Be Such a Baby

My parents drive us back to Tucson. As we take our bags from the car, my mother hugs me hard. "Be a good wife," she whispers.

"I will try," I tell her, though, once again, I am not sure what she means. Is being a good wife the same as being a good girl? Moe unlocks the door, and we drop our bags on the floor by the bed.

"I need supper," Moe announces. "What food we have here?" he asks.

"I don't know," I answer and head off to explore the kitchen cupboards. I see a note on the counter.

Susie and Moe: Your refrigerator and cupboards are full. There is a cookbook in the second drawer down in case you need it. Have fun. Love, Mom

I read the note out loud to Moe. He asks, "Can you cook?"

I have never cooked a single thing in my life. My mother, though she is a wonderful cook, never let me near the kitchen. "I – I – " I stutter back at Moe, "I don't think so." I open one of the doors, take out some canned soup, and proceed to open and close drawers, looking for a can opener.

Moe picks up the cans, looks at them, and slaps them back onto the counter. His face reddens and he begins to mutter softly. "What stupid country. What mother not teach daughter to cook?" Then, he laments in a louder voice. "This is bad sign, bad sign."

"What do you mean, bad sign?" Surely, cooking can't be the most important thing in the world to him. After all, I am sure I can learn. I bend down and look in the lower cupboards for a pot to heat the soup in.

"I am man," Moe tells me, patiently. "I am not cook." He sucks in large breaths of air and his face gets redder. "But I know some things – I teach you cooking," he finishes with a look of determination on his face.

I suggest that we ask Ahmed, as he is a wonderful cook. Moe looks at me and nods. "Okay, if I not know – I ask Ahmed. If you not know – you ask mother." He stops to look directly at me and asks, "Why she not teach you anything?"

My mother took over the household chores at the age of eight, cooking and cleaning for her mother and two brothers. She told me that when I was born she made a vow that I would never have to do anything around the house. She wanted me to study and do something important with my life. If I needed to learn how to do housework, I had enough time to do it later. I guess this is what she meant by later.

My explanation is incomprehensible to Moe. He mutters about my mother being a good woman, but a stupid one who didn't know how to raise children. He then attributes this to the fact that she only had one. I let him rant. Arguing with Moe is not possible – and it is not a good idea.

We begin our life in the little apartment. Moe spends most of his time in the library. Most of his professors allow him to use the tape recorder so he records the lectures and brings them home to me. I listen to the tapes and write out all the notes in detail, as neatly as I can. In the evening, we sit at the tiny kitchen table. I read his notes, then he reads them and then I ask him questions to make sure he understands what I have written. It keeps us both busy. I attend my own classes at university, resigned to quitting at Christmas. The baby is growing quickly and now people stare at me in class and whisper.

Moe insists I hurry home right after class so I can make his dinner. He eats, gives me his class recordings and then goes out again. He says he is going to the library to study. He is never back before midnight. The library closes at nine.

My mother has agreed to pay for the doctor and the cost of delivery and for my stay in the hospital. She has managed to keep me on my father's government health insurance, which means she will only have to pay a percentage of the final fees.

We celebrate the ten-day Christmas break with my parents at Fort Huachuca. Christmas has always been my mother's favourite holiday. Moe's out-of-date, worn-out clothes are the target of most of her energy this year. Moe, who never wears anything but white long-sleeved dress shirts and shiny black trousers, is gifted with a new wardrobe of brightly coloured short-sleeved sport shirts and dress shirts, each coordinated with appropriately coloured trousers. How she figured out his size is a mystery, but everything fits perfectly. He proudly tries on every item as he unwraps it. He shows his gratitude by kissing her hand and both her cheeks, and then thanking her over and over until she has to tell him to stop. My mother can't stop giggling.

When Christmas is over, I am glad. I wanted Moe to like my parents, but this overdone kissing and thanking ritual is not what I had in mind. My mother keeps telling me what a nice man he is. As well, Moe forms a weird bond with my father based on drinking and telling jokes.

As we are leaving, my mother hugs me tightly and pronounces that she thinks I have the best possible husband and I should do as I am told.

My father nods in agreement. "You have made a good choice. He will take care of you." Then he adds, "Even if he isn't like us, he's a good man."

In January, when Moe starts his next term, the only time I see him is when he appears for dinner with his tapes. He continues to go out at night. He never tries to touch me or kiss me. When I ask him why, he says it is not good for the baby. Moe describes how excited his friends are about the birth. They are making bets about when the baby will be born. They are also betting on whether it is a boy or a girl. Moe keeps telling me how progressive he is in that he doesn't care if it is a boy or a girl, but how his friends are all telling him it will be a boy.

One night, Moe comes home and announces that his exchange family wants to have a baby shower for me – tonight. "Get dressed," he orders. "Right now. They come in one hour to pick us up for party." I have only met his sponsoring family once so it surprises me that they want to have a shower for me. "Hurry up," Moe coaxes. "They will give us nice presents for the baby."

I have no clothes that fit. I put on bulky sweat pants and a well-worn maternity top. When I walk out of the bedroom, Moe looks me up and down. "You can't wear such ugly clothes!" he shouts. "You look like fat orphan!"

I go back to the bedroom, take off my clothes, pull back the bed covers and get into bed, crying. Moe comes to see where I am. His voice gets louder and I know he is mad. I cover my head with the covers and cry some more. I just want him to go away.

He reaches under the covers, grabs my arm, and pulls me up into a sitting position. "You stupid woman. Get up. Put on clothes and come. Now." His voice is sharp and I know I had better do what he says.

I slowly move up off the bed and look into his red flashing eyes. "I have no clothes," I tell him, the tears running down my face. I wipe them away and take a deep breath to stop the crying.

"You have much clothes. Just put on clothes. Why you so stupid?" His eyes look right through me, as if I am not really standing in front of him.

"Stop calling me stupid. I'm not stupid. You said the clothes I put on are ugly – but I have no other clothes that fit me." I burst into tears again.

Moe hangs his head and sighs. "Moe sorry. You pregnant. Moe not like you cry. Please stop." He puts his arms around me. "Please not cry. Put on clothes and come. You not stupid. I not know what to do. Host family very nice. We go."

I stuff myself into a different pair of sweat pants and a different maternity top. But, in the mirror I look just as ugly and just as fat as I did in the first outfit. I don't care. I follow Moe out of the bedroom and wait with him by the front door. He looks at me, but says nothing. I feel tired and sad.

Suddenly, we hear a loud honk. "Host family here," Moe informs me and we head down the sidewalk towards the car. Moe runs on ahead and I struggle to put one foot in front of the other. I feel more tired than usual. I have trouble walking, and I have a pain in my back.

By the time we reach his house, I learn that Mr. Thomson is a bachelor, aged 75, and he lives with his unmarried sister, Juanita who is 65. He is excited to meet me and his sister is really excited to have this little party. I discover that this party has been planned for more than two weeks, yet Moe didn't tell me about it until today.

We arrive at the house and I struggle out of the car. Moe mutters something in Arabic. He takes my hand and leads me into the house. I stagger through the door, and hear the laughter of many women. Immediately, Moe and Mr. Thomson disappear into another part of the house.

"Here she is at last," a voice shouts out. "Our guest of honour." The owner of the voice, an older women in a smartly designed flowered caftan, walks out of the gaily decorated room and comes towards me with her arms outstretched. She gathers me to her like her own child, like she is snuggling me into a warm and soft blanket. "We are so pleased to have you in our home at last. We have been begging Moe to bring you over but he keeps putting us off. We are so pleased that he agreed to this little party. It took some convincing on my brother's part that it is our custom and we really wanted to do it. Moe told us you don't have many friends. So, I took the liberty of inviting a bunch of mine. Come on in and let me introduce you."

I smile, feeling at ease, even in my sweat pants and old maternity top.

She leads me into the room and shows me to a big plush chair in the centre. I sit down gratefully. I am so tired that I wonder if I will be able to get up again. I smile.

The women fuss over me like mother hens. Juanita has gone to a lot of trouble. A wonderful red punch and a specially-baked cake shaped like a baby duck are served. Long streamers made of safety pins and pacifiers hang from an invisible wire. After the cake is cleared away, several ladies carry in armloads of gifts, brightly wrapped packages, some decorated with colourful bows and topped off with tiny stuffed animals, and others wrapped in receiving blankets or diapers. It takes two hours to unwrap and examine everything.

Halfway through, I struggle up out of my chair and go to the bathroom. I am dizzy, my stomach hurts, and I have a peculiar pain in my back, as well as one that comes and goes in my stomach. Lumbering back to the party room, I meet my hostess. She smiles at me with a tilt of her head that says, "Is everything okay?"

I smile back at her and nod.

An hour later, the party breaks up and Moe reappears. I sit in the back seat of the car while he goes back and forth to the house, bringing out all the baby gifts. "Wow," he says. "Our baby has much stuff." At home, I sit on the bed while Moe piles the gifts all around the bedroom. By the time he is finished, there is no place to stand. "I think we need new place to live," he says with determination. "I go look tomorrow."

The pains in my back and stomach continue and, by this time, I realize that I am in the beginning stages of labour. "Moe," I say quietly. "I think I might have the baby tomorrow. I think I'm showing signs of labour."

Moe looks up from where he is straightening a stack of gifts, "What is labour?" he asks, curiously.

"You know labour, Moe. Work, work having a baby."

"Oh," he says, and his eyes glaze over, "I take you to hospital?"

"No, I am okay for now."

"No. No, you are stupid girl. I take you now." He is across the room in one stride and stands in front of me.

"Moe, I am not stupid. Stop calling me stupid."

"Sorry, Moe not mean it," he bites his lip. "I scared. Women in my country call mother and men go away until baby born. I not know what to do."

"Well, let's call my mother," I suggest. "Then you can stay with my father."

"Good idea." Quickly, Moe walks to the corner phone booth and calls my mother.

At the end of my last visit, the doctor told me to pack a bag and be ready in the next week. I find my bag under the bed and go to the bathroom to add some personal items. Suddenly, I feel a pain that starts in my back and runs up through my stomach. I catch my breath. Never have I felt pain like this. It slowly subsides as I make my way to the bathroom.

Moe returns to tell me my mother isn't home. He tells me he called a taxi.

"It will be very expensive," I tell him.

"Moe not care," he answers, frowning.

A few minutes later, the taxi honks its arrival. Moe helps me out the door. I walk bent over and the taxi driver jumps out to take my bag from Moe. "Hope she ain't gonna have no kid in my back seat." His voice is deep and he spits out his words. His thick hairy brows come together in the middle of his forehead.

Moe looks at him with fire in his eyes as he gets in beside me. "Go to Tucson Medical Center, mister," he spits back.

Before he can say any more, I reach out and grab his arm. Another pain is hitting and it is bad. I wonder if I am going to die.

We arrive at the Tucson Medical Center. As I stumble from the taxi, Moe holds my arm and together we struggle up to and through the front doors. A nurse greets us with a wheelchair and I am whisked away, leaving Moe to fill out the paperwork. I wonder if he can.

A student nurse comes in. She fusses over me, taking my blood pressure and checking my heart rate and then putting the stethoscope on my belly to listen to the baby's heartbeat. Then, Dr. Bryson comes in. He examines me quickly and then fills a syringe, saying, "I'm going to give you something to help the pain." As the needle empties into my arm, the hospital fades away.

I open my eyes and look around. I can't really remember where I am. I turn my head and see my mother sitting in a chair across the room from me. As soon as I move, she gets up and comes over to the bed.

"Susie? How are you? Are you awake?" Her hand brushes the hair off my forehead. She looks worried.

I nod. "I feel awful," I say in a croaky half-whisper.

"Well, you should feel awful," she answers, sympathetically. "You've had quite the time. The doctors thought you would need a C-Section for sure, but they worked with you and you finally had your daughter." She strokes my hand. "A daughter! Imagine! I'm a grandmother."

"I – I have a baby girl?" I whisper.

"Yes, she is pretty beat up though. They used forceps. Her little head is really bad. It's looks like a pinhead. The doctor says it will reshape itself. She has birthmarks on her head, too, but they should disappear before long."

Then she frowns, "We've been so worried about you. You keep wandering in and out of consciousness. The doctor wanted you knocked out so you didn't have to feel all the pain of labour. Do you remember anything?"

The little pieces of the labour that I remember are like a nightmare. My mother is still talking. "They pretty much kept us out until you actually had the baby." She describes what I missed. "Moe was really impatient. As soon as you had the baby, he went off with his friends. I've only seen him once since then. He said to call him at Ahmed's when you wake up." She smiles at me. "I'll go do that in a minute. He should probably be here."

I ask. "Why isn't he here?"

"Oh, who knows? You know how men are with stuff like this. They manage to find other things to do." My mother fusses with the blankets and pats my hand.

"Can I see the baby?" I need to see for myself that she is okay. What my mother has told me is a bit scary.

"I think so. They brought her in to feed several times but you have been out cold." She laughs nervously. "It's been three days. I was starting to worry about you." She glances toward the door to my room. "I imagine they'll bring her in soon." Her mind then skips to another topic. "I'm not too happy with the name you two decided on, though. What kind of a name is Zohra?"

"It's his custom, Mom." I whisper, thinking Moe could come in at any moment. Surely, he wants to see his child. "Zohra is his mother's name and she is dead and they always name their first child after a dead relative."

"What about our customs? She is half-American, you know." My mother stands up and moves to look out the window. "And another thing," she continues, "Why can't she have a middle name?"

"It's the custom, Mom, it's the custom. He says nobody has a middle name in his country so it would make it difficult for us if the baby has a middle name."

"Well, I think that's so silly. How do you even know you won't live right here in Arizona? Why can't he just consider that possibility?"

"It's not a possibility, Mom, so get used to it." I feel tired again. I close my eyes, but she continues.

"You are so foolish to even consider going there. They don't treat women or children very nice. We know that from living in those countries."

I open my eyes and struggle to reply. "Moe's not like that, Mom. He's always nice to me." At that moment, I believe what I am saying.

I hear the rustling of nylon stockings, the thud of footsteps and a high pitched, small birdlike cry. I turn to see a tall, horsey-looking older nurse standing over me with a bundle in her arms.

"Well you're awake, finally," she says. She sounds disgusted. "This baby needs to eat from you. She's fussy and needs your milk. So, sit up."

I look at the nurse and the bundle, but I feel too weak to move. "What?"

"You'll have to sit up to do this. So get with it. I don't have all day."

I try to get myself into a sitting position, but I fall back because of the dull throbbing that starts in my bottom. "Oh, God. I hurt," I cry out. Another dull aching pain travels up my bottom and into my back. I start to cry.

"For Pete's sake! How old are you anyway? Twelve?" she barks at me. "You just had a baby – you're not dying. Don't be such a baby. You're worse than the baby." The nurse stares at me for a moment and then abruptly turns and leaves the room, carrying my baby.

Tears roll down my face.

My mother comes to the side of my bed. "Honey," she says in a tightly controlled voice, "See if you can't at least try to sit up. The baby needs to be fed. You've been out of it for three days."

The horse-faced nurse returns and with her is another older woman. "Okay," this new nurse says, "between the two of us we should be able to get you up and at it. First, we'll take out your catheter and help you to the bathroom. Then, we'll clean you up and bring the baby. It's time for you to get on with it."

My mother uses this opportunity to leave the room to call Moe.

The nurses help me through going to the bathroom and washing up. They guide me back to my bed. I still can't believe that I have a baby – a daughter. Moe must be really disappointed.

The arrival of my baby brings me out of my thoughts. The nurse places her in my arms. She is the first baby I have ever held. I lift the blanket and look at her. She looks like she has been in a war. Her little head is shaped like a cone with big blue bruise marks above each ear. Her eyelids are also bright red-purple bruise-coloured. The nurse explains that the bruising colour on her eyes is a birthmark that will go away with time. She says it comes from how the baby sits in the womb. She shows me another blotchy red mark that travels from the back of the baby's neck, along the base of her skull and halfway over her head. Again, she assures that it will mostly go away in time.

"The doctor had to do a lot of pulling with the forceps to get her out," she explains. The baby's little face looks swollen, again apparently normal for a forceps birth. I pull back the cover and examine her feet and toes. They are so tiny. I can't believe they are real.

Suddenly, the baby cries, a loud frantic wail. I look at her, frozen. She cries again. The emotion that crawls up my spine overwhelms me. I feel lost. I cry with her.

The nurses stand at the end of the bed shaking their heads in disgust. "Well," the first one says, "I've never seen any thing like this in my whole life."

I cry harder.

"Me neither," says the other nurse. Finally, the second nurse steps forward and takes the baby from my arms. "We'll try this again when you feel better," she announces, and both nurses and my baby disappear out the door and down the hallway.

My face is wet with tears. I don't know what to do. I feel hopeless. I am a failure as a mother.

My mother reappears. The nurses have filled her in by about my lack of mothering skills. She stands by my bed for a moment and then sits down next to me. She reaches out and brushes the hair away from my face. "Honey, things will get better, I promise. Having a baby is really a hard thing. You'll feel better when we all get home and into your new place."

"New place?" I mumble through my tears. "What new place?"

"Well, while you were toiling away in here, Moe and I went out and rented you a new place. It's bigger and better than the little room. It's a little apartment, still by the university. It will be better for you and the baby. There is a nice kitchen and two bedrooms. We also got a crib and playpen and lots of nice things for the baby. Those are presents from your dad and me. It is supposed to be a surprise. But, I thought I should tell you before you actually get there. Moe seems very pleased with everything."

My first meal in three days arrives. I eat it all and begin to feel better. I tell them to bring the baby back and I will try to feed her.

The next day, I still cry whenever the baby cries, and I still have trouble getting her to feed. The nursery staff has already decided I am hopeless at breastfeeding and tell me to feed her formula. My nipples are sore, but I decide formula will be too expensive and I make up my mind to learn how to breastfeed, no matter what.

Moe peeks around the door before entering. I look up and smile when I see him. He steps into the room carrying a large vase of beautiful peach-coloured roses.

"You already sent flowers," I protest as I point toward the large vase of red roses sitting on my nightstand with his carefully worded card. *Thank you for having my baby*, it says and it is signed, *Love Always, Moe.*

"These flowers from Arab student friends," he announces. "They also give much money." He shows me an envelope filled with money that has been tucked in with the flowers. "It is custom."

I smile again at Moe and he kisses me gingerly on the cheek. "She look like wounded soldier, no?" he asks softly.

"Yes, she does," I agree.

"She is still very beautiful, like you." He hesitates before adding, "But, she have my beautiful family eyes. I think she break many hearts someday."

"Yes, Moe. I think she will."

"What doctor say about going home?" Moe changes the subject.

"I don't know," I answer. "I haven't really seen any doctor yet. I have been asleep for three days. I don't remember much of anything. I hear you went off with your friends. Why did you do that?"

"Having baby is woman's job. Men not strong this way. It is for women to take care of women," he says again, shrugging his shoulders. "It our way."

"Moe, are you upset she's a girl?" I want to be reassured.

"No," Moe smiles. "Someday we have boy, but I like girls." His face slips into a frown as he continues, "This is new world. We not kill baby girls anymore in my country. Girls do much housework and it is good to have one."

"Oh, god, how kind of you." I say, sarcastically. He must be joking. "Do you mean that you really used to kill baby girls in your village?"

"Of course, but not in my time. In the time of my parents. They want to have boy first and they let baby girls born first die in first days." He looks at my shocked face and says, "Just a custom," as if that explains everything.

Six days after I give birth to Zohra, we leave the hospital, and Moe takes the baby and me to our new apartment. It is much bigger than the little room we had been renting, but I am not sure if it is really better. The walls are thin, and our new neighbours turn out to be cranky about the baby and her crying. They yell and bang on the walls.

I am cranky about the baby crying, too. I have mastered the art of breastfeeding, but it doesn't seem to satisfy my daughter. She cries all the time. I take her to the doctor, thinking he will know how to fix her. But, he tells me it is just colic and he has no remedy for it.

"Give her time and her system will adjust," he tells me.

I take her back home and she cries some more.

After a week of listening to her cry constantly and being unable to stop my own tears in response, I call my mother for help and she comes to stay with me. Moe, tired of listening to the crying, packs a small bag and tells me he is going to stay at Ahmed's until I get the baby and myself under control. He has to study for final exams and he can't get any work done with both of us crying.

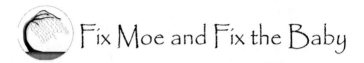 Fix Moe and Fix the Baby

My mother arrives to help with Zohra. She lasts a week. She says, "I am too old and too tired to care for a baby like this for any length of time." As she is packing to leave, she turns and says, "Granny is really good with babies and she might be able to help. What do you think of me and you taking the baby to Salt Lake City to visit Granny?"

"What about Moe?" I ask.

"Well, what about him?" She waves the clothes she has in her hands. "He isn't here and anyway, he is going to summer school. If you and the baby aren't here, maybe he can stay home and get his school work done and not have to stay at his friends all the time."

"I'll talk to him about it," I say.

The next day, Moe drops by. Immediately, I see that he is distracted. He can't sit still. He paces back and forth in our living room.

"Moe, you are really sad, really deep in thought," I try to tell him that Zohra won't be so difficult forever. "I know this hasn't been easy for you - but I hope things will get better. I hope my Granny can help."

He looks at me sadly, and then he takes in a huge breath of air. The words pour out. "Moe not sad about baby. Moe have secret thing to tell you and I am waiting long time so I not upset you. I know baby thing hard for you."

When he pauses, looking for the right words to tell me the secret, I jump in. "What secret thing?" I ask. Then, wanting to make it easier for him, I try teasing. "You have a secret you haven't told me?" I wink at him.

Moe looks at the floor, then at my face and then at the floor again, unwilling to see the humour in my words or my winking. He says solemnly, "Yes, I have big secret."

Another big breath and he starts again. "You remember how I long ago told you that I had to go away for a while? It was the same day we make love first time in adobe house. You remember?"

"I remember," I nod, as images of the stained mattress, and his body on top of mine flash through my mind. Does his secret have to do with that?

"Well, I still have to go away, but now I tell you why I go. Okay?"

"Okay," I answer.

Moe looks at the floor while he speaks, embarrassed. He launches into his explanation, and with many hesitations as he chooses the right words, he manages to make me understand. While he was studying at New York University, he got a bad flu and the doctors gave him an antibiotic that caused such an allergic reaction in him that he almost died. He was in the hospital for three months. That's the first piece.

While he was in the hospital, the doctors discover a problem that, in Moe's words, "happened before I was born." He shows me pictures and medical documents about this problem, which is in his urinary tract and lower intestine. He tells me to read them. From the medical documents, I find out that he has multiple birth defects, and that while he was hospitalized in New York, surgeons were able to repair his urinary tract, but there wasn't a surgical procedure available to fix his lower intestine.

"So, what is wrong?" I ask. I have read all of the medical explanation but I can't follow the scientific names for the various body parts, so I don't know how the problem affects him.

He explains that when he has a bowel movement a long piece of intestine drops out of his body. He gets many infections from this and it is very painful.

"In my country, my parents do nothing with this problem. They not know what to do and they have no money – so they not pay attention." He still can't look at me as he talks.

"What does this have to do with you going away?" I finally

ask, after an awkward silence. I don't want to embarrass him any further, but I can't understand what he is really trying to tell me.

Moe sighs and starts again. "I tell our father my problems when you are in hospital." He pauses and glances up at me. Then, he drops his eyes again and continues, his rate of speech quickening with each sentence. "Father is friends with surgeon and this surgeon agree to fix me. Father make appointment for operation for me with his surgeon friend. I go to hospital in a few days."

Moe's face is now full of excitement. He seems more excited than worried. He waits for me to say something.

"Is this operation expensive?" I finally ask. We don't have very much money in our savings account.

"No. Doctor tell me it is free because it is new operation and they put it in medical books. They take pictures of it – but no one see my face, only my – you know," his face turning red at this revelation. "It embarrass Moe very much, but I am happy for this opportunity to get fixed." Moe stutters. "I – I not tell you before because I not want to bother you with baby and everything."

"Moe, you told me you were going away a long time ago," I say. "That was before you knew my father. I understand where you are going now, but where were you going then?"

Moe answers, "I was thinking of going to another doctor by myself – but I lost courage. Moe is very lucky man to have Father. He help me very much. Such an operation will make Moe feel much better."

Then, Moe suddenly changes the subject. He looks directly at me, all of the embarrassment and hesitation of the past few minutes gone. "Mother talk to me about taking you to Salt Lake City to visit Granny. She say Granny can fix Zohra's problems."

"Oh Moe, I really don't want to leave you here by yourself. I can go when you are –"

"No, no. You go." Moe interrupts. "When you leave?"

"But who will take care of you?" I ask.

"Oh, nurses take care of me," he answers quickly. "Nurses and my good friends. It is best this way. You fix baby and the doctor fix Moe and it will be good."

I hug him and he hugs me back. "This is good," he keeps repeating.

Moe has his operation on May 25, 1963. My mother and I wait until the surgery is over and we are assured by the doctor that he will be fine and just needs time to heal.

I kiss him goodbye on May 27 and leave for my grandmother's house in Salt Lake City with Zohra and my mother.

My grandmother's answer to Zohra's colic is to rub her little tongue with a whiskey-soaked cheesecloth every time she cries. I am astonished. My grandmother is a devout Christian Scientist and disapproves highly of anything to do with alcohol. I watch in amazement as Granny faithfully and carefully rubs whiskey on my daughter's tongue every day for a week. Between the whiskey treatments, Granny spends countless hours carrying Zohra around the house, praying. To my surprise, Zohra starts to sleep longer and longer hours. At the end of the week, Granny informs me that my baby is cured. Granny assures me Zohra will now sleep through the night. I am not sure if it is the whiskey or the praying that brought about the change in my baby's behaviour. In the end, I secretly think Zohra has decided to shut up just to put a stop to my grandmother's constant chattering.

By this time, my grandmother is obsessed with the baby, which means my mother and I are free to do whatever we want. I have to feed Zohra, but other than that Granny is happier if my mother and I disappear from the house. We go outside looking for things to do. First, we weed my grandmother's garden and then we go downtown and shop endlessly. I have no money but my mother buys me whatever I want.

Mother and I talk to Moe and my father at least once a week. My father visits Moe every day while he is in the hospital. He is impressed with Moe's progress and so is the doctor. Moe is a minor celebrity at the hospital. Professional photographers come to take pictures of his rear-end nearly every day.

Of course, we hear this from my father and not from Moe. "Yep," my father tells us, chuckling, "I think Moe can safely say that he has the most famous butt in the medical world."

Moe, however, doesn't talk about the daily picture taking. The first few days he sounds depressed, and sometimes, his speech is slurred by the pain medication. However, after two weeks, I notice a big improvement in his spirits and I find that the picture taking has ended and he will soon move to Ahmed's house. At the end of the third week he is released from the hospital and goes to be with Ahmed and his friends. Then, every time I phone, he tells me how much he has improved and how happy he is to be *home.*

"Home?" I ask him. "You still `think Ahmed's house is your home?" I tease him. I don't want him to forget we have our own apartment. That is where his home is.

"Of course, Ahmed's house my home. He is my brother," he answers, curtly.

The sharpness of his tone cuts me. What about our home? It must be that Arab brothers thing again. Will I ever understand how he thinks?

At the end of June, after nearly six weeks in Salt Lake City, it is time for us to go home. I can tell my mother is ready to return to her own house by the way she talks to Granny. Mother's lips turn under and her voice sounds impatient. Occasionally, when we are alone, she lets her exasperation spill out with comments like, "Oh that woman is so stubborn" or "she is so-o-o-o- bossy." I smile. I feel the same way about my mother.

The daylong trip back to Tucson is uneventful. Moe and my father greet us at the apartment door. Moe is a lot thinner and looks a lot older, but he is smiling and immediately he says he is happy to see me.

"Ah," he says, as he reaches out to hold the baby. "She grows so big. Now, she is very beautiful."

After my parents leave, the three of us curl up on the couch together. I talk about my time in Salt Lake with Granny and my mother, and he talks about his time in the hospital and at Ahmed's and then at the apartment.

"Your father do shopping," Moe announces appreciatively. "He very generous man. He very kind man. I think you are from good family. I think your father is good man."

I nod. "He is a good man, Moe."

Moe takes me in his arms and holds me close. I put my head

on his chest and listen to his heart beat. It has been such a long time since I have been close to him. I feel an inkling of desire begin and I try to kiss him.

"Not now," he says shaking his head. "Moe still have pain."

In a few minutes, Zohra starts to cry. I pick her up, and bring her back to the couch. She is hungry. I automatically unfasten my bra and attach her to my breast. She drinks easily and noisily and I smile, contented.

Moe smiles, too. "You learn a lot from Granny, no?"

"Yes," I answer. "I learned a lot. I am not so afraid now."

When the baby finishes eating, I change her diaper and take her for her bath. Moe follows me around, watching everything I do. "Yes," he repeats, "You learn a lot from your granny. Too bad your mother not so good at teaching."

I ignore the remark about my mother. "And you learn a lot from my father. Your English is much better these days, Moe."

Moe smiles at me again. "Yes, I know. Your father helps me very much. I like him very much." Tentatively, he adds, "I think he likes drinking very much, no? I also think your father afraid of mother."

I laugh at his last remark. "You might be right about that. She can be bossy."

"Oh, I am right," he declares, nodding his head, emphatically. "He never argue with her." Moe tilts his head at me and with a big smile says, "Father also like ladies very much. He always looking and ladies always look at him. He take me to his club and ladies come and kiss him. He big man, I think."

"Oh Moe, my dad has many friends – men and women. He always kisses the women. It doesn't mean anything."

Moe laughs, and I notice a twinkle in his eyes, "Oh, it mean something," he says. "He kiss them on the mouth. In my country, we kiss everyone on cheeks." He grabs me to demonstrate and kisses both my cheeks. "But if I kiss woman not my wife on mouth, I want to use my penis on her."

I burst out laughing. "You are so funny, Moe. This is America, Moe. Everybody kisses everybody."

"Yes," Moe answers slowly, licking his lips and smiling wickedly, "It is America – but America not change that your father have a penis. He is true man."

I am not sure what *true man* means, but it is useless to try to make Moe understand how different we are. However, as long as he is laughing, I don't care what he thinks.

The days go by and our routine returns to normal. I spend my days taking care of Zohra, playing with her, taking her for walks, washing clothes, making meals and doing housework. Moe goes to school early in the morning and returns at supper. We eat together and Moe delivers his tapes to me to transcribe. After supper he goes back to the library. I still wonder what he does from the time the library closes at nine until the time he arrives home at midnight, but I say nothing.

Zohra is still a fussy baby. Not as bad as she was in her early months, but from time to time, I am still sitting in the rocking chair with her when Moe comes home from his nightly jaunts. He sometimes sits with her while I get some sleep.

On Friday nights, we go to my parent's house for dinner. Moe listens carefully to every word my father says and my father is delighted to have such an attentive audience for his old military stories. The only time Moe is very quiet is when my father talks politics. I can tell by Moe's expression that he doesn't like what my father says. Once, I asked Moe when we got home why he doesn't say something when he disagrees with my father. Moe answers, "It not good to disagree with your parents. It not respectful."

Most weekends, Moe studies. Sometimes, he takes time to go for a picnic in the park with us or to take us to visit Ahmed. I look forward to these outings, especially the ones to Ahmed's. He always invites such interesting people and I enjoy having a chance to talk with adults.

One Saturday night in the middle of October, as soon as Moe finishes supper with me and Zohra, he announces," I go tonight to Ahmed's. He is having party. It is not family party." He walks to the bedroom to change.

Excited at the prospect of a rare adult outing, I follow him and say, "I could ask my parents to babysit."

"No," he says, loudly. "Not good party for you or baby."

"What do you mean?" I ask. I understand that the party is not for children, but, if my parents will look after Zohra, then Moe and I will be able to go out together.

"I mean, it is party and you are mother and you stay home with baby."

I stare at Moe. I watch a darkness build around him, beginning in his eyes, and then in a tightening of the muscles in his neck.

"Calm down," my brain tells me, "don't argue." But I don't heed my own warning.

"I don't understand," I snap back. "Why –?" Before I can get the question past my lips, his hand flies towards me and I hear the loud clap of an open hand meeting flesh. The force of the blow stops my words. I reel back, slamming my head against the door and sliding heavily onto the floor.

He stands over me, bellowing, "Moe said no. You not go. I am husband. I say no. You do what I say." He grabs me by my elbow and pulls me up off the floor. "I not beat you – but you do what I say."

His eyes are blood red and above the open collar of his dress shirt, the veins in his neck are poking through his skin. He yanks me close to him and with loud staccato words and spittle flying over my face, he screams at me, "NEVER ASK WHY WHEN I TELL YOU NO. Do you understand what I say?"

Without waiting for a reply, he shoves me hard onto the bed. He stands over me for a few moments. I watch the tension drain out of him. In a quiet soft voice, like a parent talking to a child, he whispers, "Remember, you are willow. I tell you before – you must be willow."

He turns, and walks out of the house, slamming the door hard behind him.

I cannot move. The sound of the slamming door echoes in my head and I want to cry. But there are no tears, only his words. "You must be willow."

I hear the baby cry, probably wakened by his shouting. I slowly get off the bed and look in the mirror. The woman staring back at me looks sad and bewildered. I can see the outline of thick fingers across her cheek. "You better smarten up," I tell her. "You better figure out how to be a willow." I turn to pick up my crying baby and we weep.

 More Room for Us

Our lives swing back into our routine. Moe's major goal in life is to graduate so he can return to his country. He continues to go to the library every night and I continue to ignore the fact that he returns home at midnight, long after the library closes. I see him mostly at supper and late at night when he crawls into our bed. On the nights when he wraps his arms around me hungrily and searches my body for his own enjoyment, I smell alcohol on his breath. Other nights, he enters our bed carefully and quietly. Many nights I lay awake long after he has started to snore.

During the day I transcribe his class notes from the tape recorder and take care of Zohra. The friends I used to have from high school have dropped out of sight, gone away to university in other states, or uncomfortable with my marriage to a foreigner. Once a week my mother stops by and takes me shopping or out to lunch. She sometimes takes her granddaughter overnight and asks me often if I need a break. I enjoy her company these days.

One day, my mother, usually the 'Queen of Perky' - even if she has to fake it - stops in. I hug her, but she doesn't respond with her usual enthusiastic chitchat and tight little squeeze.

"What's wrong?" I ask.

At first, she says nothing. Then, she sits down on the couch and pats the spot next to her. "Is Moe home?" she asks.

I shake my head. Why would she ask that? She knows he will be at class at this time of day. I sit down next to her and wait for her to speak.

"I'm afraid for you." Her voice is almost a whisper.

"Afraid for me?" I repeat, surprised.

Looking into my eyes, she slowly pushes the words out. "I

know I shouldn't say this, honey." She reaches up and moves a stray bit of hair from my forehead. "But – you are naïve." Before I can speak, she touches my lips with her hand and continues. "All my life I've known the truth about men. I've just known." She pauses, and then folds her hands into her lap. "Never," she says firmly. "Never ever trust men. No matter what they do or say or how good they seem to be. Never trust them."

Surprised by the passion of her words, I think immediately of my father. Is there something I don't know about him? Then, I think of Moe. I am confused. Is she talking about my father or is she talking about Moe? "Why would you say that?" I ask, finally.

"I just know. You can't trust men." The words come out with a finality to them that leaves no room for questions or misinterpretation.

We sit silently next to each other. She reaches into her pocket, pulls out a check, and presses it into my hands. My mother often gives me money – but not like this. She buys me a new blouse or brings an outfit for Zohra, and she and dad help out with extra money for rent and groceries all of the time.

She folds my fingers around the slip of paper. "I want you to take this check and put it in the bank and not tell anyone. Every time you get some money, like for your birthday, or whatever, put it in the bank. Do not tell Moe about it." She emphasizes this last statement by repeating it, "Do not, under any circumstances, tell Moe. Promise me you won't tell him."

"I don't keep secrets from Moe," I tell her. But, I don't tell her what else goes through my mind. I don't say to her, "But he keeps secrets from me. He doesn't tell me where he goes when the library closes. He doesn't tell me why he comes to bed with alcohol on his breath after a late night out." I only say, "I hate secrets."

She looks at me. "Then, you're a damn fool."

I bow my head. "I'm sorry you feel that way. I thought you liked Moe." Neither of us is angry. Our conversations are so different these days. We don't have screaming matches any more. It helps that she has stopped telling me what to do, and that she doesn't try to make me feel guilty when I disagree with her.

She hugs me. "Please do what I say. You will thank me some

day. I do like Moe – as men go – but men are not to be trusted as far as I am concerned." She pauses and I think she is going to tell me something else, but she only says, "I have my reasons."

I hesitate, still not sure how to respond. Something tells me not to argue with her. "Okay, Mom." I wave the check and put it into my pocket. "Tomorrow, I will open an account." Still not sure what to say, I tell her, "Thanks."

The next day, with Zohra in her stroller, I walk to the closest bank, open an account in my own name and deposit my mother's check.

In October of 1963, we are still living in the second apartment that Moe and my parents rented for us. At first, the neighbours, students who were studying for exams and writing papers, complain about the baby keeping them awake. Now, the neighbours, students new to university life and freedom from parental supervision, are keeping us awake with parties and loud noises. We decide to look for a quieter place, even though we can't afford to pay more rent.

My daily walks around the university with Zohra become a quest to see if I can find a new place to live. One day, late in October, on Tyndall Avenue, I walk by an older-looking house with a small *House for Rent* sign and a phone number. I arrange for my mother and Moe to meet me and the owner of the house that evening. Even as I make my plans, I am filled with misgiving. I should talk to Moe first. He will really be mad that I found a house on my own.

The owner and I wander through the house while we wait for Moe and my mother to arrive. There is one bedroom, a dining room, a kitchen, a living room, and, along the back of the house, a screened porch. "You could use the porch as a second bedroom, if you had to," he offers.

Moe walks in with my mother. I glance at him. He seems to be in good spirits. He looks around the house. The man continues his tour explaining again about the back porch being used for a second bedroom. He shows us the bathroom. It has a tub and shower and looks freshly painted. I study Moe to get his reaction. He shows me nothing.

"How much for the rent?" my mother asks.

The man looks at her. "Will you be living here, Ma'am?" he asks, politely.

"Oh, good gracious, no," she replies. "I am the mother, but I still have an interest in where my chickens land – if you know what I mean?"

The owner tells her the rent is fifty dollars a month.

"Fifty dollars!" Moe blurts out unhappily. "Fifty dollar is too much for us." He turns to head for the door.

"Now, just a minute, Moe," my mother says. "Fifty dollars isn't that much for this house. With a little bit of money for some plywood, we could fix up the porch, board up the screening and you would have a nice place to live for a year or two. It's quite comfortable, actually. You'll need a bit more furniture. I'm sure we can scrounge up some for you. What do you think, Susie, would you be happy here?" She looks at me closely. She wants me to give her a truthful answer.

"I would be very happy here," I nod, enthusiastically.

"Moe not afford this house." Moe looks at my mother and frowns disappointedly.

"It's okay, Moe. Dad and I will help out here. Don't worry." She steps up and puts her hand gently on his arm. "I'll sign the lease," she finishes. "That way, there won't be any unforeseen problems."

As we walk down the sidewalk towards my mother's car, she turns and says, "I guess you have a new place to live. This is much better than where you are. We'll hire people to clean it and then you should be set."

Moe looks at my mother. "I can never repay you, Mother," he says, seriously. Tears appear in his eyes. "You are good and generous woman. I promise to take care of your daughter and granddaughter," he says, forcefully. "I promise."

My mother smiles and walks on toward the car. She calls back over her shoulder to Moe, "You make good on your word to take care of my daughter and granddaughter. That's the only thanks I need." She drives us back to our apartment.

November 1, 1963 comes. Our meagre belongings are packed

and ready to move. With the comment that moving is women's work and he has to study for a test, Moe goes off somewhere.

By evening, the little house is shining brightly and my father has arrived just ahead of a small van, which delivers a new double bed, and a kitchen table and four chairs. As the days pass, my mother visits often and each time she brings some new item, sometimes purchased from the second hand store, sometimes a castoff from one of her wealthy friends. During November, we acquire a whole household full of gently used items, till we have everything we need

"Wow," I say. "Wow, Mom, thanks." It's all I can manage. My parents have done so much for us.

"It's okay," my mom says, hugging me. "Just promise me you'll be happy." She makes me look at her as she speaks, and I think of the check in my new bank account, and the little bit of money that I have added to the original sum.

"Okay, Mom. I promise."

Moe is happy with the house. He wants to invite his friends over. They have sometimes come for coffee or dessert, but we have never had a real party. He decides that he will cook an Algerian meal on the following weekend.

Surprised, I ask, "You are going to cook a whole meal?"

"Of course." he responds. "How do you think I live before you?"

"I thought Ahmed cooked or you went to a restaurant."

"No, sometimes I cook." He looks at me and laughs. "Moe have many secrets, no?"

Two days before the party, he comes home right after his class at three in the afternoon. "We going to make a few dishes for the party," Moe begins my education in Algerian cooking. "Every Algerian meal must have four things: One is couscous, which you know about. One is meat dish – either roast lamb or lamb stew. One is mint tea. One is bread. Algerian bread. It is long like the French loaf. It is used to scoop up meat stew sauce." As he works, he tells me how he is looking forward to inviting his sisters to our house in Algeria as soon as we are settled, so they can teach me to cook.

I smile, and say I look forward to that day, too.

The night before the party, Moe sets the alarm for five in the morning. "We have to be sure we get everything done by the time guests arrive," he explains. By nine, the house is filled with the unbelievably sensual smells of garlic, cumin, roasting lamb and freshly crushed mint. Moe works busily in the kitchen and when Zohra wakes up, I get her dressed and feed her breakfast. My mouth is watering, but Moe won't let me taste anything.

He says, "You not allowed to eat until the dinner. You must keep room for this wonderful food," he teases. "If you eat anything before, you ruin whole meal. You must come to this meal as virgin comes to her wedding bed, hungry to be filled."

Moe is obviously happy. In fact, he smiles lustfully at me.

"You are happy today, Moe." I say, pleased with his good humour.

"Moe happy his friends come to eat at his house and I am host. Hosting very important in my country. I have much to, how you say, pay back to my friends. Always they feed me and now I feed them. This is good time for me."

Moe has invited ten friends to his party. I have met them all. I dress in my best dress – a full-to-the-floor cotton muumuu, with pink flowers on a black background. It has thick straps that run over the shoulders and a gathered bodice. I like what I see in the mirror. As I twist and turn to look at myself, Moe comes into the bedroom to change his clothes.

He pauses and looks at me. "You look very beautiful," he says in a low sensual voice.

I smile at him, glad that he finds me attractive.

Then, abruptly, his sensual voice ripples into his authoritative voice. "Cover up your arms," he demands sternly.

"Moe," I say, "this dress doesn't have sleeves. Besides, it's too hot for sleeves."

Moe stares at me and says impatiently, "Then wear different dress or put shirt under it. Your arms are naked. My friends not need to look at your naked arms."

I start to argue with him but when I open my mouth, I catch a glimpse of the dark look in his eyes. I sigh. I go to the closet.

"You good girl," he comments as he presses by me to go back to the kitchen. "You learning."

I find a pink blouse and put it on under my dress. A glance in the mirror is all I need to confirm that it looks ridiculous. All I need to complete the outfit is a hood and a veil over my face.

As I am about to follow Moe into the kitchen, I hear Zohra whimper in her crib. I slip into her room just in time to watch her roll onto her hands and knees and begin to rock back and forth in her crib, something she has been doing a lot lately. Sometimes, when she rocks, she bangs her head against the end of the crib. When I mention to Moe that I can't help but think something is not right about the rocking, Moe tells me it is normal. He tells me that his brothers and sisters used to rock like Zohra.

"Of course, they not have cribs, but they crawl up to a wall in our house just to bang their head and rock. It a family thing."

Now, I go toward the crib, saying, "Wow, Zsa Zsa, you are just a real little rocker, aren't you honey?" She looks at me, smiles, shakes her little head, rolls over onto her bottom and holds her little arms out for me to pick her up. I hug her close, and she clings to me. I feel my tears well up. It has taken me all these months to look forward to picking her up, to want to hold her. When she was tiny, she spent so many months crying. I was always afraid that I might hurt her in some way or do something wrong in taking care of her.

She will be joining us for our first party. Moe says that in Algeria children are always welcome at parties. He is very proud of her and has even laid out her party clothes. She is definitely Daddy's girl. I get her dressed in her pretty aqua-coloured pinafore and white tights. The doorbell rings and Moe answers it. At the sound of Ahmed's familiar voice, I take Zohra to greet him. Zohra nearly leaps into his arms. Ahmed smiles and reaches out to take her.

Then, Moe calls me to the kitchen. "You look very nice in your dress," he smiles. "See, you can cover up and you look better."

"Thanks, you look pretty good yourself – even if you're not covered up," I say, sarcastically. Moe frowns, but says nothing. I envy his shorts and t-shirt attire. He looks so free and cool. I argue with him in my head. "This is Arizona. Arizona and 90 degrees."

The doorbell rings several times in the next half-hour. Two of his single friends have their American girl friends with them. His married friends arrive alone. I greet the guests and carry bags of beer and whiskey to the kitchen.

"I thought Moslems didn't drink," I say as I walk to the counter with the bottles.

Moe, stirring something in a large pot, looks up and smiles. "Ah, well, when we are at party in foreign place, sometimes we like to enjoy drink or two." He smiles again. "You know I drink sometimes, especially when I am with Father."

I continue, "I thought your married friends would bring their wives and their children, Moe. I thought this was supposed to be a family dinner."

"Well, maybe they change their minds." He turns his attention back to the food. As he makes the final preparations, he informs me that I should wait until everyone has been fed before I fill my plate, in case there isn't enough. He stirs his stew one more time and then puts the spoon down. Dinner is ready.

Moe fills a plate for each guest and they return to their seats. I look into the living room and see Ahmed with Zohra on his knee, feeding her from his plate. Zohra loves every bite he offers. She seems to be entertaining the whole crowd. Moe walks up to me as I watch.

"Our daughter is real Algerian. See how she loves the food? She eats hot peppers and couscous at seven months. I think this is big deal." He nods approvingly and carries his plate into the living room, taking the last seat, next to one of the American girlfriends.

I turn back into the kitchen and fill my plate with some of each wonderful dish. I start toward the living room and then remember that there is no place to sit. I seat myself in the kitchen. Slowly, I savour the tastes, the smells of the stew. I have done as Moe asked. I haven't eaten a thing since the early morning. He is right about not eating until this meal. I feel like I can't get enough.

As I finish eating, Moe appears in the doorway with Zohra. "You make Zohra go to bed now. Okay?" he says.

I look at him, but say nothing. I smell liquor on his breath. The noise from the front room is getting louder, with much laughter and clinking of glasses. How will I get Zohra to sleep with this noise? I take her to the bedroom and change her diaper. I kiss her goodnight and lay her down in her crib, turn off her light, and gently pull the door closed behind me.

When I walk back into the kitchen, I see a stack of dirty dishes. The laughter from the living room suggests the party is going well. At that moment, one of the American girl friends staggers into the kitchen and announces she has to go to the bathroom. She has taken off her blouse and is parading around in a black lacy bra.

"I'm hot," she announces, handing me her blouse. "I'm hot and I have to pee." She teeters and is about to fall. I reach out and catch her by the arm. She smiles at me drunkenly and I guide her to the bathroom barely in time for her to throw up down the side of the bathtub. "Oh god," she says, "I want to die."

"Yes," I answer under my breath. "That would be a very good idea." I pause. "But, you can do it somewhere else."

Zohra starts to cry. I leave my unwanted charge and go to the crib. Zohra is on her hands and knees, consoling herself by rocking back and forth. Every second or third rock she hits her head. I lay her back down and cover her up. She is quiet.

I don't hear any more noise from the bathroom and I don't want to know what is going on in the living room, so I go back to the kitchen where I fill the sink with hot soapy water.

Suddenly, one of Moe's friends appears in the doorway. "Did you see a blonde girl?" he inquires in a thick accent.

I look at him and state flatly, "Yes, she is in the bathroom throwing up."

"Oh," he says and returns to the living room. In a moment, the other girlfriend appears at the kitchen door. "Is Candice in here somewhere?" she asks. I glance at her over my shoulder. Her face is flushed and she is holding onto the doorjamb to steady herself.

"She's in the bathroom being sick."

"Oh, damn," says the girl, "I told her not to drink with these guys. They always put stuff in our drinks and we pass out." Laughing, she adds, "The next morning I can never figure out what I did the night before."

"She threw up all over the bathroom," I say, disinterestedly.

"Oh no," says the girl. "By the way, my name is Maria. I am Ali's friend. Sorry if Candice wrecked anything. I'll go see if she is okay."

I watch Maria go towards the bathroom, thinking, "Isn't Ali the prince that is married to Sandy who will soon be having a baby?"

After a few minutes Marie returns and asks me, "Why is your baby rocking back and forth like that?"

"Oh, she always does that," I answer.

"Really? I read once that when babies rock like that, it means they are retarded."

Water splashes everywhere as I turn on the girl and explain, "She's a baby. Rocking like that is what babies do." I stare at her fiercely. "So take your friend and go home."

Maria hesitates and then mutters, "S-o-r-r-y," under her breath.

She heads back to the bathroom and then calls Ali to help her. Candice is too drunk and sick to walk. Ali goes to the bathroom and returns, balancing the drunk Candice with one hand and slopping his drink with the other. Someone, probably Maria, has at least cleaned the vomit off the front of Candice's dress.

As I turn back again to my kitchen duties, I find Moe standing in the kitchen doorway. "Why you be rude to guests?" he asks, his lips turned under in a sneer just like my mother's.

"Your friend was in the bathroom throwing up all over."

Instead of being horrified by that information, Moe laughs, "Moe have good party, no?" Then, he mutters to himself, slurring his words, "Funny people theesh Americans," He goes back into the living room.

A few minutes later, the front door opens and closes, and then it is very quiet. All the guests have gone. Moe isn't there, either. I clean the bathroom, lock the front door, check on the baby and go to bed. I try to sleep, but all I can think about is how Moe kept saying he really wanted to have a nice party. Is this what he had in mind?

Moe comes home the next day while I am feeding Zohra her lunch. He knocks on the door and I let him in. He looks tired, and he reeks of alcohol and strong perfume. He looks at me guiltily. He waits for me to say something.

I continue what I am doing and he passes through the kitchen and into the bathroom. He runs the shower. Does he think he can wash all that happened last night down the drain?

Could the shower wash it all away for me as well? A sob wells up in my throat and tears fill my eyes. In my mind, I hear the word *willow*. I picture my body in the sky, bending, twisting, floating with the wind. Aloud, I say, "Bend, woman, bend."

For a few days after the party, Moe's routine is different. He comes home for supper, hands me his tapes and goes out to the library, but reappears at 10 o'clock. He says little to me, except to ask if I will make sure Zohra is awake when he comes home so he can spend time with her. I tell him to play with her at supper, that ten o'clock is too late for a baby to be awake. After that, he goes back to his midnight routine.

On November 22, 1963, I decide to clean house and make a nice dinner for Moe. We need to talk, but I am not sure how to get that to happen. Around lunchtime, I feed Zohra, change her and put her in her little infant seat on the couch. I flip on the TV. My father insisted that we have his old TV when he bought a new one and I find it a welcome companion for my loneliness. Walter Cronkite is on the screen, tears streaming down his face. Sitting on the couch next to my daughter, I stare transfixed at the fuzzy screen and hear that President Kennedy has been shot.

At that moment, I hear a key in the lock, and turn to see Moe standing there, white-faced. He comes straight to me and taking my arm, he pulls me up. He is visibly shaken. "I just hear about your president. I so sorry. It is a moment for history." He takes me in his arms and hugs and rocks me back and forth like a baby. "I so sorry," he repeats.

We sit on the couch for the rest of the day and far into the night. "I cannot believe," Moe says over and over, "that this happen in America. I believe this happen only in backward nations. Places like my country." He is shaken to his core. Our discussion goes back and forth. Moe asking questions about American politics and me explaining. Then, me asking questions about Algerian politics and Moe explaining. It is like it used to be between us, when we first met – before the adobe house, before we got married, before Zohra. I fall asleep listening to his voice.

The next morning, I awake to the sound of Zohra crying. Moe is not in bed. By the time I get up, the crying has stopped. I enter Zohra's bedroom to find Moe changing her diapers and tickling her little feet. He looks up at me, smiling.

I follow him out to the kitchen. He puts Zohra in her high chair and moves to the refrigerator to find her some milk. He stops with his hand on the door to the refrigerator and says, "Moe is thinking these days. I talk to my sponsors. I have two more years of money. I must graduate at end of two years or I go home with no degree." He opens the door, reaches for the milk and turns to face me. "I think you go back to school."

I stare at him, dumbfounded. "What?" Not sure I have heard him correctly, I repeat, "Me go back to school?"

"You like, no?"

"Well, yes, Moe, I would love to, but what about Zohra? Who would take Zohra while I am at school?"

"I think, if you ask mother, maybe she do this," he says. "Plus," he pauses to pour Zohra's milk. "Plus you ask mother and father to pay, no?"

"Okay. My mother told me she would pay for any classes I want to take."

"Good. Then, you go on Monday and make enrolment."

 No Patience

Returning to my studies marks a major change in my life. I show Moe my report card from the first few semesters of the pre-law program I had taken. All As and Bs. He smiles and looks at me with respect. "My wife very smart. This good. Maybe she can get job in Algeria." He pauses and winks teasingly. "But I think you cannot get job in my country if you study politics and economics. You must study something useful for life there."

I open my mouth to argue, but it occurs to me that he is right. It will be difficult enough for me to get a job, let alone a job in a field not acceptable for women in his country.

Moe hands me his copy of the university catalogue and tells me we will look at the subjects and see what will work best. We find out that if I enrol in the Faculty of Agriculture, I will be able to save all the credits I have already and apply them to a Bachelor of Science Degree in Agricultural Education.

"Moe, I know nothing about agriculture," I protest. "I wasn't born on a farm. I don't know anything about crops or animals or anything in this field."

"Not matter," Moe fires back at me. "I can help you. I am son of farmer. Besides, you learn in classes and then go to my country and teach people farming. It okay for woman to teach this in my country. You can do this."

Can I? I am doubtful. But, I want to go to university and I know that fighting about it might put an end to my schooling all together. I call my mother and she agrees to watch Zohra and to pay the tuition.

The next day, I pack up Zohra in her stroller and we trudge off to the office of the College of Agriculture's Program Director. He invites me into his office and closes the door. He smiles at Zohra and asks me if she is my baby.

"Yes, she is," I answer.

"Oh," he asks, "Are you married?"

"Yes, I am," I reply.

"Well, how can I help you, Mrs. Chaabane?"

I explain about going to Algeria and why I want to study Agricultural Education.

He listens politely and when I am finished, he says, "Mrs. Chaabane, I am impressed with your plan. The only problem is that we just don't offer Agricultural Education to women. Women don't teach agriculture. Women just don't do this kind of job. I don't know how much clearer I can say it. I understand your circumstances, but I don't think you would have any hope of success in this area."

I stare at him, and I make no move to leave.

When he sees that I am not going to give in, he continues, "Tell you what I can do for you. Why not sign up for General Agriculture? I think, under the circumstances, this would work best – and since you have a baby – you are limited to enrolling in just one course."

I nod. I leave with the paperwork for a Chemistry course completed and the information about when classes start in January.

Moe and I start back to school together. We fall into a new rhythm, one that feels more comfortable. Moe comes home every night when the library closes and seems anxious to spend time with Zohra whenever he can. He talks more. Both his English and his marks improve. Sometimes, he brings his friends back to the house for a meal and he seems pleased with what I cook. He receives several letters from his father and brothers who write that they are happy for his marriage and his child and are waiting anxiously to see all of us.

Zohra comes home happy after her days with her Mimi. My mother insists on being called Mimi.

Moe is not happy about that name, but concedes that she can call herself whatever she wants. The trouble comes when my mother renames his daughter Zsa Zsa. Repeatedly, she tells Moe, "Zohra is an ugly name."

I keep thinking there will be a real fight over this, but Moe complains only to me and not to my mother. I tell him that if it bothers him so much, he should tell her.

"I not tell her," he says, firmly. "She is good woman and I have respect for parents."

Moe has always been like that with my parents. It is what endears him to them. They enjoy his company and he has certainly bonded with my father. My mother teases him when she can, which indicates she is comfortable with him. Moe always smiles when she teases and tells her how much she looks like she is my sister, instead of my mother. My mother loves the attention.

I like the routine of having something to do besides sit home and entertain Zohra. I make a few friends while in class and I look forward to talking to them every few days. In June, I finish my Chemistry class with a B. I am sad when the class ends, but my mother assures me that I can go to summer school if I want.

In the months since I started to go to class, Moe has changed in another way. He is more affectionate and more willing to take time to talk to me and play with me in bed. His interest in having sex with me has escalated, and nearly every evening he comes home wanting to kiss my face and touch my body. He takes the time to teach me about things I know nothing about. I have intensely pleasurable feelings I have never felt before. I ask him about these feelings and he laughs.

"You are really my virgin wife, aren't you?" he asks playfully and pulls me close again. It seems to excite him and he forgets to answer my question. Later in the night, after I have experienced a particularly powerful event, and we are having a cigarette, I ask him again. He looks at me funny and in a suddenly very French accent says, "I don't know what it is in English, but in French it is called orgasm."

I catch my breath. "Oh, that's what an orgasm is," I laugh. I have seen the word written and heard it laughed about in dirty jokes, but I didn't really know what it was.

Moe smiles at me and touches my face. "You are such a lucky woman," he whispers.

"And why am I such a lucky woman?" I ask, thinking he is going to tease me some more.

"Because I let you have orgasm," Moe explains seriously. "Some men in my country think orgasm very bad thing for woman. They say if woman feel that, then she will want to do sex with any man. Sometimes, they cut off that part of woman's body so she doesn't feel it. Then woman not be wanting other man to take her to bed."

In the dark, I squint at him in disbelief. "What did you say?" I ask, mortified. "They cut off her thing?"

"No, no," he says, "Not her thing, just the little piece that make her feel this. Many years ago in my village I hear about this. Some fathers and mothers make their daughters do this, but the French colonists make it against the law. Not happen anymore in my country." Then he adds, "Some African countries do this even in these days."

"I've never heard of such a thing," I say. I don't know if I am shocked that such a thing happened or relieved that it doesn't happen any more.

"Yes, I know," Moe continues. "People don't talk about such things." He adds, "And, you know little about sex."

Without thinking, I ask him, "So, how do you know so much?"

He hesitates. I can tell that he is deciding whether he should answer my question or not. After a moment, he clears his throat. "When I am fifteen, my brothers take me to whore house in the next village," he says, watching me closely to see my reaction.

"Whore house?"

"Yes," Moe affirms. "Whore house. In my country, many villages have such places. Girls with no families or women who have sex before they marry and women who go with men not their husband go to government whore houses. It is good idea. In your country, you have pregnant girls who have no fathers for their babies, children without families, and young girls, they just run wild." He pauses, and then continues.

"In my country, whore houses mean good women are pro-
tected, but bad women have job. Some are very good dancers and
sometimes they get hired to dance at weddings and special occasions. The government keeps the women in the houses and they
get examined by doctor every week, so nobody gets sick. Whore
houses good for young boys, like me when I am fifteen. With
whorehouses, I not bother good girls. My brothers go and pick
out a woman for me and pay her to teach me about such things. I
never forget this and I learn how to do this with woman."

I think about our first time together and wonder if that is
what he learned. I let the image of that night fade away. I like how
Moe acts towards me these days. I end the conversation by getting
up and turning off the light. "Teach me some more," I whisper to
him under the covers."

I hear him laugh quietly. "Pretty soon you wear out poor
Moe."

Three days after this unveiling of the benefits of whorehouses,
I wake up with the knowledge that I am pregnant again. I tell Moe
my suspicions.

"I'm not positive," I tell him, "I haven't even missed a period,
but I just feel it."

"You should go to doctor now," he instructs.

"There's no point, Moe. They can't tell anything until I miss
my period and am halfway to another one. I'm telling you what I
suspect. I just know that I'm pregnant."

Moe pulls me close and kisses me. "It's okay," he says, "It will
be a boy."

"And, how do you know that?" I ask.

"Because I know." he answers. "You know you are pregnant
same way I know it is boy." Then, in the next second, he turns on
me and suddenly snaps, "Why you not use your birth control?"

"I did." I answer, firmly but quietly. "I always use my birth
control. Why didn't you use yours?"

He pauses, and then laughs, "You not give me chance."

I laugh. "Yeah, I guess that's right, but you'd think one would
work."

Moe adds, "I just hope this baby not cry all the time. That all I hope."

I sign up for summer school because it will be practically over before the doctor can confirm that I am pregnant. I take two classes, 'Freshman Composition' and 'The Study of English Words.' These two courses go perfectly together and I love the hours I spend composing stories and studying words. What I learn, I apply in my work on the stories from under the canopy.

In the middle of July, the recognizable nausea of my first pregnancy returns and I know without a doctor's confirmation that I am going to be a mother again. I count backwards and figure that I will deliver sometime in the middle of February. Zohra will be 22 months old. I smile to myself. As an only child, I always wanted a baby brother. I am happy.

In September, I make an appointment with the doctor that delivered Zohra. After the examination, discussion and blood tests, he tells me he wants to talk to me in his office. He keeps me waiting for fifteen minutes and when he enters, he sits behind his desk, reading my file. Finally, he puts it down, folds his hands on his desk, fixes his eyes on me, and says, "Well, at least, this time you are married. That must be a relief."

I am not sure how to respond, so I say nothing.

"Look," he continues, "I've given your file some consideration and have decided that you would be better off going to the St. Elizabeth's of Hungary Clinic downtown. It's a place where you and your husband can get really good care, but it won't cost you any money. It's a charitable organization run by Catholic Social Services for southeastern Arizona. They take good care of young mothers and, like I said, having the baby will cost you very little. I have taken the liberty of referring you to them. You can phone this number for an appointment."

He stands up and thrusts a card at me with St. Elizabeth's and a phone number scrawled across the centre in thick black letters. "My nurse will phone you with the results of your pregnancy test. So, you can pay her on your way out and we'll call it square." He nods curtly and disappears out the door.

I make my way to the nurse's desk and she tells me my bill is

$50.00. I stutter, "I – I don't have $50.00 right now, but you could send the bill to my mother, if that's okay."

"Okay," The nurse glares at me. Then, she relents, "But make sure she comes in today. We close at 5:00."

I arrive home to find my mother scrubbing the kitchen floor, to me, an unspoken criticism of my housekeeping.

"Mom, what are you doing? You don't have to do that."

"I know, honey," she says, getting up from her knees. "So, how did it go?'

"Crappy. On the way out, the nurse insisted that I pay the bill right then and I didn't have the money." I sit down at the kitchen table. "She was so rude, Mom. You just wouldn't believe it. She said we have to pay her by 5:00 today."

"Forget the nurse," my mother says, curtly. "I want to know if you are pregnant again. So – are you?"

"I don't know for sure, but the doctor thinks I am." I remember his comment about me being married this time and then his dismissal of me by referring me to the free clinic. I try to make light of it. "Gotta wait for that poor bunny to die," I quip.

"Oh, honey, don't joke. I want to know if you are or if you're not."

"Mom, I am 99.9 per cent certain I am. So, let's just say I am. I'm sorry if you aren't happy." I am irritated that she isn't sympathizing with me about the nurse's rudeness.

"Well, don't take this the wrong way, honey. But, I think having another baby at this time is really foolish." She sits down on the other side of the table. Her voice is firm, and I hear anger in it. "Also, while I don't resent using our health insurance to pay for the first baby while you were still eligible, I have no intention of paying the bills on this one. It's time for Moe to step up and take responsibility."

Rage spreads through me, blood-red rage. "Well, you don't have to worry about it, Mother. Moe and I can take care of everything for this baby. And – when it's born – you don't even have to see it or have anything to do with it, or us, ever again!" I burst into tears and run to my room, throwing myself onto the bed.

A few moments later, my mother lets herself out the front

door. By that time, I feel ashamed. She has been so generous to us and I have just treated her so badly. I lay in the darkness and sob. "What am I doing?" I ask myself over and over. "What in the world am I doing having another baby? Why am I being so mean to my mother?"

Moe finds me with a tear-streaked face and sits down next to me on the bed. "My little Sewzie." he soothes, "What is the matter? Are you sick?"

"No, I'm not sick," I protest, still sobbing.

He reaches out and takes my face in his hands. "Stop crying, I hate when you cry. Tell Moe, what is this big problem?"

I babble it all out, tripping over my words about how the doctor examined me and then refused to have me as a patient and how he is sending me to the charity clinic and how my mother is mad at me...

"Stop!" Moe throws up his hands. "I not understand any word you say," He takes a deep breath. "Relax, start again, please."

But, then, he interrupts me before I say a word. He asks, "Do you fight with your mother?"

"No," I say emphatically.

"Good, it not good to fight with parents. So. Why you so upset?"

I finally calm down enough to tell him what the doctor said about going to St. Elizabeth's.

He listens and, surprisingly, he tells me he thinks it is a good idea. "I go there," he informs me. "It is wonderful place."

I look at him stunned. "You went there?"

"Yes, many times. It a clinic for immigrant people and poor people. They are very nice and they take good care of people. I like it." He smiles as if that settles that part of the problem. "Also," he moves on to the next issue, nodding his head as he speaks, "It not good for parents to always pay. Mother right. We need to pay our own things." Still nodding, he looks at me as if I have been disagreeing with him. He finishes firmly. "You know I am right in this."

I stop crying and cuddle up to him. Yes, I know he is right. I just feel tired and afraid. I am happy about the baby, but I am afraid of the birth. I listen to Moe's heartbeat and I feel better. He holds me tighter and kisses my forehead. He is a good man. I am a lucky woman.

A few days later, I apologize to my mother for getting mad at her. She pretends she can't remember why we had a spat and returns to being good-natured.

The morning of my last summer school exam, I sit studying a list of chemical equations at my kitchen table. Something catches my attention on the counter and I glance up wondering what it is. As I stand up, I see a large mouse, the size of a newborn kitten, finishing the leftovers from Moe's breakfast.

"Oh crap," I say out loud and, at the sound of my voice, the furry creature scurries down the side of the counter and across the floor. It makes its exit through a hole in the woodwork between the kitchen and the living room. I stand zombie-like staring at its escape. Later that day, I trudge down to the phone booth and call my mother.

She calls the exterminator and they arrive right away. They set traps and do an overall inspection. At the end of the day, I am holding a report that tells me we should vacate the premises while they exterminate, not just because we have mice, but because we have cockroaches and spiders as well. The report says that the entire underbelly of our newly boarded-up sleeping porch is a haven for black widow spiders.

The exterminator explains our situation, "That space under that porch of yours, Missy, is a mass of webs. It's a dangerous, scary place, if you ask me, and I been in this business just about twenty years. Shouldn't have little ones around here till we wipe them critters out."

My mother pays for the extermination. Moe and I move in with them for five days.

On September 1, I go for my first prenatal appointment at St. Elizabeth's. I put Zohra in her stroller and pack a bag with snacks, a bottle and her favourite toys. My mother agrees to take me to the clinic, but says she will go home and wait for me there. I am to call her when I am finished. She has things she wants to do and doesn't have time to sit and wait with me. I suspect it is the idea that the clinic is for poor and indigent people that keeps her home, but I say nothing.

When I arrive, I find out that all prenatal appointments are scheduled for 9:00 a.m. and they take patients in the order of their arrival. I look around the room. Brightly coloured and kid-friendly, it has a pile of toys in one corner and little tables along the walls where older children can color and play board games. A little courtyard where children are playing some sort of ball game can be seen from the waiting room. It is definitely a family place. I find a seat for myself and giving Zohra a few toys, settle us in for a long wait.

Every fifteen minutes or so, a large woman dressed in a white nurse's uniform emerges from the recesses of the building to call forward ten patients, who then follow her through the double doors and disappear into various rooms. After two hours, I become concerned that they have forgotten us.

Zohra starts to fuss and a large black woman sitting next to me leans over and suggests I let her walk around. Zohra's fussing gets louder. I take her out of her stroller. She is wet from head to toe. With nowhere but the floor to change her, I spread a blanket and lay her on it. Just as I get her diaper off, a nurse appears and calls my name.

The nurse, the black woman next to me, and everyone else in the room turns to watch. My hands start to shake. I work as fast as I can. I finally pick up my daughter, dressed and dry, but by this time, the double doors are shut and the nurse and the patients that were called have disappeared. I try to open the doors, but they are locked.

The black lady calls out, "Oops, you missed your turn, honey. Better just sit yo ass back down here and wait again. Ain't no use in tryin' to sneak in 'cause you has missed yo turn."

She is right. I finally do see a doctor, but not until after I have used up all my bottles and all my snacks and Zohra, totally miserable, is throwing herself around and screaming at the top of her lungs. I am on the verge of tears when I hear my name again. I grab my daughter and run as fast as I can to follow the nurse. Next time, I will know the routine.

In the examining room, I try to calm both Zohra and myself. I put her back into her stroller, where, thankfully, she seems content. Three young male doctors and a nurse enter. They explain that three of them are students and thank me for my participation in their learning. The one who seems to be in charge refers to a file full of papers that was obviously sent over by Dr. Bryson. He goes over the information, writes copious notes, and then tells me to undress and they will return to examine me. It is fifteen minutes before they return. The examination takes only a few minutes, but I find it uncomfortable with four people looking at my private parts.

I am, indeed, pregnant and they tell me my delivery date will be in mid-February. I dress myself and push Zohra's stroller out into the waiting room. From the pay phone in the hallway, I call my mother. She is busy getting dressed to go out for the evening.

"My God, I thought you got another ride home," she says, irritated. "I guess I'll be there in twenty minutes. Why did it take you so long?" she rants.

Half an hour later she pulls up in front of the clinic and gets out to hold the baby while I fold up the stroller. "So," my mother says, still in the middle of her rant from our phone call, "It sure took long enough. Are you pg or what?"

"Yes mother, I am pg, for sure, and everything is fine."

"There were a lot of negroes and Mexicans hanging out around that clinic. Do you think it's safe to go there?"

"Yes, mother," I respond, coldly. "It's fine."

Neither of us speaks for the rest of the drive.

Moe is standing on the front porch smoking a cigarette as we pull up to the house. By the way he is pacing, it is clear that he is upset about something. I sigh.

Even before the car comes to a full stop, Moe runs down the stairs and yanks open the door. "Where you go? Why you gone so long?" he yells.

I look at him, afraid to get out of the car. Anger wells up in my chest and I yell back. "I went to the clinic, Moe, and it took four hours. Okay? Why are you yelling at me?"

"Oh," he says, suddenly quiet, "Moe forget."

"Moe, next time you are going with me. It took four hours to see the doctor. You can come next time, if just to entertain Zohra. Then, I will dare you to ask me where I've been and why it took so long."

Moe takes the baby as I get out of the car. He kisses her little face. I walk past him, headed straight for the house. Then, I remember my mother and return to the car. "Thanks for the ride, Mom. See you soon." I say as nicely as I can.

She mumbles something undecipherable and as soon as I close the door, she tears off down the street.

"What the matter with Mother?" Moe asks, watching the car disappear.

"Same thing that's wrong with you, Moe. No patience."

I decide not to take any courses in September, 1964. Taking care of Zohra, helping Moe with his classes, which have become more and more technical, and being pregnant is enough. I promise myself I will go back to school after the baby is born.

Also, we receive a letter that informs us we have to be out of our house by November 1, as the University has expropriated the property in order to expand. I am upset. My mother has spent $500.00 to make the place liveable – and it takes so much energy to move.

My mother decides that finding us a place to live is her only purpose in life. After several weeks, she stops by to announce that she has found the perfect place and that she is here to take us to see it. The house is bright pink adobe and it has an eight-foot-high fence around the back yard. It is next to a little neighbourhood store and within walking distance of Moe's classes and the library. It looks expensive.

We knock and are invited in by a tall white-haired man in a blue golf shirt and cut-off jeans. He smiles broadly at my mother and a look of recognition crosses his face. "Well, for heaven's sake. If it isn't Franklin's wife," he beams at her. He explains, "I play tennis with your husband every Sunday morning and I occasionally see you when you stop by the courts over by the Days Inn Hotel."

"Oh, by the way –" The man turns to Moe and me and offers

his hand. "I am Jeff Newman and this is one of my little rental properties. Feel free to look around."

Moe, carrying Zohra, and I, already visibly pregnant, move forward into the living room. It is large with grey plush wall-to-wall carpeting and a big bay window that looks out onto the street. We follow a hallway off the living room and find three good-sized bedrooms, a large three-piece bath, a kitchen, and a laundry with a brand new washing machine and dryer. The bedrooms have hardwood floors and the bathroom has new tiles both on the floor and inside the bathtub and shower enclosures. Every room has pretty cotton curtains and brightly coloured walls. I know this house must be very expensive and I feel sad that we can't afford to live here because it would be perfect.

While we are still looking at the laundry room, Moe and I hear my mother talking to Mr. Newman. We look at each other, but say nothing.

"What's the rent?" asks my mother.

"I usually charge about $80.00 a month, plus the utilities," he answers. "I know it's a bit high for this area, but it's quite a big house and there is a large yard at the back. It would be really nice for a family."

"My daughter is having another baby," my mother offers, as if this makes a difference.

"Yes," says Mr. Newman. "She'll be a busy woman."

"She really needs a good place for her children," my mother continues.

"Yes, she does." says Mr. Newman.

His comment is followed by silence. I hold my breath. Moe's eyes are round.

My mother breaks the silence with, "They plan to stay at least two years. They are very clean and they would take good care of this place."

"Well," says Mr. Newman. "That is worth something. How much do you suppose they could afford to pay?"

"I think $75.00 would be their absolute maximum."

I hold my breath again until I hear Mr. Newman tell my mother. "Okay, but I would like it if you sign the lease with them."

"Of course," my mother answers confidently. "I intended to do that anyway."

"Well, I guess you have yourself a house."

Moe looks at me in the shadows of the laundry room. "I have no $75.00 a month for this house," he whispers. "It is too much for us. The last house was too much for us."

He shifts Zohra to his other arm and stomps out of the laundry room and into the living room. I follow him. Before he can say anything, my mother puts her hand on his arm and announces that she has rented the house for us and we can move in on January first.

Moe opens his mouth, as if to contradict her, but instead he says softly, "Okay, Mother, whatever you say."

My mother smiles and tells Mr. Newman we will be by his office in the morning to sign the papers. We all pile back into the car. Moe hands Zohra to me and I get into the back seat. Moe gets into the front next to my mother. As soon as we are all settled in and on our way, Moe tells my mother that he can't afford $75.00 for rent.

"Oh, so you were listening, were you, Moe?" She glances at him, smiling.

"Yes, mother," he answers, guiltily. "I was hearing."

"Well, it's okay," she says, patting his hand. "You can afford $50.00 – so you pay $50.00 and Mr. Glasier and I will pay $25.00. That way you will have a nice place to live. You will have no bugs, nobody ousting you for the university, and you will have enough room for both babies." She glances into the mirror and her eyes meet mine.

Moe looks at my mother with wide-eyed appreciation. "Again, I make bow to you, my mother. You are most generous and kind mother. Moe forever thank you and respect you."

My mother smiles in the glow of his praise and his respect. I have the feeling she gets more out of giving than we get from taking. I sigh, appreciating my mother's generosity, but thinking of the pending move and all the packing that has to be done.

"Oh, by the way," my mother adds, again meeting my eyes. "It was your father's idea. He said if the place was decent, we should rent it. So, really, you should thank him, first chance you get." She smiles again at Moe. She is happy with her solution to our housing problem.

I suspect that my mother slips Mr. Newman some money to let us in a few days early, but she says nothing about that to us. It works out well. Moe is off school and can help load and unload the van my mother rented. We finish moving in by the end of the Christmas holidays.

On January 15, Moe comes home from school with the announcement that he has purchased a car for $25.00. "I will get driver's license," he informs me. "I know how to drive from many years ago."

Ahmed arrives the next day with the car, a 1955 Chevy. I have seen Ahmed and his friends with this car before. "For $25.00 dollars, it is a good deal," Ahmed tells me. He explains, "One of my friends has gone back to Morocco. He has to sell the car." Something about the way he tells this story fuels my suspicion that the Arab students pass this car back and forth to each other. As each owner finishes school, another student purchases the car from the group.

On Friday, February 5, 1965, I pack up Zohra, her stroller, snacks, diapers and all the items I need for my now weekly visits to St. Elizabeth's. As I am about to leave the house, a man in a uniform knocks on the door. He tells me he is from the phone company and has instructions to install a phone. Annoyed at the delay, I tell him, "I didn't ask for a phone."

As he checks his paper work, my mother pulls up in front to pick me up. Seeing the man, she leaps out of the car and runs up the stairs. She asks, "Are you from the phone company?"

Then, she turns to me. "You have to have a phone in your condition with two children. It is ridiculous not to have a phone. I am paying for it – so you're having one."

She turns to the man and ushers him through the door into the house, shouting, "Just lock the door when you are done, Mr. Phone Man."

Mr. Phone Man gives her a smile and a strange look, but he nods his head. As he passes by me, he rolls his eyes and mutters,

"Lucky you, a free phone." Louder, he adds, "I'll leave your phone number next to the phone."

On our way to the clinic, my mother tells me she is going to park her car and go in with me. I explain to her that we are going to be really late for our appointment and it is going to take a long time – but she isn't listening.

"I don't care, dear. I will sit there as long as it takes. My bridge group was cancelled for the day and I am not doing anything. We'll just be together," she babbles, jauntily.

I warn her that she won't like the waiting, but she waves me off, insisting that it can't be that bad.

"Okay mom," I tell her. "I give up. You are here at your own risk."

We park, wrestle Zohra out of the car with all her belongings, and enter the building. All the seats are taken. It is going to be a very long day.

Eventually, a woman with four little girls is called and my mother grabs two of the seats. "I don't understand these people," she says, her voice way too loud for the crowded room. "No manners whatsoever. Couldn't she see that you are pregnant, and I need to sit down?" She uses her handkerchief to brush imaginary dust off the chair seat and sits down. "Those children don't need to take up chairs." She leans closer to me, but makes no attempt to lower the volume of her voice. "Honest to Pete! It's no wonder they have no money."

By the time my mother finishes her rant, the entire clinic is staring at her. I see fire in every adult eye. I wonder if we will get out of there alive. "Mom," I speak slowly and clearly to her. "I think you should take Zohra to play at your house. I'll phone you when I'm finished here." I can see the heads all turned toward us as our conversation plays out.

By this time, my mother notices all of the people looking at us and asks, "Why are all these people staring at you?"

"They're not staring at me. They are staring at you," I whisper, wanting to bring this situation to an end as soon as I can. "Take the baby and GO."

My mother grabs Zohra from my arms, dumps her in the

stroller and marches indignantly out the door. I sigh and shake my head.

The lady on the bench across from me laughs. "Sister, I thought my mother was a pain in the arse, but yours takes the cake. How do you take her uppity-uppity?"

Uppity-uppity – I like that. I smile at her. "I try to ignore her," I say. "She means well, but sometimes she doesn't know what she is saying."

The woman looks at me and cocks her head. "Oh, I think you're wrong, sister. She knows exactly what she's a-sayin'." Others nod their heads and laugh nervously. I look down at my feet and feel the heat in my face. What can I do? I know the lady is right. But she is still my mother.

Lost in my thoughts and my embarrassment, I almost don't hear my name called. I get up slowly and waddle after the nurse who leads ten of us down the hall to various examining rooms. I am as big as a house. It is time to get this baby out.

When the doctor enters, he isn't alone. He has four other men with him who are all dressed in white coats and look like interns or students. He glances at me lying on the table, reads my chart, and addresses the other men, announcing, "I will do an internal on this patient today. She is getting pretty close. It will give us a better idea of when to expect her delivery."

When the doctor finally finishes with the internal exam, which is painful and makes me cry, I phone my mother and, when she arrives to pick me up, she asks what's wrong. "I'm tired," I tell her. She has obviously forgotten the clinic episode and takes pity on me. "I'll take ZsaZsa tonight so you can get some rest," she offers.

"Thanks, Mom. I really am tired." I close my eyes and try not to think of what happened in the examining room.

When she drops me off, Moe is standing at the window waiting for me. He asks me how it went and I tell him the baby is big and it won't be born for two weeks. I don't feel like talking. I don't feel like eating supper. I walk past him and into our bedroom. The minute my head hits the pillow, I am asleep.

At three in the morning, I wake up with severe back pain. I

slowly try to get off the bed. The pain subsides and I drag myself to the bathroom. The signs of labour are there. I decide not to wake Moe until I have to. I sit on the couch until nine in the morning when Moe stumbles into the living room. It is Saturday and he doesn't have to go to classes.

Moe comes over and sits down beside me. "Are you okay?" he asks.

"I am fine. I am in labour."

His eyes grow wide at that statement. "What? Are you sure?" He half-stands, then sits back down and takes my hands in his.

"Yes, I am positive." As I speak, a strong pain begins in my lower back and twists its way around and up my front. I catch my breath and the pain continues. This pain lasts a really long time.

"You want to go to the hospital?" Moe's eyes anxiously search mine as I try to breathe through the pain.

"Not now," I tell him. "I am going to stay home as long as I can."

Moe nods. "Okay, you tell Moe when you want to go and I think we call your mother."

I can tell he is nervous because he runs the two sentences together. I am not sure if he means to call my mother when I go to the hospital or if he is asking me if I want him to call my mother now.

"You can call my mother now," I tell him.

"Okay," he responds. "Good idea."

I laugh. I feel another pain coming. I look at my watch. The pains are getting closer together.

Moe calls my mother and she arrives within ten minutes. The clock says ten o'clock. A pain begins as she comes through the door. I am consumed by it. I also feel a huge urge to push.

"You want to push?" She asks, a look of horror on her face. She stops taking off her coat and grabs her purse, which she has only just put down on the table. "You can't push now."

She turns to Moe, who is still standing by the door. "Moe, we have to get her to St. Mary's and it's clear on the other side of the city."

I try not to push, but the urge is nearly overwhelming. It seems to take forever before we finally pull up to St. Mary's emergency doors. My mother runs in and returns shortly with a nurse and a wheel chair. Moe is sent to sign us in and the nurse asks me several questions on the way to the delivery floor. They help me out of the chair and on to a hospital bed where a doctor examines me.

"She needs to go to delivery right now," he tells the nurse. They wheel the examining bed into the delivery room and a nurse helps me remove my clothes, tie a hospital gown around my swollen body and put my legs in stirrups.

I am uncomfortable lying flat on the hard surface. "Please," I beg. "I need to get up, I need to walk."

"Don't be silly," says the nurse. "The time for walking is over. You need to concentrate on having this baby."

A tall dark man dressed in white and wearing a hospital mask enters the room. He examines me and tells me in a thick very Arab accent that the baby's head is showing and I can push any time. At that point, my labour stops. After an hour of me having no heavy contractions, the doctor feels my stomach and then turns to the nurse standing next to him. "I'm going out for a while," he says. "When she decides to do something, call me." He takes off the mask as he leaves the room, saying, "I've got other things to do."

"Yes sir, we'll do that," she says in a thick accent of her own. I see disapproval in her eyes. She leans down and whispers, "I come from Ireland, honey. There, we don't use doctors in childbirth. We have midwives and that's what I used to do there. For thirty years, I was a midwife. I know about babies." She smiles kindly and brushes the hair from my face. "We are going to work on you, honey. You need to have this baby and you need to have it now. It's ready to come out, but you have to push harder. When you get the next pain, I will help you. Okay?"

Another pain sweeps up and over my back and around my distended belly. "Oh, god," I mutter between my clenched teeth, "Oh, god, it hurts."

It hurts too much to push and I scream. "Stop screaming," the Irish midwife orders. "That won't help your baby." She orders one of the nurses to come to the head of the bed and she goes to the doctor's position. "The cord," she announces quietly.

The midwife tells me not to push while she and two other nurses work feverishly, all at my bottom. Suddenly, I feel another pain. This time, I feel the baby slip from my body. The midwife catches it, the attendants heave a collective sigh of relief. I look up in the mirror and see the Irish midwife cut the cord. "Ho," she shouts, "he is one big bruiser. No wonder you had so much trouble, honey. I'll bet he weighs at least ten pounds."

"It's a boy?" I ask quietly, my voice weak with fatigue.

She puts the naked baby on my stomach for a moment. I can feel his warm little body against mine. Then, she scoops him up so I can see him. "We need to clean him up," she says softly, "so have a quick peek at your wee man. Then, we'll take him away for a few minutes."

I only get a fleeting glimpse of my son. He looks blue and wrinkled. He doesn't cry. The midwife hands him to one of the other nurses and she carries him away. A wave of longing sweeps over me. I want my baby.

Suddenly, the doors fly open and the Arab doctor strides in. "I thought you were going to call me," he declares in a loud, rough voice to the Irish nurse.

The nurse speaks softly in reply and moves out of the way. The doctor steps in and, in a minute or two, delivers the placenta. "You are ripped," he comments, "and I need to sew you up. It will only take a few minutes." When the doctor finishes and leaves, he doesn't speak to me.

A short time later I am wheeled into a room with four other new mothers and put to bed in warm blankets and a soft pillow. I can't believe how good I feel. Compared to my last birthing experience, this one is amazing.

A few moments later, Moe and my mother come in. Moe's face is alive with excitement and joy. "We have a beautiful son," he shouts. "He is so big. Almost ten pounds. Wow, you do good job." He continues more quietly. "They put him in incubator. He have breathing trouble."

"Yes, the nurse told me he had the cord around his neck and the doctor that was supposed to deliver him left." I want Moe to understand that our baby was well taken care of. "An Irish midwife and the other nurses delivered him. She knew what to do. He is lucky to be alive."

Moe listens to me soberly, all of the original joy gone from his face.

"What's wrong, Moe? You are suddenly very sad looking. What are you thinking?" I press him for answers.

Still very serious, Moe explains, fear and anger evident in every breath "I see doctor in hall while we wait for you to have baby. I ask him what is going on. He ask me if I am baby's father. I tell him yes. He ask me where I come from. I think this is strange question for doctor to ask. I tell him I am from Algeria. He looks at some papers he has in his hand and asks 'Your name is Mohamed?' I tell him yes. He looks at me funny and in strange voice, as he walk away he say, 'I am from Egypt. I am a Jew.' Oh god, I am so afraid. If he is your doctor and he know I am Moslem, he will hurt you or hurt baby. I want to jump on him. Mother hold me back. She tell me not to worry. She say, 'This is America and nobody care about religion.' I pray she is right."

How can people be so afraid of each other? I need to talk to him about this before we go to Algeria. I need to understand. Such strong feelings of hate are foreign to me.

The excitement around having a boy is overwhelming. Gifts and flowers begin to arrive. Ahmed arrives, again bearing roses, this time bringing three dozen different coloured ones in a beautiful crystal vase and a card with $500.00 tucked inside. "From the Arab students organization," he announces proudly. Ahmed asks Moe what we have named the baby.

My parents are in the room and they look up, obviously anxious to know the name of their grandson. Moe told me that he would accept only three names for his son: Mohamed Cheriff, Omar, or Tariq. We all stare at him, waiting for an answer. Moe hesitates, looks at me, and says in a clear calm voice for everyone to hear, "My son's name is Tariq."

The suck of horror in my mother's breath confirms what I expected would happen. My father says nothing. I wait for my mother to protest loudly. But, she doesn't speak. Instead, tears begin to roll quietly down her cheeks.

Moe looks at my mother. He asks her, "Mother, why do you cry? Tariq is very good name."

She sputters, "It might be a very good name in your country, but not in my country.

As if he doesn't hear my mother's comment, Moe continues, "Tariq is a name that comes from history – the history of what you call it in English, the Rock of Gibraltar. It is one of my favourite stories. In the year 711, a ruler of North Africa was sent to conquer Spain. On April 30th he lands on rock with 7,000 soldiers. His name was Tariq ibn-Ziyad. Although he was outnumbered by many thousands, he made a victory over the Spanish. The place where Tariq first landed was called Jabal Al-Tariq. Later, the name came to be Gibraltar. I like this story. I like how strong the name is. It is important to my history this name."

My mother listens and then gives Moe a small smile. "Well, I guess we can always call him something else if he stays in this country," she concludes. "We call Zohra Zsa Zsa, so I think we'll find something to call this one, at least until he leaves."

Moe frowns, but says nothing more.

Later, a lady comes to my bedside with official looking papers to register our son's birth. Moe asks me how to spell the name in English. "You decide how to spell name," he says. "Maybe, if you spell it how it sound to you, your mother will be more happy?"

I tell the lady to spell it T-A-R-E-K. She carefully writes it down and then asks for a middle name.

"He doesn't have one," Moe tells her.

She shrugs, gathers up the papers and leaves, telling us that the actual birth certificate will arrive by mail in about six weeks. Moe looks at her hand-written copy, "Tarek," he says very slowly and precisely. "It not exactly Arabic, but it will do."

Tarek isn't totally Arab, I think, but I don't speak my thoughts out loud. Moe has compromised and I am willing to let him have the last word.

On the third day I leave the hospital, waiting until Tarek is circumcised before we bring him home. When the nurse asks if we want to have our son circumcised, Moe first asks me what that is.

Then, he tells me that in his country, circumcision is done when boys are eight years old.

"God, wouldn't that be painful at that age?" I ask.

"Yes. It hurts very much but it is big ceremony," begins Moe, exuberantly. "Everyone in the village comes. They bring money. There is much dancing and singing."

Then, his voice changes and he continues in a quiet voice. "Special men come to the village to do the operation. I remember," he says. "When they come, they hold boys down and cut foreskin without any anaesthetic. I cry in terrible pain. Everyone dance around me and laugh."

"Moe," I ask quietly. "Do you want your son to go through that pain?"

Moe looks at me and says. "No. To do it now, in hospital, with no pain, is much better custom." He signs the papers.

The next day, when we leave the hospital, I feel happy and energetic. Tarek is fussy for a day or two, but his little wound clears up quickly. He begins to eat and sleep on a regular schedule. When he's a month old, he starts sleeping through the night. If Tarek had been born first, I would have thought having babies was not such a big deal.

 Be a Better Mother

By the time Tarek is six weeks old, he sleeps for so long that I have to wake him up to feed him. He is indeed a joy for me and for Moe. Zohra seems to be more content as well. Both she and the baby get lots of attention. She still rocks herself to sleep every night on her hands and knees, but she doesn't seem to have the need to bang her head against the end of the crib as much as she used to.

My mother's wish to call the baby by a different name than Tarek comes true the day we bring him home from the hospital. We introduce Zohra to her little brother and she looks at him closely. She studies his face for a moment or two and suddenly blurts out, "My Beaties." I have the feeling he might be Beaties until he is old enough to change it.

Moe studies very hard, and he makes every effort to come home as early as he can. He doesn't stay out late like he did before. "I am happy with my children, now," he coos. "And you are becoming good wife and mother."

The children become his obsession and he delights in taking them for walks and playing with them on the living room floor. He tells me how he is looking forward to Tarek getting older so that he can take him to interesting places.

Not whore houses, I hope.

Sometimes, Moe takes both children to Ahmed's house to give me a break and to show them off. They always come home with money tucked somewhere in their clothing. Moe tells me it is a custom.

This custom I like.

One morning, I wake up to Tarek crying. I am surprised because Tarek usually lies in his bed and gurgles to himself until someone comes to pick him up or until his sister pinches him to make him cry. I slip out of bed and go to him. I find his face very red and his breathing laboured. I pick him up and hold him close. He whimpers and clings to me. I feel his little chest move in and out with a weird wheezing sound as he fights to breathe. Moe comes sleepily up behind me and looks over my shoulder. "What wrong?" he asks.

"I think he is really sick," I answer. "Listen to how he's breathing."

"He has cold," Moe tells me in his *I know best* voice. "He will be fine."

Moe dresses and goes to school. I watch Tarek for a few hours and realize he isn't getting better. He is lethargic and the sound that comes from his chest gets louder every time he breathes in. It is more than a simple cold.

I phone my mother, but no one answers. She has probably gone off to play bridge somewhere. I look in my purse. I only have $5.00. It is enough to pay for a taxi from the house to the doctor's office, but I won't have enough to get back home. Surely my mother will be home by that time. I dial the taxi.

Within ten minutes, with Tarek in my arms, and Zohra by the hand, we clamour out the door. It is 10:00 o'clock. I give the driver the address of the St. Elizabeth of Hungary Clinic. I really want to go to Dr. Dew's office. Dr. Dew is a paediatrician I use for Zohra and Tarek, but I see him only when the kids are really sick and I have money. He charges $25.00 per visit and it is often difficult to find that much money in the budget. Today, I don't have $25.00. So I go to the free clinic.

We arrive and I pay the driver $4.25. All the chairs are full and there is a line down the centre of the entry hall for patients to register. With Tarek in my arms and Zohra whining at my feet, I am already tired. I stand for fifteen minutes, shuffling forward slowly as patients talk to the nurse and go to the waiting room. When I reach the check-in window, I tell the nurse that my baby is sick. She looks at Tarek. Then, she gets up off her chair for a closer look.

"You need to come in right now," she says in a calm voice.

I follow the nurse into an examining room. She talks softly to Tarek and listens gently to his chest with her stethoscope. When she is finished, she says nothing except to ask me to take off his clothes. I slowly undress him.

Zohra seems to sense the seriousness of the situation. She finds a chair and climbs up on it, then sits silently staring at her brother. "Beaties sick?" She asks in a wee little voice.

"Yes, honey, Beaties sick. The doctor is coming," I say to her, reassuringly.

"Doctor fix Beaties?"

I nod as the nurse returns to take his temperature. "His fever is 105," she announces. "He is a sick little baby. Wait just a minute and the doctor will be here."

The doctor strides through the open doorway. He grabs a stethoscope from the wall and runs it around Tarek's chest. He opens a drawer in the examining table and takes out a blanket. "Cover him up," he orders. As he scribbles notes on a chart, he announces, "I think he has pneumonia. I want you to take him to St. Mary's Hospital as soon as you can. He needs to be admitted. We'll have a bed ready for him. Tell them at the hospital that he is coming in under Saint E's and they'll take care of the paper work." He turns on his heel and is gone.

I dress Tarek and sling him back over my shoulder. He falls into a wheezy sleep. Zohra jumps off the chair and together we walk down the hallway. I don't know what to do. I have seventy-five cents. I have no car. I have to get my child to the hospital. I decide to use five cents to call my mother again, but now there is a long line of people waiting to use the phone. I step in behind the last person and stand, holding Tarek and listening to his noisy breathing. Zohra stands by me, whining and bored, but resolute in staying nearby.

The clock ticks away for fifteen long minutes. I feel weak and lightheaded by the time it is my turn. I wait while my mother's phone rings and rings. No one answers. She is still not home. I step away and look for a place to sit down. There is a seat down the row a bit and I heave myself and my limp fifteen-pound baby gratefully into the hard-backed chair.

Tarek is now in a deep sleep and his face is rosy red. Every few minutes he coughs and whimpers, but drops back again into a restless sleep. I stand up and lay him on the chair. I tell Zohra to watch him and I go back to the phone. The line up this time is not as long.

I put my money into the phone and dial a girl I know named Kathy. She is a beautiful, bouncy, auburn-headed woman with huge round blue eyes and freckles everywhere. I met her in high school when my family first moved to Tucson. She weaves in and out of my life, dependent on how much time and energy I have. Only a year older than me, she got married at seventeen and already has four children, two of her own and two stepchildren.

I have always been drawn to her because, from the day my mother met her, she labelled her a 'woman of ill repute.' That always made me want to like Kathy more than I actually do. I haven't seen her since Zohra was born, but she is the only one I can think of who has a car and is likely to be at home. She answers on the first ring.

"Kathy," I say. "It's Susie Chaabane."

"Who?" She asks.

"You know, Susie Glasier. I got married."

"Oh, yeah," she responds, disinterestedly, "Susie Glasier."

I immediately launch into my story about how I can't find a ride to the hospital and my son is sick and is there any way she can take me.

"Well," she mumbles, "I – I do have things to do, but it'll take me awhile to get ready and get my kids organized. I really can't be there for at least a couple of hours. You'd have to wait."

"It's okay," I tell her, desperate. "I'll wait. I would really appreciate a ride, whenever you can come." I wonder if Kathy hears in my voice how desperate I feel.

"Okay, I'll try to be there by two."

I sit in the clinic trying to entertain Zohra for the next two hours. Tarek continues his restless sleep, his breathing becoming more and more laboured. He squirms in my arms, moaning, trying to get more comfortable. When I can't stand the boredom of it all, I take them both outside and sit on the grass. Zohra runs around in the sunshine. There are fewer people to stare at us. I call my mother every hour, but I get no response.

Finally at 3:15, I see Kathy in her old green boat of a car pull up to a parking stall in the clinic lot and get out. I call to her. "Over here, Kathy."

"Hi," she mutters, as she comes up to us. She peers at Tarek, shaking her head. "Wow, he's big." Then, she turns back toward the car, saying over her shoulder. "Listen, I have a bunch of running around I have to do. So – if you don't mind – I'll do it first." She looks at me. "It might take a while –" she hesitates. Then, she talks without taking a breath as we walk to her car. "But I can't go clear out to St. Mary's first because I need to do my stuff before the places close."

I nod helplessly.

I peer through the dirty back windows and see four children with dirty faces sitting in the back seat. Settling into the driver's seat, Kathy offers me a cigarette. Gratefully, I take it and we ride along happily puffing away and catching up on the years we missed seeing each other. Zohra sits on the front seat between us and I hold Tarek on my lap.

From time to time, when the kids in the back get particularly loud, she yells, "Shut up, you guys or I'll belt ya one." The kids quiet down for a minute or two and then return to their original volume.

Zohra sits quietly, intimidated by the roughhousing and shouting behind her. From time to time, Tarek stirs in my arms and coughs and whimpers. His wheezing gets louder, and occasionally, he struggles to take a breath. After each struggle, he clings to me more tightly and then falls back into a restless sleep.

Kathy drives from place to place in the city. At each place, she parks and gets out of the vehicle. She tells the kids to be good and goes off, leaving me alone with them for up to fifteen minutes each time.

At five o'clock, Zohra pulls on my sleeve and informs me she is hungry and needs to go the bathroom. This time, when Kathy returns to the car, I tell her I need to go to the hospital right away. Tarek is getting sicker.

She doesn't say anything, but starts the car and heads east in the general direction of the hospital. A few miles up the road, she turns to me and says, "I can't wait, you know. I have other things to do. I'll have to just drop you off. You'll have to find another way to get back."

I assure her, "That's okay. My mother will come and pick me up."

Kathy drops me off at the front door and, with Zohra in tow, I make my way to the admitting desk where the lady takes my information and ushers me down the hall to a little examining room. I am told to take off all of Tarek's clothing and wait for a doctor. The air conditioning is going full blast and it is cold. I search for a blanket to cover him, but there are no drawers or cabinets in this particular room. I snuggle him close to me. Zohra whines again about being hungry and having to go to the bathroom. I am exhausted.

Just as I am about to go out and ask someone where the bathroom is, the door opens, and a doctor and a nurse enter. They look at me and at Tarek. "Put the baby on the table," orders the nurse.

"It's cold in here," I say.

"It'll be okay for a minute," the doctor says, grumpily. I put Tarek on the table. He opens his bloodshot eyes with a startle and tries to cry. No sound comes out. He starts to cough again.

The doctor runs a stethoscope over his chest and then listens to his back. "Poor baby. Pneumonia," he confirms.

The doctor glances at the chart the nurse hands him, and turns to me, frowning, "You were supposed to be here this morning. Do you not understand that your baby is very sick? Where have you been?" He glances at the chart again and turns back to me, his voice hard. "His bed has been waiting. This child should have been in an oxygen tent since ten o'clock this morning. You waltz in here after five o'clock stinking like cigarettes and the baby so oxygen deficit he could die. What the hell kind of mother are you anyway?"

"Wh – what?" I stammer, shocked. "I – I – didn't have a ride. I didn't know what to do."

Suddenly, Zohra, who has been frowning at the doctor throughout his tirade, rises up to her full two-year-old stature, places her hands on her hips, and shouts at him. "You bad man," she screams. "Mommy nice, you bad." Then, she runs across the floor and, with both her little fists in the air, attempts to sock the doctor in the first soft spot she can find. "My mommy nice," she yells again.

Luckily, the doctor is quick on his feet and catches her little arms before she can do any damage. He picks her up. "Well," he says. "You are a feisty one, aren't you?" He sets her down on the floor and turns back to me.

"Take your son to the third floor. The nurse will go with you. I want him admitted. He needs to stay with us until we get this under control."

I nod. "I didn't realize," I choke out, my voice nearly a whisper.

"I know," the doctor says more gently, but still agitated. "But, the next time a doctor tells you to get your baby to the hospital, remember that it means today, not tomorrow." He walks out of the room, slamming the door behind him.

I burst into tears and Zohra comes to comfort me. "It's okay, Mommy," she coos in her sweetest voice. "Zsa Zsa loves you." In a decidedly more desperate voice, she adds, "Zsa Zsa has to pee, please."

The nurse arrives with a blanket to wrap around Tarek and I gather him up in my arms. We follow her to the paediatric ward. She takes him from me and says she will put him in a bed. Then, she shows me where to take Zohra to the bathroom.

When we return, they have laid Tarek in a large hospital bed, propped up on numerous pillows. Several physicians and nurses are standing around him and he is very quiet. One doctor leaves the group and comes over to me.

"You take your daughter and go home," he informs me. "We have a lot of tests to do and we won't have anything to tell you for sure until tomorrow. Go home and call back late tomorrow afternoon. We should have some information by then." Pointing at Zohra, he adds, "We don't allow children in this part of the hospital anyway so you need to take her out of here."

I nod and take Zohra's little hand and we walk down the hall to the lobby. I find a phone and call my mother. It is 5:30. She answers the phone.

"Mom." I say, relieved to hear her voice. "Thank God, you're home."

"I just got in the door," my mother says. "What's up, honey? You sound funny."

"It has been a terrible day. I need you to come and get me. I'm at the hospital. Tarek has pneumonia and they are going to keep him for a while."

"Oh, honey, I am so sorry. I'll be there in half an hour. Wait for me outside."

"Call Moe if you get a chance. He is probably really mad I'm not home."

"Okay," she responds. "I'll call him. Better still, I'll just stop by there on my way and see if he wants to come with me."

I put down the receiver and walk to a chair in the lobby. Zohra climbs up on my lap and we both sit, exhausted. The minute my mother and Moe arrive, they go to see Tarek. I am too tired to move. Zohra falls asleep on my lap. An hour later, my mother and Moe return. Moe picks up Zohra and we walk out to the car.

"He looks so tiny in that great big bed," my mother tells me. "He is so sick. We were able to talk to the doctor while we were there and he said Tarek has to stay at least a week." The frown lines on my mother's face deepen as she explains more of what she heard from the doctor. I notice that Moe is listening carefully, but he says nothing. "The doctor also said something about you smoking cigarettes around Tarek, and not bringing him to the hospital when you were told to. What was that about?"

"I couldn't get hold of you. You weren't answering your phone." I explain. "Moe was at school. I couldn't find anyone to take me to the clinic so I had to hire a cab." I mumble. I am being put on trial by my mother and my husband. By the end of the story, I am crying.

Finally, I blurt out. "I suppose you think I'm a bad mother too, just like that doctor does."

I turn to Moe. "Go ahead." I am yelling now. "Tell me what a bad mother I am. I don't care about either of you. You always criticize me, no matter how hard I try. You never have anything nice to say. I got him here and he's alive, so you can both drop dead as far as I am concerned."

I cry and I can't stop. Exhaustion pours over me.

"Don't be so dramatic," my mother finally responds, disgusted. "For heaven's sake," she continues, "I never said anything to you except to ask what happened. The doctor was upset, that's all."

Once we reach the car, Moe takes my hand and holds it against his cheek. "Don't cry. Tarek will be well."

Every day for the next week, my mother tells me she is too busy to take me to see Tarek. Moe is either at class or studying. He makes no effort to find us a ride to the hospital. So, all I can do is call the hospital every day.

Every day I get the same response from the nursing station, "He is getting better. Call back tomorrow."

I feel lost without my baby. I spend my days looking after Zohra and wondering how Tarek is feeling and when he will be able to come home.

Finally, on the seventh day, just before supper, to my astonishment, Moe and my mother arrive home with Tarek.

"Why do you have Tarek?" I ask, shocked by their sudden appearance with him. "Why didn't you tell me you were going to get him? I wanted to go and see him."

Moe tells me matter-of-factly. "Mother and I know you tired. We go to hospital so you can rest."

I look at them, dumbfounded. "He's my baby." I yell. "I wanted to see him. Every day I wanted to see him. It's been a whole week. Why couldn't you take me with you?"

My mother interjects, "Like Moe said, honey, we figured you've been upset this past week with all that has happened. We thought it was better if you had a rest." She glances at Moe and continues,

"Wasn't it nice not to have two babies for a while? Nice to just have one to take care of?"

I look from my mother to Moe and back again. "You went to the hospital to visit him during the week, too!" I accuse them.

My mother's face turns red. "Well, yes, your father and I went in the evening and kept track of how he was doing." She looks at me, and says patiently. "Why are you so upset?"

"I am his mother," I scream. "What's wrong with you?" I run into my bedroom and fling myself across the bed, sobbing.

Nobody comes to comfort me. They stay sitting in the living room playing with the children and watching TV. I fall asleep and dream of a meadow lined with trees. I float through the light sweet-smelling air and land gently on the branch of a large willow tree. My body turns to liquid and I melt into the tree. I bend to the grasses now below my feet. We are all one.

Over the next few weeks, Tarek gradually grows stronger. As a result of him having pneumonia at such a young age, he develops asthma. It takes its toll on his lungs. The doctors tell us we have to learn how to manage his condition. We are instructed to take Tarek to the nearest hospital whenever he has trouble breathing.

Every night when I put him to bed, I remember how Moe and my mother took over when he was so sick. I never want that to happen again. It only happened because I didn't know how sick he was. I am sure that he will be all right from now on. I just need to be a better mother, and he will be fine.

* * *

In October of 1965, Moe receives a letter indicating he will graduate with a degree in Agriculture in January 1966, if he passes all of his courses in the fall term. Final exams are scheduled for the middle of January.

Our American days are nearly over. We begin to plan our lives in Algeria. We agree that Moe will leave for Algeria as soon as his exams end and he receives written confirmation that he has been granted a degree.

"What are you going to do to celebrate your graduation?" I ask him one day when he comes home from school early.

He looks at me with sad eyes and says quietly, "I not celebrate graduation. I miss my family very much. I go as soon as I can. I go home and find a job and a place for us to live. Then I think about big celebration." Then, smiling he adds, "It will be the biggest celebration anyone has ever seen."

My mother suggests that we sell our furniture and move in with her and my father. "It will be better for you, honey. You can stay with us until you have to leave. Dad and I can help you with the kids and it will cost a lot less. You don't know how long it will take Moe to get things ready for you and he will feel much better knowing you are all safe here with us."

I hesitate at first until Moe points out to me that he will have no money until he has a job. He will have to live with his relatives in Algiers until he is employed. I have no money to pay the rent or other bills. All I really have is the little bit in the *secret* bank account. I have the feeling it will be handy in the coming months. Reluctantly, I agree to my mother's idea.

In January, we start packing and looking for buyers for our meagre belongings. In less than two weeks all our household goods are gone. Moe's friends are the principle buyers. I am surprised that they don't haggle over price with him. They pay what he asks. Moe says it is because they respect him. In the end, we are $400.00 richer and we decide that Moe will take the cash with him as his stash for a new life.

On February 5, 1966, the day before Tarek turns a year old, Moe receives his ticket to Algeria by special delivery from his sponsoring organization in New York. He will be leaving in two days, flying first to New York, and from there to Madrid in Spain, and then, on to Algiers. As he reads his itinerary, his face is beaming. His smile goes from ear to ear.

He spends the rest of the day helping my father in the garden and playing with the children. At five o'clock he disappears, and when he returns an hour later, he has a set of luggage and $50.00 more in his pocket.

"I sold the car for $50.00 and this luggage," he explains. "I sold the car for $25.00 more than I pay."

My suspicions about the Arab students supporting each other

comes back into my mind. Did one of them buy the old car? Did they buy our household goods for the same reason?

"You did good, Moe," I tell him. "You did good."

"I did well," he corrects me, laughing, "I did well."

I smile at this correction, and I think, "Moe, you have come a long way from the day I met you five years ago."

On our last evening together Moe promises me, "I write every-day. I hope you and children can come soon. Maybe, even by May? I think it not take too long to get job. But I hear from friends to find a place to live is the most difficult thing."

On the morning of February 7, 1966, my father drives Moe to the airport. At Moe's request, the children and I stay home. Moe says that it will be too confusing for the children to drag them out of bed at 5:00 in the morning, but I can't help but think the real reason he wants us to stay home is that he might cry.

He kisses me one last time. I whisper that I have tucked a surprise gift into his suitcase. I explain about the book I made containing the stories about his family that he dictated to me. I have titled it *Stories Under the Canopy*. He smiles his sad smile and waves good-bye.

I cry, but I wait until he is out of sight down the street. He hates to see my tears.

PART TWO

UNDER THE CANOPY

Moe's Mother

 Zohra Khaldhi

Algeria, North Africa between 1911 and 1921

At thirteen, Zohra Khaldhi knows all she needs to know about her life. The first-born girl is always loved a little less than her brothers but a little more than her sisters. She knows she is fortunate because her mother gave birth to a son first so she, being second, was permitted to live. She has been taught that it is Allah's will to allow only a son to be first born. She also knows that Allah looks kindly on her mother, Khadija, blessing her with six more sons and then two daughters. For as long as Zohra can remember, she has risen at dawn and slept at sunset. Always she has had a baby to tend, water to haul, and food to gather and prepare. Zohra is luckier than most. Her father is a farmer and with what he can grow on the land, they are able to have the food they need.

She enters the veil at eleven, at the first sign of womanhood and experiences her first confinement at twelve. Confinement comes a couple of days a month when the blood flows. She knows it is an unclean time, so she spends those days away from the family in a little hut made from cow droppings and mud. She passes the time washing the pieces of cloth that catch the blood. She doesn't mind confinement. It is the only relief from her daily chores.

She remembers the first time the blood came. Zohra was sleeping and her mother found it all over her bedclothes. Khadija ran to tell the other women and soon Zohra found herself caught up in a celebration. All of her mother's friends and relatives came from their houses to visit her and to praise her. The house was filled with chattering, excited women. Zohra particularly remembers the time, just at the end of the visit when all the women began to chant in a high piercing yodel– the way all of the women of the region do on special occasions. The sound always makes her feel warm and excited and on that day she knew the chanting was for her. When the ululating died down, the women coloured her hands and feet with henna to ward off evil spirits and to bring her luck. It was then that she entered her first confinement.

That seems like such a long time ago to Zohra. These days, she hears the women talking about her again. The women with sons of marriageable age are beginning to look at her closely, to ask her questions, and to feel her body to see if it is strong enough for work and childbearing. They even check her teeth. Zohra is lucky - she is very shy. Shyness is the greatest character trait that a woman of this region can have. Her mother has trained her well.

Khadija always tells her, "Lower your eyes. Never speak above a whisper. Work hard. Never complain - and you will be won by a wealthy man."

Zohra already knows she is very good at woman's work. She can tell how good she is by the happy look on her mother's face when Zohra willingly takes the younger children to play in the courtyard or ties the youngest baby to her body for the day. Sometimes her mother praises her when she does a particularly good job of skinning a rabbit, killing a chicken, or milking the goat that lives in their outer compound. Zohra is also good at beating rugs and scrubbing floors, but she gets tired lifting the large pails of bleach water used for washing just about everything.

One of Zohra's favourite tasks is making couscous, the traditional North African wheat dish. Being allowed to help prepare the couscous means that her mother and her many aunties and the other women in the community think she is almost grown up. Preparing couscous is a community activity. The women gather in groups as they rub the little wet semolina kernels over large oval screens - back and forth go their hands - each woman knowing exactly how much wheat flour to add to the mix to form perfectly-sized tiny kernels. Zohra feels useful when she is allowed to drop the finished balls of semolina onto the drying trays and then gather them into large burlap bags for storage. The smell of the wet wheat and the constant funny grating sound the kernels make as they pass over the sieve reminds Zohra of many pleasant conversations between the women. One day, in the middle of a particularly happy couscous gathering, Zohra is summoned by her little brother to the outer courtyard. Her father is waiting to speak with her.

"Zohra" he says, his face very serious, "As my firstborn daughter, beloved that you are, I have great news for you. I have chosen you a husband. His name is Romar. He is from our tribe and from our village and he has offered a large price for you. I believe this is your destiny. He has many other wives, but all are barren. Therefore, my daughter, I ask only that you bear him many sons, for alas, this man has never had even one. You will find him old but gentle, and above all you will find him rich. Allah's will be done."

Zohra knows that her father's word is final and that if all goes well, she will soon belong forever to Romar. She will not see Romar until the day of her wedding. But that is as it has always been throughout time. It is the custom of her village.

Days later, what a wedding it is! It is indeed a special wedding for Zohra's family. Her father is pleased that Romar is very rich. The men and women gather in the morning as the sun is coming up. The women busy themselves with kitchen tasks making the many festive dishes; sheep, goat, chicken, fish, and rabbits made into roasts and stews, and served always with couscous.

It is the custom of the village that the bride stays in her bed during the wedding celebration. From there, Zohra can hear the women talking in excited voices and smell the aroma of the tasty dishes being prepared in the kitchen. She can feel the excitement in the air. She is so curious to see what is happening! Just as she decides to get up and sneak a look out her door, a group of giggling women, including her mother, five aunts, and two cousins, come into her room. They tell her they have come to fetch her for a special journey. They dress her in the traditional white cotton veil that covers her entire body and drapes over her head covering her hair. The final piece of the veil is a small square of white cloth that her cousin places across her face so that only her eyes can be seen. This face piece is tied behind her head.

The women cover themselves in similar veils, and they all walk like lovely white ghosts two-by-two the mile or more to the public bath. There, they all take turns scrubbing Zohra's skin until she can't stand the pain of it anymore. Their unusually loud voices echo around the bathhouse. They giggle and make rude jokes about Zohra's wedding night, the state of her virginity, and even take bets on when her firstborn will arrive. Zohra has heard the women talk like this about other brides and then she thought the sound was joyful and fun. But now that she is the object of their banter, she trembles. She doesn't understand what all of the joking and laughter is all about. As these women talk and splash and joke, they get louder and rougher and more profane. Zohra feels suddenly cold, as if she is going to be sick – or worse – as if she is going to cry.

"Allah," she prays. "Please don't let me cry. They will think I am only a stupid crying baby and they will make fun of me for all the rest of my life."

As if Allah has heard her plea, the women become quiet. The final part of the bathing ceremony begins. Two of her aunts and her mother pick her up out of the water and ceremoniously carry her to a large marble bench at the end of the pool. Here, her mother reaches down and spreads Zohra's legs apart. Zohra's heart skips a beat, sure that she is going to faint.

Her mother sees the blood drain out of her daughter's face and whispers to her, "It's okay Zohra. This won't hurt. You saw this done before when your cousin Nadia got married."

Zohra had forgotten her cousin's wedding and how she had taken part in this very bathing ceremony. She relaxes. Her mother takes a sharp straight-edged razor and gently shaves off all the hair on the dark area of her lower body. It feels strange to Zohra, but it doesn't hurt. All of her aunts and cousins continue chanting as they stare at her being shaved. Zohra wishes she could escape their eyes.

Finishing the task, her mother tells her, "Zohra, from this day forward you must keep the hair away from that part of your body or it will grow so tightly together no child will ever get out."

One of her cousins comes forward with new clothes, long flowing bloomers and a loose long-sleeved top. She carefully dresses Zohra, admiring each new item as she lovingly puts it on Zohra's body. She covers the new clothing with a new veil. Zohra is ready for her wedding. Three of the stronger women lift Zohra onto a long wooden board and the women carry her in a procession back to her father's house.

Once inside the house she is carried to a bedroom on the upper floor and laid on a large mattress that is covered by a large white linen cloth. As the women depart, they leave the door open a tiny crack, so Zohra can hear the festivities below without being seen.

Zohra hears the sounds of the first guests arriving. The heavy footsteps and deep voices tell her that the men are gathering in the living room, and the high-pitched ululating that the women are in the kitchen. It will be a long time before any of them turn their attention to her again. For the hours the festivities go on, Zohra remains on the large mattress on the floor in the upper room. She is alone in the dark room. She can smell the wonderful aromas coming from the kitchen as the women arrange the food that they have spent days preparing onto large trays. She hears the younger children being called and given instructions to take the trays of food to the men. She has taken part in that task at other weddings.

Zohra lies unmoving in the dark. She feels lonely and overwhelmed by everything that has happened to her this day. She wonders what will happen to her on this night and she prays to Allah that she will have many sons. The crude jokes and the laughter have only increased her anxiety. No one has explained anything. The hours creep past. The festive noises from below continue. Always before, she has been one of those who enjoyed the laughter and the food. She has never spent any time thinking about what the bride was doing while her wedding was being celebrated.

During the wedding the men and older boys are being entertained by local *dancers*. It is the tradition in this part of the country to bring in the women of the local brothels to dance for male wedding guests. Such *entertainers* are given some respectability during these festivities and often leave the wedding with more money in their purses than the bride and groom.

Her thoughts are interrupted by a change in the sounds coming from below. The women, cloistered behind slatted shutters in the kitchen, have begun their high-pitched chanting once again. Zohra knows that her father has just finished sealing her fate by signing the marriage contract with Romar. She is now a married woman. She hears footsteps and her door opens wide and Zohra sees her mother, wrapped in her own white veil to keep her hidden from any men who might see her as she passes by on the balcony above the crowd.

"Get up, Zohra. Give me the linen you are lying on. It is time," says her mother softly.

Zohra gets up and removes the white linen cover from the mattress. Zohra likes the embroidered birds and flowers that her mother has drawn and sewn on the cloth. It is a special cover, one her mother has sewn and embroidered with her own hands. Many times as she worked on the stitching, her mother has told Zohra that this cover will prove her worthiness to her new husband and to both families. Zohra wants to do her part in being worthy, though she really doesn't understand what that means about today, her wedding day.

Suddenly, there is a quick knock at the door and Habib, Zohra's seven-year-old cousin, enters the room. Khadija hands him the cover. He steps out onto the balcony and throws it to the crowd of men below. One of the men catches it and marks it with blue dye in one corner and gives it to another young boy who takes it back up the stairs to Habib, who then returns the cover to Khadija, who lays it back on the bed and motions to Zohra to lie down on it again.

Kadija gently kisses her daughter's cheek and says, "Zohra my beloved, I wish for you many sons." She turns and leaves the room.

Zohra is alone again.

The next footsteps at the door are heavy ones. It must be Romar. The crowd below the balcony has grown quiet. Zohra watches the light under her door. She catches her breath and closes her eyes as the door is flung wide open and then slammed shut again. She hears Romar's breathing and slowly opens her eyes. He wrestles in the darkness with his clothes. He says nothing to her, not a single word. Once his clothes are off, his hands touch her body. He pulls off her new clothes, even her underneath garments. Zohra is glad it is dark. Her body begins to tremble as it did at the bathhouse. This time, her mother isn't there to reassure her that she won't be hurt. Romar still says nothing to her. He doesn't seem to notice that she is trembling. Abruptly, he lowers the terrible weight of his body onto her and roughly shoves her legs apart. Zohra feels his hand touch the area that her mother has told her to keep shaved for the rest of her life so that the hair won't tangle and prevent the babies from being born. He grunts and adjusts his body. Then, Zohra feels a terrible searing pain like none she has ever felt in all her life.

She wants to scream and fight to run away. Her mother's words echo in her mind, *"I wish you many sons."* In the instant before she faints, she realizes that her father is wrong about Romar. He is not a kind man, not a gentle man. He is a man consumed by his own sense of urgency and the need to produce sons.

She awakes to find her mother pulling the linen out from under her. The cover that once was white is now stained crimson. Her mother smiles at her and tells her what a good mother she will be. Zohra understands that somehow this bloody stain means that she is now half-worthy – she has proven her virginity. The final sign of her worthiness will come when she is the mother of sons. Once she has a son, she will have brought to her family all the honour a girl can bring. Habib returns and takes the blood-stained cloth from Khadja. He opens the door and steps out onto the balcony. As he throws the bloodied cover to the crowd below, Zohra can hear the wild cheering and clapping and cries of *"long life"* and *"many sons."*

Zohra remains on her mattress until all the guests and dancers leave. When she hears the quiet, she sits up, bruised and still trembling uncontrollably. Her mother appears at the door carrying a large container of wash water.

"Wash yourself Zohra, and get dressed. It is time for you to leave this house and go with your husband to his house." Her mother helps her kindly, but silently, and in a few minutes Zohra is dressed again in her new clothes and her veil. Her face piece is a new one that her little sister has made from beautiful lace. Under the soft fabric of the clothing, she feels her body pull into itself, almost as if she is exposed even while hidden, as if she walks naked even while covered.

Her mother hands her a small bag containing all her possessions. Then, in a procession with Romar and several of his brothers and sisters, Zohra joins her new family to walk the five miles to her new home.

And so it was that thirteen-year-old Zohra and fifty-year-old Romar were married.

* * *

Allah doesn't look any more favourably on Zohra than he did on Romar's other three wives. Zohra came to live in her husband's house more than a year ago and still she is confined each month, just as when she lived in her father's house. The only difference is that from time to time she is required to go to Romar's bedchamber and endure what he does to her. She can do nothing else. The other women in the house explain that it is the things he does that make sons. Zohra thinks that she must have done something awful to cause Allah not to give her a son, but she has no idea what it is.

Except for the times she is forced to spend the night with Romar, Zohra finds herself enjoying living in his house. Her father is right about two things: Romar's house is big and he is rich. The house has many separate rooms furnished with richly carved wooden tables, brightly tiled floors, thick rugs, large mattresses and warm covers. It has running water and inside bathrooms. She always has plenty to eat. Zohra shares the house with Romar's first wife, his mother and father, five brothers and their wives and

all of their children – children are everywhere, babies are everywhere – everywhere but inside of Zohra.

On the day of Zohra's fifteenth birthday, she awakens to find
the house strangely quiet and a young boy about twelve years old
standing over her. "Romar wants to see you," he says, and pauses
for emphasis, before blurting out the final part of the command,
loudly and forcefully, "Now!" She leaves her bed, dresses in a long
skirt and a long-sleeved blouse, walks down the stairs to the living
room and knocks on the closed door.

"Enter," says a voice.

She opens the door and steps into the room. She is shocked to
find that Romar is not alone. Her father and four other men she
has never seen before are in the room. She covers her face with her
arm and turns to run out in shame at being seen.

Romar's voice barks out, "No. Stay. There is no need to cover
yourself in the presence of these men. You have born me no sons.
No children at all. Only a whore bears no children. These four
men with me say that you are a harlot. Allah's law is that you
must die for this." He pauses and gestures toward her father, "But
your father, the merciful soul that he is, has agreed to take you
back into his house."

Zohra peers out from under the arm she is using to hide her
face. She can't believe what she is hearing. She looks at her father
but his face is hard and a deep frown makes the veins in her neck
stick out. He is clearly angry. What did she do that was so terrible?
She knows that she cannot speak in her own defense. Even if she
could, she wouldn't. She wants to cry, but there are no tears. She
stands in shocked silence.

Romar's voice again booms through the air at her. "So, Zohra
Khaldi, according to Allah's law, I divorce you. I divorce you. I divorce you. Be gone." A fling of his arm finishes his speech and he
turns away from her.

In this region where Zohra has been born, there is no greater
disgrace than being a divorced woman – unless it is being divorced
with no children. Zohra accepts the disgrace. She agrees that it is,
indeed, her fault that no sons have come to her. She knows that

she will now be relegated to the position of servant within her father's household, that that will be her life.

Even as she feels the shame, relief spreads through her body, relief – and astonishment that she is going home. As she turns to leave she notices that her father is looking kindly at her and she wants to smile.

Moe's Father
Abdullah Chaabane

Mascara, Algeria, North Africa between 1901 and 1921

Abdullah Chaabane is a special person. His mother says so and so does everybody else. It isn't so much the things he does but the way he is – wise beyond his years. He has a quality of tolerance, an ability to accept change, which is important because he is living in a country that is changing everyday.

Abdullah is eighteen when his father, Tohamy dies. According to Allah's way, the eldest son inherits the farm and takes on the full responsibility of his mother and his eight younger brothers and sisters. Abdullah knows, however, that this responsibility will last only for one year. At the end of the proper grieving period, his uncle, Ahmed Benthedid, the brother of his father, will marry Abdullah's mother and adopt her young children as his own. This is the way of the village.

When his mother moves to the home of his uncle, Abdullah decides it is time for him to find a wife of his own. He decides he wants to look for a wife in another village, which is unthinkable in this region. Abdullah doesn't really understand why he decides to do this, but it seems a *different thing to do* and Abdullah is excited by doing different things. Sometimes his friends tell him they think he is a man before his time. Abdullah isn't at all clear what this means, but he likes to be thought of that way.

Through some negotiating with a cousin who lives in another village, he and his mother are able to negotiate marriage to a woman named Hira Khaldi. Hira is typical of the girls of her region. Her hair is very curly, somewhat like the black people living south of the Great Sahara, but not as coarse. She has small eyes, nearly oriental in shape, and soft brown skin, the color of honey. When she comes to live with Abdullah in his village, she is shy and very sad. She seldom talks to the other women and keeps to herself in Abdullah's house. Abdullah's mother comments to her son about this sadness, but Abdullah doesn't notice. His mother wonders if she is sick. Abdullah tells his mother that his wife is just shy.

As the days turn into months, however, Abdullah begins to watch his wife as she works in the house preparing meals. He sees how adept she is at woman's work and he grows fond of her. He sees that she is fragile and he feels he needs to take special care of her. He appreciates that, along with not speaking very much, she also never complains, not even to the other women.

One day, a year into their marriage, Hira lays down to sleep and never wakes up. Abdullah is shocked. No one understands how this could happen. Abdullah and the people of his village bury her in the cemetery near the top of the hill overlooking the village. *"It is Allah's will,"* they all murmur after the ceremony.

Abdullah turns his life to his work, to developing the farm and vineyards that he loves so much. He is truly a farmer at heart. It is hard work – enough to keep two or three men twice his size busy. His hands become callused and his back grows strong as he works the land. People begin to talk about the grapes he grows, fine grapes that the French *colons* buy and send to France to make into fine French wine. Abdullah is one of only a few Arab landowners. Mostly, *colons* own the land and the native Algerians work for them. The French have ruled Algeria for as long as Abdullah can remember. He sees that many of his people have been kept away from good schools, professional jobs, and thus, from a decent way of life. His father, Tohamy, has always maintained a special working relationship with these *colons* and his family has been allowed to keep the land they farmed from one generation to another.

Abdullah has learned from his father: Show respect to the French *colons* and landowners but stay away from them unless you are doing business.

Abdullah continues to work hard for the next three years, building up his farm. He begins to yearn for more than having meals with his mother. He builds a small house on the farm and decides he wants to fill it with children.

One day Abdullah goes to pay a customary call on the family of his dead wife in the neighbouring village. One of Hira's younger brothers answers the door and lets him into the house. As Abdullah enters, he happens to look into an adjoining room where he catches sight of a beautiful young girl who is not wearing a veil. She is so intent upon scrubbing the last crumbs of food from a large table that she doesn't realize that the door is open and that a man is staring at her.

Abdullah knows that he shouldn't be looking at her, but he can't help himself. He thinks, "She must be one of the family's servants. She doesn't resemble Hira at all."

Even though Abdullah was once married to Hira, he is still a stranger to the woman in this family. It is the custom. Women who marry join the families of their husbands.

Suddenly, the boy shouts at the beautiful girl to get her attention. The girl looks up and startled, she runs from the room, covering her face. Abdullah can feel her embarrassment almost as though it is his own and he wonders why his heart beats so quickly. "A creature as lovely as she is must be married," he thinks. Still, he asks the young boy about who she is.

"Oh," says the boy, embarrassed. "She is my sister, Zohra. Romar, her husband, gave her back to us because she gave him no sons."

Abdullah searches his memory and recalls the gossip that surrounded this unfortunate marriage. It happened near the time of his wife's death so he doesn't remember the details, but he knows that one of Hira's sisters was divorced and that her father took her back to be the family servant. "How tragic," Abdullah thinks. "How terribly tragic." As the days pass Abdullah cannot help but think about Zohra. All he can hear are the boy's words, "She gave him no sons," but all he can see is her face.

Abdullah makes it a habit to take at least his noon meal at the home of his mother. He enjoys her company and the company of his many brothers and sisters still at home. On this day, Abdullah notices that his mother is in a pensive mood. This is an indication that she has something important to say to him. He knows she will wait until the rest of the family leave the table.

Sure enough, as soon as the last person leaves, she turns to him and announces, "Your cousin, Heathera, is ready to marry." She adds, "It is time you fill your house with children."

Abdullah doesn't want to marry his cousin. He has noticed that the children of these marriages often are sickly or deformed or stupid. He stares at his mother and from somewhere deep inside of him, these words come out, "I don't care if Heathera is ready to get married. I intend to marry Zohra Khaldi."

This announcement comes out of him before he can contain it. In this region, it has always been a mother's duty to pick the bride for her son. However, Abdullah's mother knows that when this son of hers makes up his mind, there will be no way she can change it. She tries anyway.

"Abdullah, this woman has disgraced her family. She has never borne a son or even a daughter. They say in the village that she is a whore. Do you wish to bring a whore to your family? Do you know what this will do to your family?" She can't believe her son would choose to marry someone who would disgrace their family as she has disgraced her own.

"Mother," Abdullah tells her respectfully, "These words about disgracing families are the words of old women who have nothing better to do than to say unkind things about others. Zohra Khaldi is the woman I want. I will not be happy until she is my wife. I will not be happy till my family agrees to the marriage."

And so, it happens that on a bright spring day with birds chirruping and the smell of cultivated earth in the air, Abdullah marries Zohra. The wedding is held without the usual array of friends, neighbours or relatives. Both sets of parents oversee the ceremony, but the only guests are the number of holy men required to make the marriage legal.

Moe's Story

 Mohamed Chaabane

Mascara, Algeria, North Africa in the 1930s

In the first three years of marriage, Zohra gives birth to three strong healthy sons. When her third son is born, Zohra senses that he is special. Once the pain of his birth is over and she holds him up for Abdullah to see, she begs him to name this child Mohamed, after the prophet. Abdullah isn't sure why he says yes, he guesses it is as good a name as any and every religious family must have at least one son named after the prophet.

His mother doesn't call him Mohamed for very long, however. By the time Little Mohamed has reached the age of three, he is only called *Masheesh*, which means little nose. His mother tells him, "You have the smallest nose anyone has ever seen in this family. You are my *Masheesh*."

The years pass and one child follows another. Mohamed remains his mother's favourite. By the village standards, he is a gentler child than most. He has an unusual regard for his little sisters. When the other brothers speak harshly and try to beat them, Mohamed rushes to their aid. As he grows older, he shops for his mother, tells her stories and spends time with her, unlike his brothers who spend as little time in the house as possible.

As the family grows, the older boys begin to help their father in the vineyards. The French *colons* offer little in the way of schooling for the Algerians – a few years in the primary schools for the boys and then most of them head back to the land. Mohamed, unlike his brothers, has no great attachment to the work of a farmer. He has ideas and thoughts in his head. He wants desperately to learn. Abdullah needs Mohamed to help on the land but more often than not, he finds him lying beside a creek dreaming his usual dreams and wasting the day. Abdullah decides that perhaps this one has it in him to be a holy man.

When Mohamed reaches the age of ten, Abdullah offers him the chance to go to the school run by the holy men of the village – the Koranic school. Mohamed is happy. He will learn to read and write. So every day, when Mohamed's brothers go off to work the land, he goes off to learn the ways of the priests and the prophet. Mohamed learns quickly that working the land may be an easier path. There are days when he is sure he has made a mistake in his choice of life work. His job is to learn to recite the Koran backward and forward day after day. Some days he goes for ten hours or more with no food. He and fifteen other boys sit cross-legged and recite word by word, hour by hour the words of the holy book. For every mistake they make they are beaten across the calves with a wooden rod until Mohamed doesn't think he can take another thrashing. To cry is unthinkable; to quit so shameful that he cannot even entertain the possibility. He tells no one. He stumbles home every night nearly unable to walk and too exhausted to do anything but sleep. Days pass into weeks and weeks into months. Slowly, very slowly his mistakes subside and so does the punishment.

When all the students seem to have their recitation perfected, they are given paper, pots of ink and special pens. The slow process of learning to write begins. At first, the students seem only to scribble as they try to copy what is given to them. Day after day, year after year, until the lines begin to have meaning and take on form. It is a time of light for Mohamed. Something turns on in his head. He finds that he can write nearly anything he can recite from the Koran. All the pain and long hours now feel worthwhile. Reading and writing is truly a miracle. He begins to see himself as a man of letters; at least, in the world of his religion.

Then, one day when he goes to the village market for his mother, his eyes fall on an old newspaper used to wrap vegetables.

He sees the words on the paper. The lines make sense to him. He thought only the holy Koran contained words he could read. Now he knows that everyday things do as well.

Just before Mohammed's fifteenth birthday, as suddenly as his schooling began, it ends. The French authorities shut down all the Koranic schools in the country and arrest and take away the mulahs who run them. People talk in hushed tones about *guerrillas*, about *freedom*, about *life*. He has never thought much about the French *colons* before. They always treat his father well and pay for his grapes on time. He has never known any of them personally though he sees their big villas and big cars. "Well," he thinks, "These things didn't concern me in the past but if my school is shut down, perhaps they should concern me now.

* * *

Mohamed has a difficult time adjusting to his life after the French *colons* shut down the Koranic School. He is used to his routine of getting up every morning to attend classes. He now finds himself enveloped in a heavy lethargy brought on by both boredom and worry for the changing world around him. There is too much talk of war and politics.

He tries to talk to his father, Abdullah, but his father only replies, "Don't worry Mohamed, it will turn out alright. However, you need to work or you need to study. This sitting around like you do is no good. Come out to the vineyards with me and your brothers. Hard work will stop this brooding of yours."

Mohamed smiles. His two older brothers seem to love to work in the vineyards, and his two younger ones already beg to go along even though they are not old enough. If there is one thing Mohamed is clear on, it is that he hates farming. He wants to learn.

One day when he is walking with his friends, trying to find a way out of this dilemma, he passes behind the villa of a French schoolteacher. On the ground near the high fence surrounding this property, he finds a book written in a language he can understand. The book looks very old and some of the pages are torn out but Mohamed picks it up and leafs through it. It is written in a strange format. He has never seen anything like it before. He shoves the little book into his pants and continues down the street with his friends. He will look at the book later.

That evening when he is safely home, he curls up in a corner of the room he shares with his five brothers and pulls out the book. It is covered in soft brown leather and when he opens it the pages smell of tanned cowhide and dust. The words jump from the pages and flow into his head. A few words are new to him and he doesn't know what they mean, but others are the same words he reads everyday in the Koran. He is determined to make sense of what they say. In time he determines that he has found a small book of classical Arabic poems. He falls in love with the rhythm of the verse. The book becomes his passion and he reads it over and over. He doesn't want to put it down.

Abdullah notices his son's new past time. He shakes his head from side to side as if he can't believe it and walks away. "Someday," he thinks, "This strange son of mine will be a great teacher, if it is the will of Allah." He leaves his son to his books. He has eleven other children to help him in the fields.

As the days pass and the spring turns to summer, Mohamed continues to wake late in the day, study his book and then go to the street to meet his friends and drink coffee in the coffee shops. He remains moody and distant from his family and continues to avoid going to the vineyards. He wonders why his father no longer insists he go to work.

Early one hot July morning, just as Mohamed is seriously considering pulling himself out of bed to face another rather boring tedious day, he hears his mother, Zohra, call out to him from her room.

"Mohamed. Mohamed, are you there? Are you awake? Come quickly, I need to talk to you."

"That's strange," he thinks. "The sun is already up and my mother is calling out to me from her bedroom. She is always up and busy tending the children by now."

He hears her call out again, her voice anxious. "Mohamed, are you there? Please come here."

He pulls on his clothes, sensing that something is wrong. His mother is heavy with child again. He has never known when she wasn't. He has six brothers and five sisters all born within the past eighteen years. With her other pregnancies, the babies just seem to appear one day and everyone was very happy. However, during the past few weeks, he has seen worry and trouble on her face, and a certain sadness that he doesn't understand.

"Mohamed," she calls out again.

He answers, "Yes. Mother. I am coming."

He walks quickly down the hall and across the living room to her bedroom door. "I am here mother, what's the trouble?" he asks, standing in the doorway. "It's really quiet today without the little children. Where are they? Did you bury them in the dung pile out back?" He is half-laughing as he waits for her to answer.

"Mohamed, my *Masheesh*. I am so glad you are here. If you must know, I sent all the little children to your Auntie's house on the other side of the village. I didn't bury them in the dung pile. Son, please come closer."

He steps inside the door and notices that she has stretched her hand out from under the covers and something about the way she is reaching for him is almost desperate. "My son," she repeats. "I need to tell you something."

"Yes mother," he replies, crossing the room to the bed. "I am here." He takes her hand gently in his, surprised by the rough calluses he feels there. He slowly lowers himself onto her bed. "What's wrong, Mother?"

The rough hands pull him closer to her, close enough that he can see into her eyes and smell her familiar smell. In a voice nearly too weak to hear, but yet clear and confident, she tells him, "Mohamed, you know you have always been my favourite son. You are such a good boy, always, good to your mother. I must tell you something very sad, my son. I had a dream this night. I dreamed that I died and your father married my sister, Aisha. I think," she falters, "I–it is my time."

She stops speaking. Mohamed sees that she is trying hard not to cry. He looks away from her, embarrassed by this sudden out-pouring of emotion. After a moment of silence, he turns back to see tears are rolling uncontrollably down her face. She looks at him mournfully and then, pulling herself together continues, "My only regret is that I shall leave so many children with no mother. I shall leave so many children for my poor husband to look after. Promise me you will suggest Aisha to your father. She will make a good wife and a good mother."

Mohamed looks into his mother's eyes and sees a sorrow he can barely comprehend. He feels fear rise up from his soul and he turns away from her. "Oh, Mother," he growls. "You are talking such foolishness. You will be fine just like all the other times. Go back to sleep and soon you will have another little one to tend and we will all be happy." He lets go of her hand and runs from the room.

"This must just be a silly women's ramblings," he thinks uneasily. But, it isn't like his mother to be silly. It bothers him that she has sent the younger children to his aunt's house on the other side of the village. The only time she ever does that is when she is ready to give birth. He doesn't think it is time yet. Maybe she really does know something. He shakes his head as if to knock his mother's words from it. Then, he pauses. None of this behaviour is like his mother. He will stay home today instead of joining his friends in the street.

Mohamed returns to his mother's room several times to make sure she is all right. Each time he peeks through the door at her, she opens her eyes and smiles at him. He thinks that he should call someone, maybe one of his other aunts to come and sit with her. If he does, however, it will mean a half-hour walk to find someone and, in his heart, he is afraid to leave her alone. He will wait until the others return from the vineyards.

By early afternoon the heat inside the house is oppressive. It is the kind of a day where the dust sticks in your throat and you only want to lay in the shade until the sun sinks away and the cool of the evening descends. Mohamed can't bear the heat of the house any longer and he wanders outside to sit under a tree, close enough to hear his mother if she needs him, but far enough away from the house to feel any breeze that might stir. He makes himself comfortable under the tree and within a few minutes falls asleep. Suddenly, he is shocked from his comfortable sleep by what he thinks is the cry of some tortured animal. As he comes out of the fog of sleep, he realizes the sound is coming from his mother. He stumbles to his feet and runs into her room.

She has moved from her bed to a huge pile of sheepskins on the floor. These skins are used for women in labour and for new babies. He steps closer to his mother. The smell hits him first, a mixture of dust, urine, and the sweat and toil of his mother in labour. The once-white skins his mother lies on are red with blood. His mother is as still and quiet as death.

He stands over her. For a second, he thinks she is dead. But, she stirs painfully and looks at him, "Go, my son. Get the doctor in the village – hurry."

The words twist and turn in his mind. *Get the doctor.* In all her life, his mother has never asked for a doctor. No matter how difficult things got during labour and delivery, the problem was always solved by his mother herself or by the other women in the village.

Mohamed knows that this run for the doctor is a run for his mother's life. The only mode of transport the family owns is an old bicycle. He runs to get it from the garage but when he gets there, the garage is locked. He will have to make his legs run the five miles to the village. It is the longest run of his life. By the time he reaches the doctor's house, he can barely speak. It takes him a moment to catch his breath enough to knock on the door.

After what seems an eternity, a woman's half-covered face appears in the upper window of the house, "The doctor is in Mosteganem today, and won't be back until tomorrow," she yells down at him.

He has to find someone, anyone to help. He turns and runs from the doctor's house to the house of his closest uncle and aunt and bangs repeatedly on the door. "Hurry up. Hurry up," he keeps saying to himself as he waits for his Aunt Muna to answer the door. When she finally opens the small wooden peek-hole at the top of the door he can hardly speak. "Please, please come, Auntie," he stammers. "My mother is in great difficulty and there is no doctor."

When Muna sees his troubled face and hears the anxiety in

his voice, she immediately agrees to accompany him back to his house. Her sister-in-law is not due to have her baby until later in the summer. Muna shouts for her young son to go to the town square and find his father. She calls after him, "Abdul-kadar, tell your father to bring the taxi and hurry." At the word taxi, Mohamed feels some comfort. Perhaps this means they will be in time to help his mother.

But by the time Mohamed returns to his house with his aunt and uncle, his mother is beyond help. As he re-enters her room, Mohamed knows that they are too late. The same sour smells are there, but there is an eerie silence penetrating everything. He knows at once that his mother has left the world. It is his fault that he could not run fast enough to save her. He falls to his knees, covers his head with his arms and hands and sobs uncontrollably.

He feels two strong hands take his shoulders and shake him hard.

It is Muna. "Mohamed," she says firmly and loudly. "Mohamed, stop this immediately. There is nothing we can do except clean up. I need you to help me, so leave your weeping to a later time."

Mohamed stumbles to his feet, wipes his eyes and nose on his shirt, and stares at his aunt. "I–I'm sorry, Auntie, I–"

"Never mind," she interrupts roughly. "We will both cry tomorrow when there is time."

Mohamed regains his composure as much as possible and looks around the room. Because of his own sorrowful crying, he had missed another cry. He blinks. There, right before his eyes, he sees a tiny slithering mass still with its cord attached, but alive. He can hear it whimper ever so softly from the dark red pool between his mother's legs. He sucks in his breath and then points, skipping over his own words, trying to make his aunt see what he is seeing. His aunt moves towards the place where he is pointing. She tells him to get a basin of water and when he brings it to her, he watches as she cleans away the blood from his mother's legs. Then she brings out a kitchen knife and cuts the child free. He knows he shouldn't watch but his aunt says nothing to him. Eventually, she wraps the baby in some old rags she finds in the corner of the kitchen and lays the baby at the dead woman's side. "It's a girl," she offers, as if it will make things easier.

Mohamed stands straight up, unsure of what he should do, unsure what it all means. The sorrow he feels each time his aunt touches his mother's dead body, wells up inside his throat like an oversized apple, choking off his breath. Finally, Muna looks at him with compassion and says, "Mohamed, go and find your father. He needs to know before the whole village finds out. Your uncle is waiting in his taxi by the barn. You will have a ride."

When the men leave, Muna finishes cleaning up as best she can. She walks over to her sister-in-law's body. She sits down at her side and picks up the baby in her arms, rocking her gently. The baby is not a beautiful child. She has grey skin and dull eyes and the boney thinness of a child born too soon. Muna talks to the child in a singsong voice, "You will be in a better place soon," she coos. "Even if your mother had lived, you probably wouldn't. You know you cannot stay here. Everyone will say you murdered your mother and your life would be a living hell. Poor pathetic little one."

She gently places the child back in its dead mother's arms, gets up and leaves the house. She finds a place to sit on the front veranda of the house. She wants to be far enough away so she can't hear the child whimper. She sits down and finally allows herself to cry. She has but a few moments left for her grief. The men will soon return.

Mohamed and his Uncle Ahmed find his father at the market with several of his brothers and other family members. He is glad the other men are here. It will make the job of telling his father the news easier than if they had been alone. As it turns out, Mohamed doesn't have to tell his father anything. Ahmed simply announces that there is an emergency at his house and he must go home.

All the men arrive at the house together. As they approach, they see a veiled woman sitting on the veranda. Abudullah approaches her, thinking it is his wife, Zohra. But, as he gets a few steps closer, he realizes it is someone else. "Woman," he says expectantly, "Where is my wife?"

Muna answers from under her veil, "Abdullah, it is I, Muna, the sister-in-law of Zohra. Zohra has passed to another place giving birth to the child. I am sorry for your pain, my brother-in-law."

Abdullah flings himself into the arms of his brothers who stand there stony-faced. They help him to a bench on the porch and cry out with him in his sorrow. Mohamed stands alone at the bottom of the stairs, his own grief long silenced by all he has seen. His younger brothers and sisters will learn of the death of their mother from their aunt. How sad that will be.

The news of Zohra's death travels fast in the small village and many relatives come to sit with Abdullah and his children. The long wait has begun. As each new visitor arrives, they bring an article of food, a live chicken, a rabbit, potatoes or vegetables. The women sit on the floor in a circle around the mother laid out on the sheepskins and the child who whimpers at her side. They tell women's stories, mostly about their own pregnancies and the deaths of their own babies. Every woman has lost at least one child before it reaches the age of two. One or two of the women leave the group from time to time to prepare meals. The mourners will remain until the child takes its last breath. This is how it is in Mohamed's village.

Mohamed eventually joins the men who congregate in the front yard of the house. In his heart, Mohamed wants to save his newborn little sister, but he knows he cannot. So he sits outside in the heat of the setting sun with his father, his brothers, his uncles and all the other visiting male villagers talking and telling old stories. Between the stories, they listen to the village holy men read verses from the Koran.

As the sun sets and the heat of the day subsides, a great sound begins. It is the sound of singing women, of women ululating, a high-pitched sorrowful, wailing sound that seems to open up the night as no other sound can. With this sound, the men know that the long wait has ended and that the real mourning can now begin.

The following day they name the little girl after her mother, Zohra, and bury her in the same grave as her mother in a family plot, under a pile of white rocks, high on a hill overlooking the village. Though Mohamed knows it must be Allah's will that his mother has died, and that the child has died, he has a feeling of emptiness, an emptiness that he will carry for the rest of his life.

* * *

Mohamed never mentions his mother's dream to his father, but even not telling him doesn't alter destiny. Within six months of becoming a widower, Abdullah marries Aisha, Zohra's sister, just like in the dream. Mohamed understands the practicality: Abdullah has all these children to look after and Aisha seems willing to take on the task. Mohamed, seeing that this marriage gives his father some comfort, struggles to accept it.

As time passes, however, it becomes clear that Aisha doesn't love children the way Zohra did. The children run away from her instead of toward her. She develops the temper of a shrew, screaming and hollering at one or the other of the little ones until her voice itself becomes harsh and ugly.

When Aisha doesn't immediately become pregnant, she blames Abdullah. She becomes more and more obsessed with the desire to have a child. Mohamed overhears her curse Zohra's children because they are not her own. Abdullah tries to comfort her and tells her that it doesn't matter, that they have enough children. But, she complains incessantly. In time she begins to complain about the house as well and then, about everything. At the end of his patience and under extreme pressure to be sure his children have a mother, Abdullah promises Aisha that he will build her a house of her own in the village. Abdullah still has some money coming from the French every year. They still buy his grapes at a good price. He trades a small piece of his farm for a lot in the village of Mascara and begins to build a house for Aisha and his many children. It won't be a very big house, but maybe big enough for them to grow up in. Maybe, the house will make Aisha satisfied to be with them, instead of obsessing about more children.

Abdullah is content with the children he has and he and Aisha are growing older. The thought of the move and the new house mellows Aisha for a time. She attempts to mother the little ones.

Mohamed feels less anxious around her. The family begins to clear out the farmhouse and pack up what few belongings they have for moving to the new house.

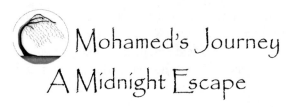

Mohamed's Journey
A Midnight Escape

Algeria, North Africa in the early 1950s

Time passes at an achingly slow pace for Mohamed. As Aisha seems more content with the children, he begins to spend more and more time with the young men in the village. They talk of politics, war and women. He reads any newspaper he can find. His country is entering a troubled time. He travels often to the big city of Oran on the Mediterranean with his brother, Tahar. They have relatives there but visiting relatives is only the excuse they use to appease their father when he asks where they are going.

The young men find many things to do in a big city like Oran. Things Mohamed has never experienced before - movies, large department stores, markets with all kinds of products for sale. He asks himself, "Why are my people living is such poverty while the French *colons* are living so well?" The *colons* live in large villas and their children attend the finest schools. The large department stores with escalators and elevators and merchandise from every strange sounding place in the world cater only to these *colons* and their families. His people have none of these opportunities.

He begins also to question Allah and Allah's ways. He doesn't understand why his sisters have to cover themselves in the presence of men, while the French women go about the cities uncovered and yet still marry and bear children. Those who follow

Allah's ways have only hard work, misery and death. He talks to his friends in the village about these things and discovers he is not alone. Other young men are asking the same questions. He and his friends meet to discuss these issues – issues for which there are no answers. The discontent among the young men in Mohamed's village grows quickly. When he goes to the city, he sees discontent there as well.

Mohamed is also learning more about the outside world from his Uncle Tohamy who was drafted into the French army during the Second World War. For years Tohamy remained silent about his adventures, afraid that people in his village would not believe what he had seen. Now, ten years later, Tohamy talks about his travels through France and parts of Europe. Mohamed hears about how other people live. Inside him, a desire grows – a desire to discover other ways of life. He worries that maybe this desire is Allah's way of testing his faith. He has so many unanswered questions.

Life in the village is rapidly changing. French troops are everywhere. Mohamed can no longer meet his friends on a street corner without being asked for his identification papers. Mohammed's brothers and some of his friends plan clandestine meetings late at night and they make plans to rid the land of the *colons*, to take what is rightfully theirs. Mohamed hears much talk of war and hate. Every day, he reads the newspaper accounts of bombings in the cities, of assassinations and atrocities perpetuated on the *colons* by the various and ever-growing groups of discontented Arabs.

One by one, his friends from school begin to disappear. Mohamed questions their families and learns some have gone to the hills to join the *guerrillas*, the fighters who have vowed to save Algeria – to bring Algeria back to Algerians. Sometimes, Mohamed hears the *gendarmes* have taken one or another of his friends, arrested them for subversive activities. Some friends never return, but if one does, he tells of severe beatings and terrible tortures. Public executions become commonplace – even for the slightest offences. Mohammed senses that the more severe the punishment inflicted, the greater the determination of his people to fight back. "When there is no hope," he thinks, "then there is only the will to fight for hope."

The work on Abdullah's house in the village stops because the money from the *colons* stops. Abdullah moves his family into the half-finished rooms anyway. The farm will not be safe for them with all of the unrest around them. Mohamed's brothers go off to the mountains to join the *guerrillas*. Businesses are shut down. Red tape and bureaucracy take over. Arabs are no longer allowed to travel from one village to another without police permission and identification cards.

For Abdullah, it is a very difficult time. Word comes to him from a secret sympathetic policeman in the village that all young males with any education will soon be picked up and shot. This is the new colonial policy to rid the country of troublemakers. After much consideration and planning, he calls Mohammed to his side, embraces him, and tells him he must leave the country as quickly as he can.

The very next night, Mohamed and two cousins, Ahmed Ben Freha and Mohamed Geldahanigel leave Mascara under cover of darkness and head for the Tunisian border. The Tunisian government is sympathetic to the Algerian *guerrilla* movement and Algeria's fight for freedom. Tunisia takes in refugees and *guerrillas* alike. Mohamed and his cousins have only to make their way from Mascara in Western Algeria to the frontier of Eastern Algeria and then across the border, and they will be safe.

The three travel mostly by night following rivers and roads when it is safe, sleeping in forests and tall grass, and hiding, always hiding from the French and their ever-searching troops. One day passes into the next. Sometimes, they eat and sometimes, they don't. Mostly, they find the people along the way sympathetic. They have little trouble in the major towns and villages and become quite adept at slipping into a new village or town and disappearing into the crowds. It is in the countryside where the danger lies. French troops patrol the major roads leading from village to village and often sweep the fields for people traveling illegally. Mohamed and his cousins are forced to stay far off the roads and paths on their journey and often get lost. These detours take time and money, both of which are dwindling.

One morning the cousins wake in a farmer's field to the sound of their own language. They stand up and greet the strangers. "Hello there," Mohamed says. "Hello."

Three men, dressed in the clothes of the countryside, look at them with fear in their eyes. One holds a gun and he points it at the cousins. "Who are you? What are you doing there? Why are you hiding?"

"We are traveling to the border from Mascara, and we heard you speak in our own language. We only want directions," Mohamed explains.

The man with the gun relaxes and points it away from the boys. "It is very dangerous in this area," he says. "The army is everywhere. If they find you without papers or in hiding, they will shoot you on the spot." He looks at Mohamed and asks, "Where do you want to go?"

"We want to cross the border into Tunisia but I think we have lost our way."

"No," the man responds, "you have not lost your way. You are but five miles from Tebessa which means you are nearly at the border. From Tebessa, you have another twenty miles to cover. However, you will need the help of Allah to cross. The border is tightly guarded and no one goes over, not even if they have papers. I advise you to wait until night falls and then slip into the city of Tebessa. Go to the hotel *Caracalla*. It is a place that takes travelers like you and it will be safer than walking the streets at night. Do you understand?"

Mohamed nods. He finds the Western Algerian dialect strange to his ears but understandable nonetheless.

Early the next morning, the farmers return, bringing them bread and cheese and homemade sweets for the rest of their journey. Mohamed and his cousins are grateful and "if it is Allah's will," they promise to someday return the favour.

Mohamed and his cousins head for the city immediately as it is less risky and easier to walk in the daytime than to sneak in the darkness. They leave their field camp and carefully wind their way towards the city of Tebessa according to the directions given by the farmers. They are happy for the bread and other food given to them for they realize it will take most of their money to pay for the hotel.

With the farmer's directions and using back roads with high-grassed ditches for cover, they make their way to the outskirts of the city. They hear the voices of many people as they approach a main road. Mixing in with the walking traffic, they slip onto the road and enter the city. They pray that no one is checking papers today. Within an hour they find themselves standing in front of the *Caracalla* hotel. The old sign flashes a neon *vacance*. They push through the wooden doors and enter the building. It is rustic and seems as old as the city itself. Mohamed knows that isn't possible because he remembers reading somewhere when he first discovered he could read, that Tebessa existed since the seventh century B.C. when it was established as an outpost of Carthage.

Mohamed approaches the desk clerk to ask for a room. The clerk looks at him and his cousins suspiciously, but asks no questions. He agrees to rent them a room. They give the man some money and he gives them a key. They take their few belongings to a small room furnished with one large bed and a broken-down couch. The room looks clean but in need of maintenance and repair. There is a bathroom down the hall with toilets and sinks, reminding them that it has been a long time since any of them has had a bath. They agree to spend the hours before dark at the public bath.

They head out to find the bath, and spend the next few hours washing and shaving. The bath is crowded and they stand out as strangers in the city. They keep to themselves. They listen to many conversations in the same dialect that they heard the farmers speak, but they hear no politics and nothing about the mounting dissent.

It is sundown when they return to their room. As they enter the hotel, Mohamed notices that the lobby is deserted. Even the clerk who was behind the desk is absent. They make their way to their room. They open the door to find three French *gendarmes* waiting for them with machine guns.

226 Bend Like The Willow

"You will go with us," one barks in French, handcuffing the three to each other and hustling them out the door, through the lobby and down the street to the office of the *prefecture*.

"We are in deep trouble," thinks Mohamed. "This may be my last day on earth."

When they are ushered into an office, Mohamed is surprised to see their meagre belongings and a newspaper lying on a desk. The man behind the desk seems to envelop the room. He is stocky and muscular with greasy hair and a ghost-like thin-skinned complexion. He addresses them in French but swings easily into the local Arabic dialect when he gets no response.

"Whose newspaper is this?" the *prefecture* blusters, his saliva spraying in thick droplets across Mohamed's face.

No one answers.

"I will assume, then, that all of you can read." He opens the door and calls to a guard. The guard enters and is told to uncuff Mohamed from his cousins.

The *gendarme* then points at Mohamed. "Take this one," he spits.

Mohamed is taken alone out of the prefecture's office and into the night. He and his two guards walk silently a hundred yards to another building. All that Mohamed can make out in the darkness is that it is some sort of square brick shed, no more than ten feet long by ten feet wide. One of the guards takes out a large set of keys and opens two locks on the thick wooden door. As the door slowly creaks open, the guard takes Mohamed by the shoulders and suddenly gives him a push through the doorway. The momentum of the guard's push sends him forward into a wall. It feels cold and greasy and wherever he puts his feet, they sink into slime. The smell overwhelms him – excrement – he is standing in it. The door slams shut. The last bit of light disappears and he is left alone in total darkness.

Even hell must surely be better than this. He reaches out in all directions. His knuckles touch the roof above him. As he tries to inch his way around the space, he brushes up against something. He reaches out to touch whatever it is – it is hard and cold. A chill climbs eerily up his spine. The more his fingers explore, the more he wants to stop them. But he can't, not before he is certain what it is.

His head swims. It feels as if time has stopped. He hears screaming – an echo of his mother's last cry – or his own? He isn't sure. In his mind's eye, he is flying. He sees his own body bent in this hell, still touching and still screaming.

Suddenly he returns to his body. The screaming stops and the sweating starts. He feels warm vomit enter his throat and gush down his chest. He leans against the greasy wall and waits.

After a long time, he hears footsteps coming towards him, heavy footsteps, many of them. He thinks, "I have lost my mind. I am really dead and this is hell."

A key sounds in the lock and a thin band of light invades the shed. From his place in the far corner, he can count the men as they are pushed and kicked, one after the other, through the door. Some cry out or curse, others cough or moan. More and more are pushed inside until Mohamed no longer has room to squat – only to stand. Someone is leaning against him, pushing him hard against the cold greasy wall. Finally, the door swings shut and the light goes out.

Mohamed envies the dead body he touched. For an instant, he wonders who is standing in his vomit. Suddenly, a rasping male voice calls out over the cries and moans. "Escape," it calls, "we must find a way to escape." Curses are the only response the voice gets.

Mohamed stands in the muck with the others. He is sure many hours have passed. His legs are tired and cramping. The reality of where he is and what is happening sinks in. Most of his hell-mates give up their cursing and crying. One man begins to tell a story of his younger days, another man follows suit but tells of his days spent traveling from village to village to circumcise young boys. One after another, they each tell their stories.

Mohamed suddenly calls out to the crowd, "Yell out something one by one, so we know how many we are."

Nobody answers.

He calls out again, "Come on, people. That way, at least we will know who our partners are in this hell.

Still no response.

"Please," he begs into the silent darkness.

This time he gets a response. A man with a young voice says, "I am a student from Algiers." The second is a storekeeper from Tlemcen, the third, a farmer, and on it goes, each identifying himself by what he does for a living.

When Mohamed thinks they have all have been identified, he is shocked to hear a small feminine voice from the middle of the group. "I am Sara. I am a mother," it says.

The crowd goes stone quiet. Then, someone shouts, "Bastards, these *Pied-Noir*. It is bad enough they put us men in hell! Are they so evil that they torture our women as well? We will damn their souls in hell."

Everyone yells in support and someone begins to chant, "Death to the *Pied-Noir*." The chant only lasts as long as it takes for them to realize that no one can hear them.

They go back to counting their numbers. In the end, they know that there are twenty men and three women in the small brick shed. They also discover two dead bodies. The smell of the rotting bodies tells them they have been here a long time. Eventually, the group decides to move the bodies. They stack one on top of the other in order to provide more space for people to stand.

Mohamed wonders who will be the last of them to die. He hopes he will be the first.

Time passes and as it does, the stories get fewer and less hopeful. People on the outer rim of the room lean against the greasy walls and the others lean on them. Some try to squat down and others try to make room for them. At the end of the first full night and day in this hell, one old man takes his last breath and dies. Others near him stack his body on top of the others. When they finish that chore, the group invites the sickest to come forward and sit on the bodies.

Mohamed imagines that it must be daytime outside. The temperature inside the building is increasing. Nature has solved one problem – he can no longer smell the human excrement. Diarrhoea is rampant in the group. There is no dignity here. At this rate, without food or water, in the intense heat, many will not last another twenty-four hours.

Mohamed thinks about the time he has spent reading and drinking coffee with his friends. He thinks about how many others must be suffering under the French. "If I ever get out of this place, I will do all I can to fix my country," he vows in the darkness.

Poetic words start to run in and out of his brain. At times, death looks sweet. He hears his mother's voice whisper to him.

> *Death, like words unspoken,*
> *Babes unborn,*
> *Ideas unformed,*
> *And lives unlived,*
>
> *Is sometimes prayed for,*
> *Sometimes cursed,*
> *Sometimes not thought of, and*
> *Always at one time wondered about.*
>
> *It can be quiet and quick,*
> *Or painful and long,*
> *Or just happen,*
>
> *Death is a lot like love,*
> *Except that death happens to us all,*
> *Love to only some of us.*

Time now means nothing. A new enemy is rampant – thirst. Every time he closes his eyes he sees the ocean. From his companions, he hears that more have died.

Death is the only thing he can think of clearly. It is calling to him as if it was his mother. "Come," she whispers. "Come to me," and he tries, but each time he reaches out to touch her, she is gone.

Those who have been leaning against him for a long time are now gone. He can hear moaning and breathing. He reaches down, down to the floor around him and feels a mass of people lying there. He traces their bodies with his hands. They are intertwined together in a marriage of death. His legs give way and he collapses, not caring where he falls. This time, the floor is welcoming. His body feels as though it belongs to someone else. He feels nothing. He smells nothing. This time, his mother will reach out and take him.

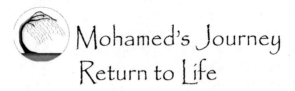

Mohamed's Journey
Return to Life

Algeria, North Africa in the late 1950s

Mohamed's mother doesn't take him after all. The FLN (National Liberation Front) *guerrillas* do. He wakes up in a make-shift hospital somewhere on the Algerian-Tunisian frontier with needles in his veins and a hell of a headache. A Tunisian doctor tells him to rest, to stay on the cot and to regain his strength before he tries to walk or talk. He is extremely dehydrated. They thought he was dead when they found him.

After several days of rest, he feels stronger and he begins to ask questions. Where am I? How did I get here? Who rescued me? His questions all bring the same reply. "The *guerrillas* who pulled you out of the *hell-box* are on missions."

Mohamed tries to do as the doctors and nurses tell him and not think about any of it, but the memories are there. Every time he shuts his eyes he feels the darkness and hears the screams. It takes days to wash the smell off his body, the smell of vomit and excrement. The dead ones come to him in his dreams. Even though he never clearly saw any of them, he pictures their faceless bodies. "This must be what it's like to be blind," he thinks, "to be blind and to know hell."

It takes three more weeks in the camp for Mohamed to re-cover physically. He knows he is better when he begins to feel restless. It is time to move on – time to complete his journey – time to help where he can. He spends his days resting and eating.

Most of what happens in this camp happens at night. When he wakes up in the morning, there are more wounded men in the beds near by. They either die right away or are up and gone within a few days. None of them talk very much.

One night when Mohamed is lying awake in the darkness, he hears the sound of footsteps coming closer. Someone calls his name, "Mohamed, come. We are moving away from here. It is time for you to leave."

He gathers up what few things he has and follows his rescuers out into the night. There are three of them, all dressed in the clothes of the countryside and carrying automatic weapons.

"We have been told to guide you across the frontier and into our headquarters in Tunisia," one of them announces. "It will not be an easy journey."

Mohamed nods, not certain what to say. He follows the men. It takes four days to cross the frontier, four days of slow arduous walking. The entire area is mined. He is told where to step and where not to step, when to start and when to stop. He is told where to pee and where to sleep. One false move, he is told, and his journey is over, permanently.

In the little time they have to talk along the way, his guides tell him the circumstances of his rescue. His cousins were released from the jail at Tebessa the night he was locked up. They made their way to a *guerrilla* outpost and told the *guerrillas* about Mohamed. A team was dispatched to find him. His guides don't know how they were able to enter the building and pull him out without incident, but they did. When they brought him back to their camp, everyone was certain he would die. Mohamed asks about the others in the *hell-box,* but the guides know only that two others were pulled out with him. They don't know where those two are now. They can only surmise that they joined the *guerrillas* or went back to their families.

On the fourth day of their journey, Mohamed becomes aware that the others are more relaxed and walk more quickly. They joke and smile and tell Mohamed they are now in Tunisia and only a few miles from their destination.

At the Tunisian headquarters of the FLN he is greeted like a returning hero and taken into the fold. Over the next few days, hundreds of other young recruits who dare to tempt fate and cross the frontier arrive. Some, like him, are guided in by seasoned fighters. Others come alone. The journey to get to the headquarters is just the beginning of the difficult life on which they are about to embark. The training is harsh and dangerous. Food and other items are in short supply.

Mohamed looks forward to completing his training, and anxiously awaits the day when he will return to Algeria to fight as a *Mujahedeen*. That, however, is not to be. On the day he expects to join a group of fighters heading back to Algeria, he is surprised to learn that he has been given a permanent assignment in the training camp as a teacher. The commander tells him that the men spend too much time sitting around playing cards while waiting for orders. He wants Mohamed to teach them how to read and write. "When the battle against the *colons* is won, someone will have to run the country," he explains and shakes his head. "Too many of our people lack even basic skills like reading and writing."

Mohamed spends the next two years teaching and, though the living circumstances are difficult, it fills his life with meaning. He is content. Then, one day, his troop commander enters Mohamed's class and announces that the Tunisian government is sending him to Egypt for formal education. Mohamed spends two years in Egypt studying subjects that allow him to enter high school. Once this upgrading is complete, he applies for a special scholarship offered by the royal family of Kuwait to Algerians displaced by war. He applies and is accepted. If he completes these studies, he will have a high school diploma, something he could never even dream about a few years before.

Kuwait is a land of dichotomies. It is a land of money, oil, cars and men. Everyone is rich and lives well. He rarely sees a woman outside. He wonders where they are all hidden. Sometimes he sees burka-clad women climbing into Cadillacs, but they disappear behind tinted windows. He never sees them on the street.

When Mohamed finishes school in Kuwait, his advisor suggests that he apply for a scholarship to the United Soviet Socialist Republic. There is no sign that the Algerian war will end, and there is nothing for Mohamed to do until he can return to Algeria. It has been nearly five years since he has heard from his family. He wonders if they are even alive.

Most of the other Algerian students that Mohamed meets in his travels are applying for these government scholarships. Many countries are now offering to help the war-displaced youth of Algeria. He hears there are opportunities not only in Russia, but in the United States. Mohamed applies to Russia. He feels his political ideals are closer to Russia than to the West. He is shocked when he hears that all his friends have applied to the West. It takes six months to get the papers processed.

One day he opens his mail and discovers a letter from the International Students Association based in New York. He has been accepted to learn English at New York University for six months and then to travel to Tucson, Arizona to do a Bachelor of Science Degree in Agriculture. He is stunned. He calls his friends. His friends tell him that they also have been accepted to study abroad, but they are being sent to Moscow, Russia. They laugh together over this news. Those who applied for the East, go to the West, and those who applied for the West, go to the East. He wonders about this twist of fate as he prepares for the next steps in his journey.

PART THREE

ALGERIA

 The Waiting Game

I sit on the shaded patio and absentmindedly stare at the orange trees. It is the first day of week four and there has not been a single word from Moe. Today, I decide to stop waiting for the mailman. Every day for three weeks, I have planned my days around his arrival. As soon as he steps onto our sidewalk, I dash out the door. Every day I thrust a newly penned epistle bearing the address of Moe's cousin, Ahmed Ben Ahmed, in Algiers into the mailman's hand. I long to tell him – to tell anyone – that Ahmed has a secure job and a nice apartment and he has agreed to let Moe stay with him until he finds a job. But I don't say anything.

Every day, the mailman has nothing to give me in return for my letters. I can barely keep from ripping the mail out of his hand to see if there is something for me. After a week, I feel embarrassed by this daily ceremony. Even though he smiles as he takes my daily offering, I think I see pity in his eyes.

I ask my mother ridiculous rhetorical questions: "Why doesn't he write? Do you think he was in a wreck? Do you think he found another wife?"

To make it even more difficult, Zohra keeps asking, "Where's my daddy? Why did my daddy go away and leave us?"

I become more and more desperate. My parents try hard to be hopeful and optimistic. "He is probably just busy getting himself settled and finding a job," my mother says one time I ask why she thinks he hasn't written, and "the mail service doesn't work well," to my second or third queries of the day.

They talk in the kitchen, whispering at first, but lately they are loud enough that I can hear them. They, too, are wondering why he hasn't sent any letters.

It's a beautiful home, this middle class grey adobe house nestled on the outskirts of Tucson. The patio is warm, restful and shaded, and surrounded by gardenia bushes and citrus trees. A high adobe fence encloses the yard and blocks out the desert. "I could live here forever," I think. And then, I find myself thinking, "I might have to – if Moe has left me and gone back to his life in Algeria." With that thought, the patio begins to feel as if it is closing in on me.

Suddenly, my mother pushes open the patio doors. "It's here!" she shouts, joyfully. "It's finally here!" She thrusts an onionskin envelope into my hand. "Thank god," she continues. "Thanks be to the lord above. I have been praying for weeks for this."

I close my hand on the letter. "I had nearly given up." Tears stream down my cheeks. "You must have wondered, too, if he was going to write."

"Don't you talk like that," my mother snaps at me. "I knew that boy would come through for you. He just had to – or – or – I would have personally gone over to that god-forsaken country and killed him myself!" She turns and marches back into the house. The past three weeks have been as hard on her as they have been on me.

My tears continue to fall, and my hands shake as I look at the envelope. My fingers trace the wide black letters of my address. I caress the letters in my name, relishing in the familiar shape of each carefully drawn letter of the script. I can see Moe's many years of writing in Arabic showing in the carefully inscribed letters.

I admire the row of beautifully coloured stamps and note how the swirls of black ink around them indicate the postmark. February 8 – he sent the letter the day he arrived – three weeks ago.

With that realization, I rip open the envelope. I am relieved to know for certain that it is the postal system that caused this delay – and not my Moe. How could I have doubted him? I read:

February 8, 1966

Dear Susie (Sewzi, I hear)

Moe is sorry this letter is short. I am so tired. The trip is very long and difficult. My cousin Ahmed came to pick me at the airport. I am now at his house. You have his address so you can write to me here if you want. Kiss my children. Tomorrow I try to write more but this is to tell you I am finally (praise be to Allah) in the land I love so much.

Love from MOE

My mother opens the door and leans out, trying to let me have my privacy but too anxious to wait any longer. "So, what does he say? Is he alive?"

"Yes, he's alive. The letter was sent on February 8. You were right about it being the post office." I hold the letter close to my breast, as if that will bring Moe closer to me.

"I thought so." My mother smiles. "Well, what else did he say?

"Only that he couldn't write much because he's so tired after the trip."

She nods. "It was a long trip."

"He says he will write more *tomorrow*. I hope that letter arrives *tomorrow*." I absentmindedly reach up to brush away my tears. "I really miss him."

My mother pauses, then she whispers, "Remember how much you miss him," she says and though she isn't crying, I hear tears in her voice. "When you and the children are gone," she continues, "Remember it double – because that is how I will feel."

I go and hug her tightly. "I'll remember, Mom. It's hard, isn't it?"

"Yes," she answers. "It is hard. Are you sure you have to go? And take your children?" She pauses again, and then the words rush out, "You could stay here. You could tell Moe that he can come back and get a job here."

I study my mother's face. Her statements are nothing I haven't said to myself over and over again during the past five years. But, I know that I must go. I have a reply ready, one that has been carefully crafted over time – as much for myself as for her.

"Mom, I have to go," I say slowly. "If I stay here, I will always regret that I didn't try to do it his way. If I beg him to come back before he tries out life in his own country, he will spend his whole life unhappy and never know how it might have been."

My mother is crying.

"Mom," I continue, my voice soft and gentle. "Some things in life people just have to do – and for me, this is one of those things. I know it will be difficult, but I have to give it a try." I hug her again and tell her how it will all work out the way it is supposed to.

She nods through her tears and goes back into the house. There isn't anything else to say and she knows it.

The next day when I hear the mailman, I open the door. I find him standing smiling broadly, with one arm extended, holding a large pile of letters. "For you," he says, and I detect relief in his voice. I reach out hungrily and discover four more onion-skinned envelopes covered in colourful stamps and accented by beautiful black letters carefully drawn across the front of the envelope. It is like receiving a whole bunch of familiar friends. I take the envelopes and walk to my bedroom. I intend to relish every word of these wonderful gifts.

I arrange the letters on my bed in order according to their postmark dates. The first one, dated February 11, describes the joy of reuniting with his family. His cousin, Ahmed, a government official in the diplomatic corps, commissioned a car and a driver to take him to visit his father and siblings in their home village of Mascara. Moe says the village has changed much since he left fifteen years ago, and that his family is not as well off as they once were. His father has run out of money to finish building his house and his brother who lives in the same compound still has a dirt floor. Between the lines, I read that Moe is disappointed and shocked at the amount of poverty he finds. Everywhere he goes, he sees damage caused by the war. Hundreds of bombed-out houses. Water systems that have just begun to be repaired. Even in Algiers, he has water only a few hours a day. He reminds me that this war with the French has killed 1,000,000 of his people. Eventually, he turns to a happier note, his father's health.

My father is in extremely good health and looks much younger than his 64 years.

At the end he writes,

He almost looks younger than I do.

The first four letters are dated between February 11 and February 20. I reread them all again in the evening and share them with my parents. I wait eagerly for more the next day. But, it is a week before I receive a clump of three more. I don't worry any more about receiving one letter a day. I accept the joy of having them arrive at all.

As the days and weeks go by, I begin to get ready for my trip. The children and I go to the doctor to get our required inoculations. The typhoid injection is the most difficult. My body reacts to it almost immediately and by the time I get home from the doctor's office, I can barely stand up. My mother puts me to bed and takes my temperature. It is 102 degrees and climbing. She gives me an aspirin and tells me to sleep. For three days, I lay in bed feeling achy and miserable. I only get up to go to the bathroom and to eat small amounts of food.

On the third day, I am awakened by my mother standing at the foot of my bed, shouting at me. "It's time for you to get the hell out of bed," she yells. "I am tired of being your maid servant and your babysitter. Suck it up, Princess, and get to work. I am tired of doing it all for you." By the time she gets to the end of her sentence, she is screaming.

Both children are standing by the bed, staring at their grandmother.

When my mother comes to the end of her tirade, Zohra screams at her. "Mi-Mi mad! Mi-Mi, you shut up!"

I know from long experience that when my mother gets like this, I need to go somewhere else in a hurry. And I need to take my children with me. Today, however, I am too sick to move fast enough to stop what I know is coming. I hear the sound of a firm slap followed by a blood-curdling scream from Zohra. I stumble out of bed and pick her up.

She sobs uncontrollably. "Mi-Mi hit me," she sobs. "Mi-Mi not nice. Bad Mi-Mi."

I feel Tarek's hand fasten onto my pyjamas with an iron grip. He stands next to me, not making a sound, sucking his thumb with his free hand, and looking up at his sister crying on my shoulder.

My mother turns her back and storms down the hall to her bedroom, slamming the door behind her, reminding me of the pattern of my mother's behaviour, extending back to my childhood. When my mother can no longer cope with things the way they are, she lashes out. Sometimes she slaps. Sometimes she pulls hair. Sometimes she lies on her bed and sobs loudly for hours. The loud sobbing is always the worst.

The only thing missing in this episode is my father. In the past, when my mother would go into one of her rages and stomp off, my father would look at me coolly and say, "Now look what you've done to your mother."

To this moment, I never really understood what I had done to cause her moods. Now, I realize that, at least this time, I have done nothing. My mother just has a low ability to cope with things when she gets tired. Looking after me and Zohra and Tarek for three days has worn her out.

I gather my children to me and we inch our way back to my bed. On Zohra's little cheek I can see the outline of my mother's hand. I silently ask God to help Moe find a job. We need to get out of here soon.

Moe's letters continue to arrive in bunches and are filled with his experiences of looking for a job and a place to live. In his first letters, he is very upbeat and happy but as the days and weeks go by I can tell that things are not going as well as he had hoped.

Susie, he writes, the government in my country is one big nightmare. It is bureaucracy. I must learn how to deal with bureaucracy if I am to get anywhere in Algeria. I see that this bureaucracy is one big tangle of officials who don't know what they want.

First, I must have my degree studied by some officials to see if I know what to do to work in my own country. I take the degree to the officials to have it judged. Then, I am told my papers must be translated into French if I want to find work with the government.

I spend my days standing in long lines. I fill out more papers – forms that tell what I know and what kind of job I can do. I explain, first to one official and then to the next official why I go to school in America and not in Russia. I explain about the money to pay for my school classes and the money paid so I can live in America. I have to keep explaining that I learned to speak English so good – no, so well – because I do my studies in English. Of course, I speak English better than I speak French.

As the weeks come and go, he confesses that he is shocked by what he finds in his country.

Moe thinks all wrong, he writes in another letter, I think I be greeted with open arms. I think that I be respected by officials in government because I come to help, because I bring back skills to help my people. I think that I be seen as a valuable person, important to my country, coming in to help Algeria grow and recover from the big war.

But biggest shock to Moe is that most of the agricultural jobs are still filled by Frenchmen. I not understand this. The war is over. The French should be gone. Algeria is now free country. Independent country. I not expect to find the enemy still have power, still run government. I not expect that the enemy still do jobs that should go to Algerian people.

Moe spends most days looking for work. Finding job is hard. But Moe thinks that finding house might be even harder. It is hard to find job with no money and no car. It is many times long distance to go to see about jobs. Many times, people who have jobs are not best people for those jobs. I see that jobs are not many – are scarce. There is not enough work for everybody who want jobs. People who do not have skills to do educated jobs try to block those with more education from getting jobs. At the end of many days, Moe's head feels like he is going crazy.

I can tell that Moe's days are long, bleak and terribly frustrating. I have no way of reaching out to him except through letters. Phone calls overseas are so expensive that even my parents won't attempt such a thing. I think of calling anyway, but the truth is, I would have to phone a public phone in a post office. According to Moe, there are few phones available in private homes. So I write letters of happiness to my poor suffering husband. I tell him all about the children and what we do everyday. I can think of nothing more I can do for him except hope that eventually he finds a place for himself and ultimately, a place for us.

Then, on May 7, 1966 I get the letter I have been longing for.

> Susie, I have good news! I have very good news! I have found job – and job comes with apartment. It small apartment, but it is in new building, No one lived there before. I will be engineer agronomme – in English, an Agricultural Engineer at Baba Ali. Baba Ali is a 1,000-hectare farm outside village of Birtouta – twenty-nine miles south of Algiers. Baba Ali was French plantation. It abandoned by French. Now, government take over this farm. Moe's job be to help oversee orange groves, goats and experimental research plots. I can do this work.

At the end of the letter he tells me in curt little writing without further comment that his new boss is French and so are two of his co-workers.

The only part of it that I really care about is the sentence that says we can finally join him.

> I happy to find job. Now, Susie, you and children can come.

I read the letter again and then I go screaming to my mother. She is standing at the kitchen sink staring out the window. When she turns, tears are streaming down her face. She knows what the letter says. She hugs me. I help her wipe her tears.

"I am happy for you, honey," she says, "but unhappy for myself."

My father comes in from the garden, and fills a glass of water from the faucet. He turns toward me as he drinks it and asks, "So, what are you looking so excited about? Another letter?"

"Yes," I shout. "Another letter. Daddy, Moe says I can come. He got a job and an apartment and he is going to meet me in Algiers and..."

My voice trails off.

My father slowly finishes his water and sets the glass down. "Well," he says. "I guess if it makes you happy, then that's all we can do. We will miss you so much." He turns to go back out to the garden. With his hand on the doorknob, he stops and says, "When are you going?"

The question echoes back and forth in my head. When am I going? How will I get there? I'll have to fly. Moe has taken all of our money... I am suddenly struck by the logistics of the trip. I have no money to pay for tickets for the children and me.

I look at my parents. They have the power to make me stay with them forever. All they have to do is to refuse to give me money to buy tickets.

"Darn, I have no money for a ticket," I blurt out.

My mother looks at my father and they both smile. "We know," they say together. "We know."

"Except," my mother smiles again, and adds, "You do have money."

I look at her curiously. "What do you mean?"

"In 1960, when you were seventeen, your Auntie Alice died and left you and your cousins a whole pile of mining stocks. Your father and I have held on to those stocks for a number of years thinking they might come in handy someday. I think today is the day. We checked their value with our banker just the other day and he tells us you have close to $10,000. There are some papers to sign and the money is yours."

"Ten thousand dollars?" I ask incredulously. "Ten thousand dollars? Holy cow. That's amazing."

My father interjects, "It will cost you $1,000 of that for your tickets to Algeria but the rest will make a good nest egg. I suggest you put it away for a rainy day. You may have to come out of that country some day and it would be good to have the money to do it with." My father pulls open the door, eyes filling with tears as he finishes the sentence.

Once my mother is sure my father is out of earshot, she tells me, "Put that money in the account with the cheque I gave you last year. Actually, maybe we should open a new account with my name on it so I can get in there and send you money when you need it. That way you know your money is safe and I can wire it to you when you need it."

My mother is right. I will put the money into an account that she can draw from if I need money.

The very next day my mother and I hire a babysitter and go to the passport office where we renew my passport and discover that I will need a visa. The Algerian Embassy in Washington assures me that, as the wife of a returning citizen, I can get a visa issued within seven days. They will send it by special delivery. I should have it by the 15th of May.

The paperwork for everything takes nearly a full day. My mother and I enjoy our day away from the usual and decide to eat lunch at a fancy restaurant. We talk about how my life might unfold once I am in Algeria. She is afraid for me, but she tries to be positive. I tell her again how I have to go to Algeria with Moe or I will regret it for the rest of my life.

She shoots back with "If you go, you might regret it for the rest of your life, too."

I can't listen to her. I can't let her fear persuade me. My heart tells me I have to go.

Our flight is booked for May 18, 1966. I look at the package the man behind the TWA desk hands to me. "Long ride for a woman and two little ones," he muses. "What on earth are you going to Algeria for?"

I don't answer. I take the package, smile, and walk away. Once I am in the car and on my way home, I open it. I am leaving at six in the morning and arriving in New York in the afternoon. In New York, I have a five-hour layover. Then, I have an eleven-hour-and-fifty-minute Air France flight to Madrid. In Madrid, the plane is on the ground for an hour, but I don't get off. Then, it is on to Algiers. The total flight time is more than 24 hours. The time changes confuse me and I don't know how much more than 24 hours the trip will take. Right then, however, I don't care. I have the tickets in my hand and all I can think is that once I am on my way, it will be only 24 hours – maybe a bit more – before I see Moe and we are together again.

A Trip to a New Life

The night before my flight, I am anxious, but mostly I am excited at the prospect of seeing Moe again. I am awake at 4:30 a.m. when my mother knocks on my door. Everything has already been packed into three large suitcases and two carry-ons, one filled with snacks, milk, diapers and a pile of toys. Everything I own is in these bags.

"I don't want to eat that yucky cereal," wails Zohra. The children are both upset at having their sleep interrupted. Tarek is bleary-eyed. He just sucks his thumb.

As we head out the door, my mother hugs each child tightly and only smiles when they struggle against her. "Bye-bye," she tells them and secretly pushes some special treat into each of their pockets. "I'll miss you so much." She turns to Zohra and orders, "You write to Mi-Mi, you hear?"

I smile and reach out to my mother. "She will. I promise." When I hug my mother close, I feel her sadness.

"You take care and you take care of these babes for me, okay?"

"Yes, Mom, I will," I assure her. There is nothing left to say. Days ahead of time, it has been decided that only my father will take us to the airport. My mother can't stand the thought of actually seeing us leave.

I pick up Tarek, along with the two carry-on bags, and herd Zohra in front of me to the car. My father has already loaded the large bags in the trunk. The kids climb into the back seat and I tell them quietly that at the end of the big airplane trip they will see Daddy.

"See Daddy?" Zohra asks.

"Yes, honey, finally, we will see Daddy."

My dad takes the wheel of the Caddie and we shoot off in the direction of the airport.

"So," he asks immediately after we pull out of the driveway, "are you sure you have all your papers? Got your passport and health stuff? Tickets?" His question masks his sadness and fear.

"Yes, Dad, I have it all right here in my purse. I'll be fine," I assure him. "You know that, right?" I ask. My voice is timid. It is hard to see my father worry about me.

"Yes, I believe it will," he responds, talking as much to himself as to me, and then adding, "Sometimes, we gotta do what we gotta do."

I smile. Those are the words I have been using when my parents ask me why I have to go to Algeria.

We pull up to the airport departure doors. My father struggles to retrieve the bags from the trunk. I realize that he has aged so much since I have become a mother – or maybe I have just noticed it more these days. His hair has turned gray and he grimaces when he extends himself, even a little bit. I will really miss my father, perhaps more than my mother. He always seems in the background of my life, but I feel a special kinship with him, especially when he struggles with my mother and her bossy ways. How will they manage when I am far away?

I pick up Tarek, then bend down to pick up the carry-on bags, and again herd my daughter in front of me, through the airport doors and into the terminal. "Wait for me inside," my dad tells me. "I'll park the car and help you get on board."

He brings our bags up to the TWA desk where the lady processes our tickets, checks our baggage and gives my father a boarding pass so he can come all the way out to the plane to help us get settled.

"You can go right on board, folks. Have a nice flight."

My father picks up one of the carry-on bags, takes Zohra's little hand and guides us out the airport gate and onto the tarmac where the plane is sitting.

Zohra looks up at it in wide-eyed wonder. "Look, Papa," she says, "a big plane. I going in a big plane."

I look at my dad and smile. He looks at me and then looks away. Tears begin streaming down his cheeks. I haven't seen my father cry since my wedding day.

As we walk across the tarmac, a friendly, blonde stewardess takes my small bag and directs us up the many stairs to the door. When we step into the plane, another stewardess reads our tickets and directs us to our seats.

"Lots of room for you," my father says as he stuffs the carry-on bags, one into the overhead racks, and the other at my feet where I can get at the snacks and diapers easily.

One of the drawbacks of having a free ticket is that I may have to hold my 35-pound son on my lap for the whole five hours to New York City. For now, I strap Zohra into the seat by the window. My father lifts Tarek into the middle seat, and I take the aisle seat.

"Well, pumpkin, I guess this is it," my father says. "Good luck, honey, and make sure you write often. We love you all." He turns abruptly and heads down the stairs.

I watch as he makes his way back inside the terminal. I lose sight of him as the door swings closed. Tears well up in my eyes and, for a moment, I wonder what I am doing sitting in this plane with two babies, about to embark on a journey to the other side of the world to live in a culture that I know very little about. Resolutely, I turn back to the business of getting ready for take-off.

The plane is loaded and ready for take-off within fifteen minutes. I am in luck. No one has booked the third seat. Both children sit wide-eyed at all the noise. Once the plane is in the air, they settle down and Tarek falls into a light sleep with his thumb in his mouth and his other little hand twirling his curly blond locks. Zohra sits like a little lady and plays with her dolls. Halfway through the trip, the stewardess brings us a wonderful dinner of chicken and vegetables, complete with apple crisp and chocolate cake. Tarek wakes up enough to eat a few bites and then falls back asleep. I lay him down in the middle seat and he sleeps until we land in New York.

I am allowed to disembark before anyone else. Juggling the

two carry-on bags in one hand, and carrying Tarek in the other, I gently encourage Zohra as we make our way down the steep steps to the tarmac.

I am met by a male land attendant at the door to the terminal. He checks my ticket, and hands it back to me. "Your flight doesn't leave for another five hours, Mrs. So, you need to claim your suitcases right now and then find a place to wait for the next few hours. About an hour before your flight, you take your bags through that large set of doors over there, the one marked *International Flights Here* and line up so the officials can check your bags. The Customs checkpoint is actually in another building. Just follow the signs." He points in the direction of the marked doors. "See, over there?"

I look at the attendant and nod. Then I ask as politely as I can, "How am I supposed to get three large suitcases, two small bags, one toddler, one baby, and my purse through that door and into another building on my own?"

The attendant says, "I don't know, Mrs. I guess you'll just have to figure it out." He turns to the next passenger.

My arms are aching from holding Tarek and the carry-on bags. Zohra is standing so close to me that I am worried I will trip over her if I move a step. I consider screaming at the attendant.

But just then, I hear a familiar voice, my father's voice, calling my name. "Susie. Is that you, Susie?"

I turn and discover, not my father, but a shorter, bearded version of him, approaching and smiling at me. I heave a sigh of relief. It is my father's twin brother. I let Tarek and the bags slide to the floor in front of me. Zohra moves to my side and clutches my skirt.

"Uncle Marshall," I say in a much-relieved, too-loud voice. "Oh my god! How did you know I'd be here? How did you find me?" I rattle on in excitement.

Marshall laughs, reaches over the bags and the children, and enfolds me in a big hug. As he talks, he picks up the bags and moves into the open space inside the terminal. I herd Zohra and take Tarek's hand to help him manage a few steps.

"Ah, Oz told me where to look. It turned out he was right." Oz is my uncle's name for my father who calls his twin Mung.

"Oz said you'd need a hand for your five hour wait-over. Not sure I can stay the whole five hours but we can give you a hand for a while. You might want something to eat while we're here." He steps back and looks down. "Hey, cute kids you got here."

A few feet from us a small, pretty young woman watches intently. Marshall steps towards her. "Susie, this is my friend, Ellen. She goes where I go." When she nods a hello, but says nothing, he adds, "Ellen isn't that good with strangers. She'll warm up in a while," he says, and then finishes, "– or not."

Suddenly, Ellen holds out her arms. She wants to take Tarek. I welcome the offer, but I wonder how Tarek will take to her. She smiles at him and Tarek reaches out to her. She gathers him up in her arms and carries him to an empty seat by the wall. She sits next to him and talks to him. When she pulls out a cookie from her pocket, I hear him giggle. He has found a friend.

Marshall and I stand next to the carousel waiting for my bags to come down the chute. I have never had the chance to get to know my uncle. My mother always refused to have him in her house. I can hear her say, "He lives like a Bohemian and he gives me the creeps."

Marshall is an amazing artist and he teaches drawing at the Art Students League in New York City and at the University of Pennsylvania. My dad says that my mother doesn't like him because he lives the life of an artist.

When he was fifty years old, he married his 18-year-old model named Jo and they had a child named Philomel. After a year or so, Jo disappeared and he hasn't seen her or their child since. My mother maintains that Marshall fills his New York apartment with his protégés. My father told me once that Ellen is Marshall's favourite student but she has mental issues. Marshall looks after her.

As if reading my thoughts, Marshall suddenly confides, "Ellen is my best student."

Not knowing how to respond, I stutter, "She–she seems nice."

Then, I go on. I want him to know I appreciate what he is doing. "Thanks for coming to help me."

We retrieve my three large green, well-worn vinyl suitcases and he loads them, along with my other bags, onto a cart. He lifts Tarek into the front basket seat and we begin our walk to the next terminal building so we can be close to my departure gates. Zohra trots along beside me. Ellen walks next to Marshall on the other side of the cart, talking to Tarek all the way.

Marshall and Ellen play with the children for a while. Then Marshall offers to get us something to eat. While they are gone, I suddenly find myself fighting back tears. I take stock. I haven't eaten since the meal on the plane, and my lack of sleep is catching up with me. "This trip is going to take forever," I think. "I am already over-tired and we are only in New York." I can't cry now. "I'm on my way to a new life," I tell myself.

Ellen and Marshall return with a wide array of sandwiches, sweet drinks, coffee and goodies. The food and coffee take away some of my exhaustion.

We walk around the terminal one more time before Marshall announces, "Well, you should be able to go through customs about now. We have to go home. Ellen is getting tired and she isn't quite right when she's tired." He guides me to the Customs line-up area and gives me a hug. "You write to me once in a while," he commands, his voice soft. "It's been a good visit and I'm glad I got to know you a little better."

I promise to write and watch Marshall and Ellen as they walk down the corridor toward the other building. Suddenly, I feel lonely.

I grab the handle of the cart, make sure that Tarek is securely in the basket and tell Zohra to hang onto the side. I push our way into the Customs area and am immediately directed by a uniformed man to the proper line.

"Mommy," Zohra pulls at my skirt and I can hear anxiety in her voice. "Mommy. Zohra has to go pee."

"There are no bathrooms in this area, Ma'am," the security guard informs me before I can even respond to Zohra.

This is not a good sign.

"Zohra," I say quietly. "You will have to wait."

"I can't wait, Mommy," she whines. "I have to go pee now."

"There's nothing I can do," I tell her.

She looks at me shocked. Then, she pees her pants. Her pants darken with the wetness and a small puddle forms around her feet.

I sigh.

We proceed through the Customs line.

Twenty minutes later, luggage checked, Zohra is still wet, and now angry. We are allowed to board the plane. My seat assignment is for two seats, one on the aisle and the other next to it, in the middle of three over the wing. There is less space in front of our seats than we had on the first flight. I sit down, with Tarek on my lap. He doesn't fit. He has nowhere to put his legs. He will have to sit crossways on my lap, with his legs facing the aisle or the window. Maybe, with any luck, the window seat won't be sold. I put him down on that seat while I reach inside one of my bags and find a clean pair of underwear for Zohra. I make her change right there in the narrow space between her seat and the next row. She does what she is told, but she isn't happy. She keeps asking me where the bathroom is and I keep telling her there isn't any for now. I put her wet clothes into the small bag I have designated for dirty diapers and other laundry.

We only just get our bags put in the overhead rack and settle into the three seats when a woman with a two-year-old appears with a ticket that says she and her child have the window seat. I get up and let her squeeze by to get to the window seat.

It is going to be a very long trip.

Zohra curls up on her seat, and as soon as the plane takes off, she falls asleep. The child with the woman in the window seat cuddles up on her mother's lap and also falls asleep.

Tarek, however, is in no mood to be scrunched up in any position and proceeds to kick his feet against the back of the seat in front of me. I try to move so his feet can't reach the seat in front but he is determined to kick no matter what.

The lady sitting in the seat turns around and glares at us

through the space between the two seats. She makes funny fussy indignant noises.

I try to hold Tarek's legs still, but he screams until I let them go. He kicks the seat again.

This time the lady stands up and pokes her head over the seat. "Do you mind keeping your brat from kicking my seat?" She glares at me, waiting for an answer.

"Sorry," I whisper.

Tarek looks at me with his huge brown eyes and smiles. He leans back against me, sucks his thumb and twirls his blond curls around his middle finger.

I wonder what is going on in that one-year-old brain.

I find myself smiling. That habit of him twirling his hair gets to me every time. Maybe, he will settle down quietly and go to sleep.

Just as I think we have an understanding, he kicks out with all his might and jars the seat in front again.

The lady stands up and looks over the seat at us again. Sparks fly from her eyes. "If he doesn't stop it, I'll – I'll – tell the pilot," she sputters loudly.

Other passengers turn to stare at all of us.

Tarek sucks his thumb and twirls his blond curls.

I am dumfounded. The pilot's job is to fly the plane, not referee arguments between passengers. I smile back at her. "Okay," I say, calmly. "Go ahead. Tell the pilot. With any luck, he'll open the door and throw us both out. Do ya think?"

She looks at me menacingly again and settles back into her seat. As mad as she seems to be, she never says another word to me for the whole flight. I try my best to keep my son's feet off her seat, but from time to time I fail.

Changing Tarek's diapers on my lap is just about impossible. Zohra is in the middle seat and there is no space anywhere to lay down a large baby. Each soiled cloth diaper goes into the little bag that I brought along for such things. I tell myself, "I should have bought some of those new fangled paper diapers that have just come on the market. They might have worked better for such a long trip." But it is too late to consider that now. We are over the Atlantic.

At midnight, the stewardess turns off all the inside lights. The only ones still lit are those on the floor. I am so tired I eventually fall asleep and so does Tarek. An hour later, the lady with the two-year-old in the window seat beside me wakes me up to get out. She doesn't return to her seat.

I think about asking one of the stewardesses to watch the children while I use the restroom, but Tarek won't be happy to be disturbed again. I decide to wait. Both children sleep until the lights go on and the captain announces that we are approaching Madrid.

Our final decent into Madrid gets very bumpy. I see grey storm clouds and rain out the window. The captain announces we have to circle, waiting for clearance. The seat belt sign keeps flashing. Nearly an hour later, we are finally allowed to land. My body aches from Tarek's weight. I move Zohra into the window seat and Tarek sits happily in the middle seat, playing with his toys and talking to himself.

Once we land in Madrid, the other passengers disembark and I am left on my own in the plane. Even the stewardesses leave. I feel sticky, really sticky. I am wearing some of the drink that the stewardess brought the kids during one of their noisier moments. I decide that while we are on the ground, I will use the airplane rest room, get myself cleaned up and try to get the kids changed into some fresh clothes.

A stewardess comes back onto the plane. She looks fresh and has obviously just begun her shift. "Hello," she offers smiling at Tarek and Zohra. "Can I get you anything?"

"Yes," I say, nearly breathless. "Could you watch them just for a minute while I go to the bathroom?" I smile at her anxiously, and in case she is thinking of refusing my request, I add, "It's been a really long time."

She smiles, "Sure, go ahead. Be careful to lock the door though because you might run into the cleaning crew."

I jump out of my seat and dash toward the rear bathroom. I am free. For one small moment, I am free. I take my time washing my hands. I even wash my face, thinking how nice it would be to wear a little make-up. Then I remember that Moe doesn't like women to wear make-up. Tiredness threatens to overwhelm me. "No wonder," I think, "I've been up for more than 24 hours and I didn't sleep much the night before we left."

I stumble back to my seat. The stewardess has refilled Tarek's bottle with milk and given Zohra some juice. They are both eating crackers and looking very pleased with themselves. I smile at them. "Overall," I tell the stewardess, pushing the thought of the lady in the seat ahead of us out of my mind, "they have been really good kids for such a long journey."

Within a few minutes the plane begins to fill up again. Someone announces that we will be departing for Algiers in fifteen minutes.

"Algiers," I think. "Wow! The last step."

It is still raining quite heavily. This time the take-off is not smooth. As we leave the tarmac, the plane bounces up and down, groaning and creaking, more like some lumbering old sailing ship on the high seas than a modern flying aircraft.

Zohra loves the motion. "Plane dancing?" she asks with shining eyes.

"Yeah, I guess so, honey. Plane dancing." My stomach is not taking to this dancing plane. I swallow several times and try to relax.

The captain comes on the loud speaker, "Ladies and gentlemen," he announces in a thick French accent. "We have just been informed of a weather system over the city of Algiers. The visibility there is just about zero. Chances are good that the system will lift by the time we get there, but if not, we will have to divert our trip today to Tunisia. I will let you know as soon as any decision is made. Sorry for the bouncy ride, but we are on a short jaunt and there's no place to go to get away from it."

Tiredness descends over me and I feel tears trickle down my cheeks. I close my eyes. Suddenly, I feel a sweet little breath on my face and a soft little body trying to climb onto my lap. I open my eyes to find Zohra hugging me. Her dark brown hair is stuck to her little face in patches from some previous treat and her beautiful dark eyes are filled with sympathy. Her nose is scrunched up as she tries to poke a sticky finger into my eye.

I take her little hand, and ask, "What are you doing trying to poke Mommy in the eye?"

"Zsazsi want Mommy to be happy. Don't cry Mommy. Why are you sad?"

"Oh, Zsazsi, Mommy's not sad, just tired. Mommy needs the rain to stop so we can see Daddy. If the rain doesn't stop, we have to go to another place."

She looks at me with wise, all-knowing eyes. "Okay, Mommy," she says, "I'll ask God to make the rain go away so we can see Daddy."

I smile. "Okay, little one, you ask God to do just that." I wonder where she gets the God stuff. Moe and I never talk about religion. It is a subject that stands between us, best left unspoken until time and place make it a priority.

Minutes later, my daughter points out the window and tells me in her most adult voice, "See Mommy, God is listening. The sun is here."

And indeed it is. Hopefully, it is also shining in Algiers.

I smile at my daughter just as the captain comes back onto the loud speaker. "Ladies and gentlemen, we have begun our descent into Algiers and will be landing in approximately ten minutes. Please fasten your seat belts."

I settle back into my seat for the last moments of this journey. The plane taxis to a stop at the terminal gate. This time, no one tells me I can get off first. The children have scattered their toys, bottles, and food crumbs all over the seats and the space between the rows. I hurry to get everything tucked into my bags. Tarek starts to jump up and down on the seat and Zohra makes an effort to help me. People stand in the aisles while they wait for the doors to open. I don't hurry too much because it will take a while to clear all these people ahead of me. I carry on a running conversation with myself, "Moe might get anxious if I am last off the plane. He might think I am not coming." I heave a huge tired sigh. "Well, this time I guess he'll just have to wait."

The doors finally open and the other passengers file out. I have gathered my belongings and am reaching into the overhead compartment when I hear my daughter scream, "Daddy! Daddy!"

I glance at her, saying, "Not yet Zohra, we have to get..."

Then, I look up the aisle to see a familiar dark figure rushing towards me. I smile with relief. But, when I look at Moe, he is grim faced.

"Aren't you happy to see us?" I ask, bewildered.

"Of course I am," he snaps, "My cousin give me pass to get on plane and help you. He told me hurry up." He adds, "We can hug later, " and he smiles.

I am suspicious that he might be embarrassed to hug me in public, but I accept his explanation with no comment.

He grabs a startled Tarek and kisses his cheeks like a hungry man. Then, he latches onto my two bags and hustles back down the aisle and out the door without looking back.

I smile to myself. "Okay, Zohra, let's go. I think we are on our own, at least to the door."

From my vantage point at the open door of the plane, I can see over the airport buildings and into the outskirts of the city in the distance. The beauty of the city with its white buildings and the sparkling Mediterranean takes my breath away.

"Hurry up Mommy," Zohra tells me as she starts down the steep steps to the tarmac below. "Daddy is waiting."

I look below and there he is, holding Tarek and looking up at me anxiously. I begin to make my way down, step by step behind Zohra, each step taking me further into the new life that awaits me here in Algiers.

As I reach the bottom of the stairs, Moe smiles at me, but curtly orders, "You let me talk. You have papers and everything?"

"Yes, I have everything, Moe."

I have arrived.

# Introduction to Algiers

   The terminal doors swing wide automatically and we hurry inside, Moe carrying Tarek and Zohra walking beside me. The building is packed. People scurry like ants rushing all in the same direction. I brace myself to avoid being knocked down by the crowd behind me and quickly pick Zohra up, relieved that she hasn't been trampled. Tarek is ahead, on his father's shoulders, and I follow him like a beacon to the edge of the crowd where he and Moe stand pressed against the wall, waiting for me.

   An official in a uniform appears, whispers something in Moe's ear, and whisks us through side door. The door slams behind us. Moe takes Tarek down from his shoulders and I let Zohra slide down my body to stand on her own feet. My arms are shaking.

   Moe and the uniformed man smile at each other and embrace, kissing each other's cheeks. Moe then presents me to the man, saying to me, "This my cousin, Mukhtar. He have title Commissioner de Police."

   His cousin shakes my hand politely, then takes me by the shoulders and kisses each of my cheeks. I smile, not sure what I should be doing. In English, I ask Moe why this man is kissing me.

   Moe tells me, "It is our custom."

   The ritual over, the man steps back and Moe tells me, "Now, we go with Mukhtar to Customs to give your papers. I carry children, and you go with Mukhtar. Okay?"

   I nod and follow Mukhtar. We enter a larger room, this one filled with people standing in various lines. Mukhtar leads me to one of the lines in the middle of the room and, in Arabic, says something to the people in the line. In unison, they take a step back. Mukhtar leads me to the front of the line, and signals to Moe to join us. The clerk behind the counter speaks in Arabic.

"He want your passport and health papers," Moe says firmly.

"Okay," I nod, reaching into my purse for my documents. The clerk leafs through the passport and the paperwork and eventually bangs a heavy stamp onto a page in my passport.

We walk to another room, where I see my suitcases piled on a long table. Moe tells me they are going to search my luggage. Moe puts out his hand and I give him my passport and my papers.

After a short conversation, Moe says, "They want us to sit down and they will ask questions. I tell you what they say, and then I answer what you say. You understand?"

I nod.

"Do you have any American dollars?"

"Yes," I answer.

"How much you have?"

"Two thousand dollars."

The man writes it down.

"Where do you live?"

Moe gives him the address.

The man examines the papers Moe has given him.

Zohra and Tarek are both getting bored. Zohra interrupts the man and his questioning with a request to pee and I tell her she has to wait. She starts to cry, probably remembering the last time this happened. Seeing his sister unhappy, Tarek begins to whine loudly. Moe tries to quiet them, but they want their mommy.

The man looks at me and then at the children. He says he will look in only one of my small bags and then we can go. I see him choose my *special* bag, the one where I have stashed all of the dirty clothes from the flight. Before I can stop him, or tell Moe the problem with that bag, he opens and bends forward to peer inside. The shocked look on his face makes it clear he is not pleased. He slams the bag shut quickly and mumbles something under his breath. I look away, hoping they don't put women in jail for carrying dirty diapers in their luggage.

"We go now," Moe announces. As we re-enter the terminal building, several young men surround us and Moe instructs them to take our luggage to the front door. All of the men smile at me respectfully. Moe steps out onto the road in front of the terminal and signals in the direction of a car parked by the side of the road. The vehicle slowly moves forward and stops next to us. The friendly young men load my luggage into it. I have never seen a car like this before. It is a Citroen. It is on hydraulics and goes up and down like a small elevator when it starts or stops.

The driver's door of the car opens and out steps a very European-looking gentleman, a short, stocky, handsome man, with flashing blue eyes. He takes off his beret, steps in front of me, and introduces himself in English, punctuated by a heavy French accent. "Ah, Madame Chaabane. How long Mohamed has waited for you to arrive. I am pleased to meet you. I am Claude Ducont. I work with Mohamed at the farm."

"I am happy to meet you," I tell him.

Claude looks at Moe and asks, "Are you ready to go?"

"Yes, thank you. I am now ready." Moe responds in such formal English that his politeness sounds artificial and forced.

Claude opens the door for me and I get into the back seat. Zohra clamours in behind me and Moe sits in the front passenger seat with Tarek on his lap.

Claude announces, "It is a fifty-nine kilometre trip home, but as you will find out, sometimes it takes a lot longer." As we turn onto the road leading into the city, Claude asks Moe, "Did you tell her about the roadblocks?"

"No, I not tell," Moe answers.

Though he is driving down a busy road, Claude turns his head to look at me sitting wide-eyed in the back seat. He smiles at me. "The trip back to the village may be interrupted by a roadblock or two," he says. "Whatever you do, don't say anything when they stop us. Okay?"

"What does that mean?" I ask, curious about what he means by roadblocks.

"Well, it's just the way it is around here. The military likes to throw its weight around and the less said the better." He returns his attention to his driving.

I nod as if I understand, but I am not sure that I do.

The children soon fall asleep. Tired as I am, I am overwhelmed by the beauty of this city. The city centre is filled with stately domed mosques and lovely modern department stores and apartment buildings, all beautiful white buildings in contrast to the main government buildings, a group of marble and stone buildings standing as a grand testament to the city's age. The streets are grass-lined with red and purple bougainvillea vines running from wall to wall around large houses surrounded by gardens. I am stunned by the richness, and I express my awe at the grandeur of it all.

Claude tells me that I am in the good section of the city and that I will have a different outlook when we pass through other neighbourhoods.

Moe leans over the front seat and laughingly tells me, "What he mean is that bad sections belong to Arabs."

I hear, not only the laughter in his voice, but something else underneath – maybe bitterness. I remember from Moe's letters how frustrated he is to have a French boss in his own land. Now, between the two men, I sense resentment, coupled with grudging respect maybe brought on by the necessity of working together. Maybe, this not-entirely-friendly laughter about the inequities is how Moe has learned to handle his frustration.

As we travel on, Claude chats about his Finnish wife, Benita, and his little boy named Laurent who is the same age as Zohra. "My wife speaks English," he says. "You will have to get together for a visit soon."

"We live in the same *batiment*," he tells me. "But, we won't be there for long, however, as we are having a house built for us on the farm."

"What is a *batiment*?" I ask.

"It is the French word for building." Claude answers. "Sorry. I forget you're American."

His emphasis on American sounds forced as if he isn't fond of Americans.

"Thank you very much for coming to pick us up. I appreciate it," I tell Claude.

"That's okay," he answers. "Actually, this is a government car.

Mohamed doesn't have his license so I thought I could pick up some things for my house while I'm at it. No trouble."

"Well, here we are. My first stop," Claude announces as he stops and manoeuvres the funny little car into a parking space. Claude tosses the keys to Moe and heads to a nearby store.

Moe and I sit looking at each other. I am too tired to talk. The silence stretches between us.

Finally, Moe asks, "So, you have a good journey?"

"Some was good and some not so good. My father's brother met me in New York. That helped a lot."

"Good," Moe nods. "I happy you here. It is a lonely place without a wife and children."

The children continue to sleep and we continue to look at each other. We wait, and Claude returns laden with packages and interesting smelling boxes. He unloads them into the back of the car, and slides into the driver's seat, handing a box to Moe. "Here, you both look like you could use a sweet treat."

Moe smiles and takes the box. Claude starts the car and we are on our way again. Moe opens the box and says, in an exaggerated French accent, "Ah, napoleon."

"What's a napoleon?" I ask, guessing that he is not referring to the French dictator.

"A treat from heaven," grins Claude.

"Yes, yes. Indeed it is," agrees Moe. He reaches into the box and hands me a large pastry, five inches long and five layers high, toasted a golden brown, each layer filled with thick gooey creamy yellow pudding. Moe dumps the pastry into my hand.

Immediately, I know I will be a sticky mess if I eat it. "Oh, no," I blurt out. "How will I eat this without a fork and plate?"

Both men laugh as they each cram a velvet bundle into their mouths. Moe has his eaten in three bites, and Claude in four. They finish. I am still staring at what is in my hand, unable to get it to my mouth without the stickiness getting all over me.

I am too exhausted to stand the thought of another sticky mess. "I better put this back in the box for later," I tell them.

They both look devastated at my lack of a sense of adventure. Moe holds open the box and I tuck the treat away. I return to gazing out the window and see that we have now reached the city limits and are heading into the countryside.

Suddenly, I hear Claude exclaim, "*Sacre blue!* I thought we might be lucky today."

We slow down. I look ahead and see that the road is blocked by uniformed men – each one holding a huge gun. I remember Claude warning me to say nothing. He doesn't have to worry. Claude pulls up next to one of the men and rolls down the window. The uniformed man looks into the car, points his gun at us and says something in Arabic. Moe answers, and tells me to show the man my passport.

I push it through the open front window and the man grabs it with a grubby hand and a grunt. I watch him turn the pages. Suddenly, he smiles and looks at me, "Ah, *Americanea?*"

I nod, reluctantly, not sure if this breaks Claude's caution that I don't say anything. The man hands me back my passport, says something to Moe, and waves us through.

"Evidently, the pass of the day is an American passport," Claude offers sarcastically when we are out of earshot of the soldiers. Talking over his shoulder, he tells me, "You will get used to this Mrs. C. It's a fact of life for this country. Notice how he didn't talk to me when he found out I was French. A couple of days ago, a friend of mine was stopped at a roadblock. When he presented his French passport, they shot him dead right there in the road. We never know what our reception is going to be."

I push myself up against the back of the seat in disbelief. Fear rushes over me. I wonder how many times we will have to go to Algiers. Frantically, I think, "What have I gotten myself and my children into by coming to Algieria?"

Claude glances at me in the rear view mirror and laughs. "No point in being afraid, Madam, it's the way it is."

Moe says nothing. Luckily, we aren't stopped again, but Claude assures me that there are days when he has encountered as many as four roadblocks. "It all depends on who they are looking for," he explains.

When I ask what he means, he says, "The military is always looking for somebody."

To help myself calm down, I watch the countryside go by, thankful the children are sleeping. By the time we reach the small village that is our destination, I, too, am nearly asleep. However, I shake myself awake, when Claude pulls up in front of a four-storey concrete apartment building and announces, "Here we are. Your new home. Welcome to Batiment HLM Number 36 in the village of Birtouta, Algeria."

I stare at the building. Obviously newly built, it reaches up into the sky like a great gray chimney. It dwarfs the small village that surrounds it.

As I am pulling my half-asleep children out of the car, other children appear. By the time I am ready to head towards my new apartment, at least twelve, dirty, pathetic-looking, wide-eyed children, stand staring at me.

Claude waves his hand toward them and says with disgust in his voice, "They seem to think Europeans are famous or rich. Every day you will be swarmed by these urchins. They beg – for money – or anything you want to give them. Be careful that you give them nothing – or they will hound you forever!"

As he finishes his rant, he looks at Moe, who says nothing. Claude turns, and one by one, he lifts out my suitcases and sets each one on the ground. Moe picks up two of the large suitcases. I stumble behind him and take the three small bags. Claude takes the remaining large bag and slams the trunk shut. The dozen dirty children are still staring silently at us.

Claude and Moe wait for me as I struggle to guide a sleepy Zohra in front of me. She suddenly stops when she notices the group of children staring at her. She stares back at them. Tarek is grumpy, but quiet and is content to rest his head on my shoulder while I carry him up to the entrance of the building. We slowly climb the steep steps to our apartment. Claude comes up behind us and as we reach our apartment door, he puts the suitcase down and walks away.

"Thank you for picking me up," I call after him, and he nods.

"Yes, thank you very much, Mr. Ducont," Moe adds, "I am thankful for your trouble."

Claude nods, but doesn't smile. I watch him until he arrives at his door and takes out his key. He and his family live five doors from us.

I turn from watching Claude to stumble across the threshold of my new home. It is bigger than I expected. Inside the entrance, there is a closet on the right and the door to the kitchen on the left. I set Tarek down and he immediately toddles over to his father.

Moe picks him up and kisses him. "I miss my little family too much," he says.

I smile at him. "We missed you, too. I missed you more than I can say."

"That is good," Moe smiles. "Now, come and look at kitchen. If you remember this not America, you will be happy."

"Okay, it's not America," I say. "I promise to remember that."

The kitchen is small, but clean. In one corner is a small refrigerator, the smallest refrigerator I have ever seen. It only comes up to my waist.

"We buy fresh food every day at local market," says Moe. "No need here to have big refrigerator."

The stove has two burners and a small oven. Moe continues his appliance tour. "This stove runs by bottle *gazz*. It run for a few hours. Then we go and buy more fuel. It very efficient."

"Come," says Moe, "I show you how we do hot water." He walks me over to the small sink that takes up one end of the kitchen. On the wall is a small tank, about the height of Tarek and a few inches around. "This also run on *gazz*." The hot water tank makes enough hot water to wash a few dishes and maybe a few clothes. The sink has a faucet that runs hot and cold water.

Moe explains that the water goes on and off during the day. Some days we will have no water at all. Evidently, it is the same for the electricity.

There are three kitchen cabinets containing a few glasses, a plate and two bowls. The two drawers below the cabinets hold a knife, a spoon and two forks. Moe says he has been waiting for me to come so we can shop together.

Next to the kitchen is a room that Moe calls the washroom, very small with a large laundry tub in the centre with one faucet. Very literally, it is the washroom – a place to do laundry.

"This is also bath tub," Moe says, laughing. "It is big enough for child or small adult. He looks at me awkwardly, and adds, "Sorry, is only bathtub. Mostly Algerians go to public bath."

I try to smile.

We move on to the next room. When Moe turns on the light, I discover three steps leading up to a platform containing a western-looking toilet that flushes when a long chain hanging from a tank on the ceiling is pulled.

The next room is our bedroom. Our bed is a three-quarter mattress on the floor, covered with thick wool blankets and numerous pillows. "You will find it very warm and comfortable." Hugging me, he says, "It will be especially warm now that you are here."

"So you are happy I am here?" I tease.

"Yes," he answers.

I hear anxiety in his voice.

He sighs, "I am happy, but I not sure you be happy."

He takes another deep breath, "I have very bad time since I come here. I am sick for many days. I visit many doctors. It is difficult to find good doctors here. I go to one and he gives me medicine and then another gives me other medicine. I hope we can find a good doctor and I get help."

"Why didn't you tell me this in your letters, Moe?" I ask, concerned.

"I think maybe you not come if I am sick."

"Don't be silly. You must know me better than that."

"Yes, I know. But, I not know what to say."

"What is wrong?" I ask.

"I cannot sleep so I always tired. Sometimes I have hard time walking. Sometimes I not able to work." He turns and walks toward the window. There, he waves his arm toward the surrounding village. "I am in shock by everything I find here."

He shakes his head, "I not know where I belong. Sometimes I sit and read newspaper at my job because the stupid French do everything."

He looks at me, sad and bewildered. "They not trust me with anything. I am mad at this."

"Oh, I'm so sorry, Moe. I had no idea." I give him a hug of encouragement. "Moe, we will work it out. You have your family now. That is good. The rest, we will make work. I promise."

Moe smiles at me weakly, "We talk more later. Come and see rest of apartment."

The living room is a large lovely area with a balcony at one end and a single bed mattress draped with a beautiful cover at the other end. Three beautiful rugs on the floor, and a table with four chairs complete its furnishings. "This our living room," Moe announces proudly. "The rugs are gifts from my father for our wedding present. They are made by hand in the Sahara." The rugs each have a unique, intricate design. Each is very primitive – and very beautiful.

Off the living room are two more bedrooms. Zohra has a small mattress on the floor for now. Moe explains that we will eventually buy her a bed. In his room, Tarek has a crib that one of Moe's friends bought as a gift.

Suddenly, I am overwhelmed by exhaustion. At the same moment, Zohra pulls on my arm and says she is hungry.

"We have no food," Moe interjects. "I not have time. I want you to get here before I spend money on food. I go now and buy things." He waves toward the living room. "You stay here and rest. I walk to the market. It only take a short time. We have bread and cheese tonight and then my friend is coming in the morning with his car to take us to Algiers for big shopping."

"Moe, don't you have to work?" I ask.

"My boss give me few days off to help you. I do nothing anyway," he adds, bitterly. "But that is good for now, no?"

"Yes," I smile. "I think it is very good."

"Can you get some milk for Tarek and some fruit or something?"

"We not buy milk from store. It only have milk in can. It very expensive. We will get real milk from cows at farm where I work. For now, he have to drink juice or water. Also, you not drink water from faucet like in States. Water here not safe. You boil water for five minutes and leave it on sink for few hours. Then, we put in a jar to drink. Very bad to drink water from faucet." He looks at me as if he expects me to argue with him. "Okay?" he finishes.

I nod and go to the kitchen to boil some water. Moe leaves to buy food and I get the kids cleaned up as best I can with cold water. I put them in clean pyjamas and lay down with them on our mattress to wait for Moe to come home with some food. It has been a long journey. They are happy to see their daddy but are as exhausted as I am. After an hour I hear the key in the door.

"Food is here," he shouts as he enters the apartment.

I meet him in the kitchen. He slowly takes his treasures out of the string shopping bag. Two loaves of delicious-smelling bread. Next, a large can. The label is in French. *Confiture.* "That mean jam in French," Moe tells me, proudly. "Well, it like jam, but it thicker," he adds.

Then, out comes a small white package. "Goat cheese," he informs me.

Coffee, a tiny container of tea, several large oranges and some butter are next out of the bag. Finally, he pulls out several containers of French-made yogurt with fruit and informs me they are for the children to be served with a newspaper-wrapped stack of special Algerian sweet cookies.

"Now we have plenty for tonight – and tomorrow we go to Algiers to buy more." He glances down at all the packages on the counter, looks at me, and smiles. "Moe do good job, I think. No?"

"Yes, you did a very good job, Moe. It all looks delicious. I can't wait to eat."

At that moment, there is a knock at the door and before anyone can check who is calling, Zohra jumps up and pulls the door open. A tall blonde woman carrying a container of eggs steps across the threshold.

"Hello," she says in English with a strange thick accent. "I am Benita."

"Hello," I reply. "I'm Susie. You must be Claude's wife. Please come in."

"Yes, I am," she says, smiling. "I want to welcome you to

Algeria and I brought you some eggs so you have something for your breakfast. I feed my son a lot of eggs here. There is not a lot of safe food in this country."

"What an odd statement," I think. I ignore the unsafe food comment and invite her to come in,

"Oh no, it's late and you are tired. I just wanted to say welcome and to meet you. I will come by next week when you are settled and take you shopping in the village, if you like."

"That would be nice." I smile at her as she hands me the eggs and waves goodbye as she backs out the door.

"She seemed really nervous," I observe as I turn back to Moe.

"I think she not like me," Moe answers. "She say nothing to me. Even when I first meet her she only nods."

"Maybe she is aware of your customs and is trying to abide by them."

"No, I not think so. I think she just not like Algerians." He sighs, and then says, "She have a car and she drive, so it is good if you know her. Also, you need someone to talk English to."

Zohra and Tarek whine that they are hungry, so I pull the bread into large chunks and slap on large blobs of butter. I look for a can opener and find a simple little hand-crank one in the drawer. I open the *confiture* and smear the thick plum mixture over the bread and butter. I hand pieces to the children and they eat hungrily and ask for more. I begin again just as Moe wanders into the kitchen.

Moe smiles and breaks a piece of bread off the second loaf. He slathers on the butter and jam and joins his children in their feast. I am too tired to eat. I lean against the counter and look at my husband, really look at him for the first time since my arrival.

He is the one that looks worn out. His skin is sallow and his cheeks look swollen. He is thinner than I remember him, and it is not a healthy thinness.

At that moment, a loud mechanical groan erupts from somewhere and the lights go out. Moe tells us to stay where we are. He returns with a lighted candle and some matches.

"Welcome to Birtouta. Sometimes we have light, and sometimes we not. Sometimes we have water, and some times we not. It is a good time to go to bed."

While Moe puts both children in their beds, I crawl into my new bed and fall asleep.

# A Full Day in My New Life

May 1966

On my second day in Algeria, I wake up in the arms of my husband, feeling warm and finally rested after my long trip. The clock says 11:30. It is morning and I hear a loud knocking at our door.

Moe throws on his robe and answers the door. I hear him mumble something in Arabic and then I hear the voices of several people. I huddle under the covers hoping they will go away so I can get up and dress in my own time.

But, Moe returns, and pulls the covers off my head, smiling. "Get up, sleepy one. My friends are here to take us for shopping and lunch in Algiers. They wait for us."

"Oh, Moe," I complain, "I need a bath and I need to dress. I can't do that with people here."

"Yes, you can. Hurry, I get the children ready."

He pulls his pants on, the same ones as he wore yesterday, and a wrinkled shirt that has been thrown over a chair. He looks so uncared for. As he slips out the door, I roll out from under the covers and search through my suitcase for something decent to wear. My first choice would be slacks, but I have been forewarned that slacks are not allowed. I didn't bring any. I find a navy-blue fitted suit and a white blouse. I put on nylons and my slip, and then I examine myself the best I can in this room without a mirror.

"I should be conservative enough for any crowd," I decide, and I run a brush through my hair and slip into my shoes. On my way to the living room, I visit the bathroom and pee as quietly as I can, praying that no one can hear me. As I come out of the bathroom, Zohra, her hair unbrushed, but wearing a clean dress, comes running up to me.

"Mommy, hurry up. Daddy is waiting for us," she says. "But," she adds, in a voice that declares she is surprised to find something that her Daddy can't do, "he doesn't know how to do my hair."

"Okay, honey," I smile. "Let's go meet the people and do your hair."

We go into the living room and find ourselves facing three men who are sitting on the living room mattress. They all leap to their feet, smiling and staring at me.

"Haven't they ever seen a woman before?" I think. Then, I remember Moe's warning to avoid looking directly at men in Algeria. I try to look down. But as I do that, I stumble into the table and nearly upset a nearby chair.

I look up nervously at the men, and then at Moe. "Sorry," I mutter.

"It's okay," Moe says. "These are my friends. You can look at them."

He indicates each of the men as he introduces them. "This is Mohamed G. It's not his true name but it is name we call him," announces Moe. "He is a journalist."

"Bonjour," I venture. He takes my hand and shakes it and steps back, nodding several times. "*Madam,*" he says.

"This is my cousin, Ahmed Ben Freha." Moe continues the introductions.

Ahmed steps forward, takes me by the shoulders and kisses each of my cheeks. "Welcome to *Algerie,*" he says in English. "Welcome."

Surprised, I blurt out, "Do you speak English?"

"No, he doesn't," Moe answers for him. "But, he wanted to welcome you in your own language."

I blush, pleased by the effort Ahmed has made. "Moe, tell him how nice that is."

"I already did," Moe replies, smiling.

"This man is Omar," Moe says as he indicates the third man. Omar barely looks at me, nods politely and turns away.

"Omar is driver of government car we have for today." Moe explains. "He is not family and he is not friend."

As we make our way to the car we encounter the same little ragamuffins that greeted us on our arrival yesterday. Today, they stand like little statues by the curb, but not one of them calls out the now-familiar *Bonjour Madame*. I wonder if they are afraid of the men.

There are no roadblocks on this trip into Algiers. Moe and I sit in the back seat, me with Zohra on my lap and Moe, with Tarek on his. The three men crowd into the front seat.

We fly down the highway at a dizzying speed and, after a moment or two, I close my eyes, not wanting to see how fast we are going.

"Why you are hiding your eyes?" Moe asks me a few minutes later. "Are you sleeping?"

"No, I'm not sleeping," I answer. I lean toward him and ask quietly. "Why we are going so fast? Are there no speed limits in this country?"

Moe laughs, "No, here people go as fast as they can or want. The only thing that makes people go slow is when they hit somebody. If you kill a person, then you run even faster because his relatives for sure come and kill you."

This addition to the conversation does not make me feel any better.

As we approach Algiers, Moe tells me we are invited for lunch at the home of his friends, Aouf and Yarka. He explains that they met when they were both students studying in Moscow. Yarka is from Czechoslovakia. They got married in Russia, and when Aouf finished his studies, they moved to Algiers.

"You will love their little boys. They are twins of ten months age. They have blond hair and blue eyes," Moe says.

"Oh, that will be fun for Tarek and Zohra," I assure him. "They will make good playmates in the years to come."

We get out of the car in front of a shiny grey skyscraper. We enter the building through beautiful brass doors, and Mohamed G automatically pushes a button on the brass nameplate that hangs just inside. It is obvious that he has been here before.

A voice comes over the speakers on the wall and Mohamed G says something. The lock clicks and the inside brass door slowly swings open onto a large lobby, the walls covered in blue and white tiles, and the floors laid with shiny terrazzo stone. I am startled by the opulence. From the outside, the building looks like an ordinary tall apartment building.

Seeing my surprise, Moe explains that, before the war, this building was a hotel used by the French and by foreign government officials traveling to Algiers on business. Recently, the building has been converted into apartments for Arab government workers.

Aouf and Yarka's apartment is on the fifth floor. We are rocketed there by an elevator that seems to go twice the speed of sound. The force of the take-off threatens to force my feet through the floor, and then, in what seems to be only an instant later, we screech to a halt and I need to grab onto Moe to keep myself upright. Luckily, Moe has taken this ride before and has braced himself by hanging onto the brass handles strategically placed along the inside of the elevator. He laughs at my wide eyes and shocked look. "You see," he assures me, though his voice has more sarcasm than reassurance in it, "Even in my poor backward country, we have modern methods to move people."

We meet Aouf and Yarka at the door to their apartment and, in turn, they wrap me in their arms, and plant kisses on each of my cheeks. Aouf is a large dark round man with a Santa Claus-like belly and a huge smiling face. Yarka is a blonde female version of Aouf. They look more like brother and sister than husband and wife. Having greeted me, they bend down and grab Tarek and Zohra, hugging each in turn and planting kisses on their little faces. Both children laugh at this behaviour and that surprises me. They usually run away from strangers.

I am given soft gold satin slippers to replace my street shoes.

We are led over terrazzo floors decorated with beautiful intricately designed oriental rugs. As we pass from the entryway to the dining room, I am so mesmerized by murals of dancing cherubs on the tiled ceilings that I nearly trip at the doorway. The conversation stops dead and I feel everyone's stares.

Seated at a long white linen-covered table are fourteen very western-looking diners, both men and women, all smiling at us. Aouf introduces me in Arabic. Moe translates. As each person's name is called, he or she comes forward and kisses my cheeks. The names I hear are either very Arabic or very Slavic. I hope I won't be expected to remember them all. After the introductions, Yarka ushers us to seats midway along the length of the table.

"You are the guest of honour," Moe says. "This whole party is for you. Yarka says that you need to feel welcome and she hopes you do."

I smile at everyone and say to Moe. "Tell her I am very flattered and thank her for me."

"You can tell her yourself. Just say *merci* and she will know."

I turn to Yarka and smile, "*Merci*, Yarka."

She smiles back at me.

I hope we will one day be able to have a real conversation.

As everyone sits down again, Moe tells me that it is a very international table. Many of the guests studied in Russia and speak several languages. Yarka speaks French, Russian and Czech. They all visit in languages that are not their own, sometimes switching from one language to another when they turn to talk with a different person. I find it frustrating to only speak English – a language that no one seems to speak, except my husband and my daughter.

Yarka serves a seven-course meal consisting of Algerian and Czech dishes. I am told that Aouf is also a very good cook and that he has created most of the Algerian dishes. The meal continues for two and a half hours with course after course of wonderful new tastes. After the second course, all the children get up from the table. When I ask about where they are going, Yarka explains that they are going to play with toys in the children's room and that a nanny will look after them.

I miss most of what is said, but Moe translates as much as he can, speaking to me in English and carrying on conversations in Arabic at the same time. Towards the end of the meal, the conversation turns to politics.

Mohamed G looks at me across the table and I hear what sounds like a direct question. I don't understand. Moe translates. "Why is the United States fighting in Viet Nam?"

It is a question I haven't given much thought to. I don't know how to answer.

After a minute of silence on my part, Moe rescues me by telling them some night he will invite them all to our house and we will talk politics, but that tonight is just a time to socialize.

Through Moe, Mohamed G apologizes, explaining that he is just interested in my *American perspective* and will look forward to the opportunity to ask me questions at another time.

"Doesn't Mohamed G know that my politics are your politics?" I ask Moe quietly.

"Forgive my friend. He is journalist who study in Russia for long time. He is always hungry for debate." Moe smiles at Mohamed G while he talks to me.

"I should study politics more closely." I think.

Exactly at 2:30, Moe stands up, and announces that he has to pick up a car from the government rental lot at 3:00. We retrieve the children and Ahmed, Mohamed G, Moe and I say our goodbyes and thank yous. Once outside, we walk a short distance to the campus of the National Institute of Agriculture and Research. Moe shows me the gardens surrounding the building. It is cool and quiet here. The flowers are in bloom and very beautiful.

A dark swarthy man comes out the front door and, suddenly, turns to come down the stairs towards us. I look at him and he looks at me, smiling. Moe greets the man with a handshake and a tiny respectful bow.

"This is my boss," he explains, "Mr. Shelig."

"Hello," I say, offering my hand.

Mr. Shelig shakes my hand weakly. "*Bonjour*," he says, and then launches into Arabic.

Moe translates, "Welcome to Algeria, Madame. May your visit here be a happy one. You have beautiful children."

Mr. Shelig turns away from us, moves on down the sidewalk and disappears across the street.

"He's strange," I remark.

Moe nods, frowning and looking off into space. He mutters something in Arabic and then says in English, "It is time to get the car I have ordered for the afternoon."

Ahmed walks down the sidewalk a few feet and whistles at a man standing in the distance. A few moments later, a car pulls up in front of us.

"Your chariot waits," Moe says. He is smiling again. "We go now to see some sights, shopping and make a trip to your American Embassy."

Our first stop is the *Galeries de France*. From the name, I expect it to be an art gallery, but the tall regal-looking building turns out to be a huge department store. The inside is as opulent as the outside with escalators, elevators, shiny tile floors and many glass counters and displays of cosmetics, clothes, and every household item imaginable. The customers are nearly all Europeans.

"I bring you here to prove my country not so backward as you think. Also – I want you to see my people have little money to shop here." Moe speaks quietly to me as I gaze in awe at the wide array of expensive items.

"I see," I nod.

We walk down one of the main streets of Algiers. Fancy dress shops with clothing made by the finest designers from all over the world are interspersed with hairdressers, pharmacies, and little shops offering jewellery and perfumes.

Suddenly, Zohra announces she has to go pee.

Moe pulls her panties down right where we are on the sidewalk.

"What are you doing?" I ask, horrified, and glancing around to see if anyone has noticed.

"She has to pee," Moe answers.

"Yes, I say, still mortified. "But here – on the street?"

"Yes," Moe explains. "She is baby. No one care if she pee here."

Zohra frowns at her father. "Zsazsi is not a baby," she says in her loudest most grown up voice. She does pee, however.

Moe says something to his friends and they look at me and laugh.

I am embarrassed, first by Zohra peeing in the street and then, by Moe's friends finding my reaction something to laugh at. This is one custom that will take getting used to.

The next area we visit is called *El Biar* District. "These houses are big, like mansions," observes Moe. "See the colourful gardens. This district has foreign embassies, rich sports people and rich businessmen. We never afford to live in a place such as this."

I hear resentment and longing in Moe's voice.

"We go now to your Embassy." Moe gives instructions to the driver.

As we approach the American Embassy, the driver tells Moe we have to walk in through the gate. He can't take the car onto American property. He drops us at the head of the driveway leading up to the Embassy grounds. There is no guard and I reach out to open the door.

Moe points to a sign written in French. He says, "Sign says to ring buzzer."

After several minutes, we hear footsteps.

A petite woman with dark brown fuzzy hair opens the door just enough to poke her head out. She frowns at us.

"Hello," I say, "I am an American. I just arrived in Algeria and I want to sign in with the Embassy."

The woman looks at me, not understanding. I pull out my American passport and thrust it at her. She looks at me blankly for a few moments and then steps back and indicates we can enter the building. As we enter, she says in very broken English, "I not speak English. I find someone."

I shake my head in disbelief. We step into a large rotunda and she indicates some wooden seats where we sit down. In the background is the sound of typing and phones ringing. The lady disappears through a door.

Twenty minutes later, both Moe and I are ready to leave without speaking to anyone.

However, just as we stand up to leave, the door opens and a young man comes towards us, his hand outstretched. "Good afternoon folks. I am Gordon. Welcome to Algeria."

I stand up and take his hand.

"Thank you," I say.

"How can I help you today?" he asks.

"I just arrived with my children. I thought I should sign in or register or something with my Embassy." Pointing to Moe, I add, "This is my husband, Mohamed."

"How do you do, Sir," Gordon shakes Mohamed's hand gingerly and then steps back. He sits down on one of the wooden seats across from us and indicates we should sit down again.

"I'll take your name and address – but that is about all I can do for you," he states matter-of-factly. "As an American woman married to a local," he nods towards Moe, "there aren't many services I can offer you. Your children are considered Algerians while they are here. We have to work under the Algerian law – even if they were born in the States. It's just how it is."

I interrupt him and ask if the Embassy can help me get a visa so that I can stay in Algeria for a year. Right now the visa I have is only for three months.

"No," says Gordon, "that is not our job. You will have to go to the Algerian Immigration Office for that. It is very difficult to get such visas these days," he adds disinterestedly.

"Well, then," I say, "can you tell me if you have any Embassy doctors that I can use for myself or my family?"

"Unfortunately, the embassy doctors are only for Embassy personnel, but if you look in the phone book you will find a list of physicians that can help you. Now, if you will just give me your name and address, I am really busy today. Seems to be a lot of things to do and I'm the only person in the place that speaks English, except the Ambassador and he's never here."

I give him my name and address, and Moe and I get up to leave. When we are nearly at the door, Gordon calls out, "Good luck to you, Ma'am. You are going to need it."

Moe pushes the door open and we step outside. Through all of this, the children have been unusually quiet and unusually good. But, as soon as the door closes, Zohra looks up at me and declares, "Mommy, I hate that place and I hate that man. It was scary in there."

I look at Moe and smile, "Yes, Zohra, I think you are right. We will make it a point to never go there again. Okay?"

"I can't believe only one person speaks English in the whole place. Not the most welcoming, helpful place, is it?" I say, shaking my head.

"No. But, you are married to me and they not know what to do with you, Moe smiles and continues. "They think you will soon run away from me and then you will be a problem to them."

"What? Why would they think that?"

"I think it happens much. Don't you know you are married to very bad Arab man?" Moe scrunches up his face and makes the growling sound of a monster. The children scream in delight as he chases them, tickling as he goes. Sometimes, he is so funny.

When we reach the car, Moe talks to the driver and to his friends who are standing smoking. They decide we should go for coffee and a treat at a street café. Once seated, we order sweet mint tea from the young boy who takes our order and Mohamed G orders ice cream for the children. It is pink and comes in tiny little cones. Both children are delighted. The café is packed with Europeans, and I hear French rather than Arabic. Reading my mind, Moe leans towards me, and speaking in a low voice, explains that sometimes Arab places are not that clean – and they don't serve ice cream.

Zohra finishes her ice cream, and then, jumps off her chair, and runs over to Mohamed G.

She climbs up into his lap and plants a big sticky kiss on his cheek. Mohamed G whispers something to Zohra in Arabic, and then the men laugh.

Moe laughs with them. Then, he explains to me, "Mohamed G says he wants to marry our daughter but he is waiting until she is fourteen."

The men laugh again, but I only smile weakly. I wonder if Mohammed G could be serious.

We leave the café refreshed and move on to a grocery store filled with imported American and European products.

"I bring you here so you know we have everything," Moe says proudly, "but it is too expensive for us. Pick something you need but we not come here again."

The store is large, very modern, and shines with cleanliness. I pick a few things that remind me of home: A small container of Maxwell House Coffee, a small bottle of Heinz Ketchup, a bar of Dial soap, and some Tide laundry soap.

Moe frowns at my choices, but pays without saying anything.

From the expensive European and American store, we go to the street markets in another part of the city. At one stall, Moe buys some fresh fish and three pieces of lamb. At another, we buy lettuce, tomatoes, couscous, and some potatoes.

At that point, Zohra announces to her father, "Zsazsi can't walk anymore. Zsazsi is dying." Everyone smiles indulgently at her and Mohamed G picks her up, puts her on his shoulders and carries her to the car. By the time they reach it, she is asleep on his head. We decide to go back to Birtouta.

Our trip home is interrupted by a roadblock manned by a group of uniformed men carrying automatic weapons. I hear Moe say *shit* under his breath. Tarek immediately repeats the word, adding his own variation, "Shit daddy, daddy shit."

Moe looks at Tarek and says. "You not know any language. Now your first word is *shit daddy*." Moe shakes his head, trying not to laugh, especially since we are approaching soldiers carrying submachine guns.

We stop beside the nearest soldier. Our driver rolls down the window and thrusts his papers out the window. The tall dark soldier bends down and looks inside the car.

I flash him a smile and hug my daughter tight.

His face registers surprise, and then, confusion. Why would a European woman and two children be packed inside a small car with four Arab men? He straightens up and barks an order at our driver.

The driver opens the door and gets out. Two more guards approach and talk to him. Then, suddenly, the back door on the passenger side is yanked open and another soldier orders Moe out of the car.

As Moe gets out, he speaks to me softly in English, "Don't worry. It will be okay."

I am not reassured. I say nothing. But, I hold Zohra more tightly and I reach out and take Tarek's hand so he doesn't follow Moe out of the car.

Moe gives the man his papers, including his Arizona driver's license.

Another soldier comes up to my window and motions for me to roll it down. I feel my hands shake and my heart pound. He tells me in French to give him my papers.

Astonished that I understand what he says, I reach into my purse and take out my passport. He looks at me and he looks at the children. He asks me if the driver is my husband. I shake my head no, and I point to Moe saying, *"Mon mari."*

He pages through my passport and spends some time studying the visa page. Then, he hands it back to me, smiling broadly. "Ah, *Americanea*," he says, before switching to Arabic. He walks over to Moe, and gestures towards me as he launches into conversation.

Moe smiles and nods at everything the soldier says. The conversation goes on for a few minutes and it becomes quite lively. During the entire exchange, Moe smiles and nods. They both laugh as if they are old friends.

Finally, both Moe and the driver get back in the car and we are on our way. We shoot away from the roadblock like a rocket and sail down the highway at breakneck speed.

"Why are we going so fast?" I ask Moe.

"We go fast before they take us to jail or shoot us," Moe declares.

"What? Would they really do that?" I ask, suddenly frightened. "You looked like you made friends with that man. What did he say?"

"You not need to know," Moe answers. I can tell he is determined not to tell me.

But my fear pushes me to know what Moe and the soldier were talking about. "Yes I do," I persist.

Moe looks at me. He announces, "I will tell you – but you not like."

"I don't care, Moe. I want to know."

"Well, first thing he tell me is they look for a big criminal that is running from police. If this is true, then we meet other road-block up the road here, near Village of Blida."

"So, what was the second thing he said?" I am still curious.

"He want to know where he can get wife like you and how much you cost."

"Oh," I answer, dismayed.

"So, you better be good wife or I sell you to the gendarmes," Moe teases.

"Moe," I smile at him. "You are silly sometimes." Then, I continue, "I was scared."

"They just stupid people. We must play game with these idiots. They can be dangerous – but sometimes we have to laugh."

Mohamed G turns around from his place in the front seat, and asks Moe what the two of us are talking about. Moe relays our conversation in Arabic.

The car erupts in laughter. Clearly, Moe has only translated the part about how to get a wife like me.

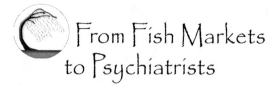

From Fish Markets to Psychiatrists

After seven days, Moe has to return to work. I don't think he is ready. He hasn't been sleeping well – for the past three nights I have awakened to find him sitting on the edge of the mattress with his head in his hands rocking back and forth.

Every night I ask him what I can do, and every night he just shakes his head and says, "Nothing." He promises he will go to the doctor next week.

Benita and her little boy, Laurant, knock on my door the first morning that Moe goes to work. She invites me to bring the children for a drive to Baba Ali, the farm where Moe and Claude work. I quickly dress the children and follow Benita to her car.

On the drive, I learn more about the farm from Benita. It is a beautiful peaceful plantation surrounded by high palm trees and thick lush greenery. It once belonged to a wealthy French man who grew oranges and limes and many kinds of vegetables. He, like thousands of his fellow French Algerians, abandoned his land during the war and returned to France. This particular property was taken over by the new government and is now designated as a research farm. The researchers still grow oranges, but they are also experimenting with new varieties of other fruits.

Benita says, "They are soon going to bring in sheep, pigs and dairy cows – and with dairy cows we will be able to get milk for our children."

"Pigs?" I repeat when she tells me. "Isn't that rather unusual in a Muslim country?"

"It's true," Benita insists.

After a short tour, we stop at an area where a high fence still surrounds what was once a tennis court. The only thing missing is the net. Benita smiles as she points to the space, "I think of it as the ultimate playpen," she chuckles.

She is right about that. The old wire gate can still be closed so that the children are safely confined inside. Tarek and Laurant get right down to playing with their toys and trucks. Even at fifteen months old, the boys find a way to play together with little conflict. Benita and I pile dirt in little mounds for them and they pretend to be building roads. Sometimes Zohra joins them, but mostly she plays alone in one corner with her little dolls.

When the boys get bored with their trucks and road-building games, they run around and around the court as fast as their little legs will carry them. Zohra jumps up to join them. After one lap around the court, her longer legs and faster pace result in her herding the little ones like cats.

Benita and I settle down to read in a couple of chairs that are conveniently placed under some trees just outside the tennis court. I choose a book from her large library bag of English novels, and have just turned the first few pages when I am interrupted by a strange noise, like the a thousand wooden boards all clattering against one another.

"What is that?" I ask Benita, putting my book down and looking around to locate the source of the unfamiliar noise.

"Storks," she says, glancing up at me, and then returning to her book.

"Storks?" I interrupt her reading again.

Benita marks her place with one finger and gestures upward with her other hand. "Look up in the trees," she says. "They're huge birds. You can't miss them."

She puts her book down beside her and continues, "I am surprised you haven't seen them before. They breed here and nest here. Claude told me that they have been coming to this farm for centuries. I saw one the other day with a wingspan of almost six feet."

The clattering goes on, and though the sound is all around me, I can't see the birds. "I've never seen a stork," I tell her. "Where do I look?"

"Come on. We'll walk to the clearing," Benita gets up. "You'll have a better view from there."

She leads me away from the tennis court and out from under the canopy of trees where we have been sitting. The children continue their running game, oblivious to us.

From the clearing, I look up, following where Benita points. I see a giant nest made of sticks, perched precariously in the crook of a high branch. Then, I catch sight of a beautiful gliding beast of a bird, completely white and bigger than any bird I have ever seen. It lands on the edge of the giant nest.

"Oh my god," I whisper, "it's beautiful." I am transfixed by its size, its whiteness against the blue of the sky and its silent graceful landing so far above me that I have to tilt my head back to watch it.

"Yes," answers Benita, "it is that." She too watches the bird's wings flap up and down as it balances on the edge of the nest.

After a while we walk back to the tennis court and to my book under the canopy. The storks' clattering continues all afternoon.

Near the end of the day, on our way back to the village, Benita drives by a construction site about half a mile from the tennis court. She stops the car and points. "See the workers?" she asks me. "They are building three houses. One is for me and my family, one for Shelig, and one for Thomas." She heaves a big sigh. "My life will be bearable once I move out here. I am working with the architect to build what I want."

She puts the car back into gear and we pull back onto the road. "In case you haven't noticed," she says, glancing at me, "I hate that apartment. Those dirty Arab children are always there." Her very proper English contrasts sharply with the vehemence of her statement. She takes one hand off the wheel and rubs it on her upper leg, as if to brush off something stuck to it. "– and they touch my son." Her voice hardens. "I hate that."

I catch my breath as she speaks so coldly. I look down at the floor of the car. "How can she be so unfair – so unaware that the 'dirty Arab children' that she hates to have near her son are the rightful occupants of the apartment building – of the country?" I think. "She is the interloper, the intruder. They are the ones who should be looking forward to moving into the newly built houses – not her."

But I don't say any of this aloud. I only avert my eyes and remain silent as Benita drives us back to the village. I know that Moe is angry about the houses, angry that two Frenchmen should get the new houses on the farm. He doesn't understand why he and his family aren't eligible for the same housing as the French.

I think about Benita. She and I should have a lot in common – we are both foreigners in this country – but we don't. She views the Arabs as being beneath her – grubby locals that intrude on her life – and she assumes that because I am American I should agree with her.

I listen to her rattle on about how she can't wait to move out to the farm, away from the *batiment* that she is being forced to share with 'those dirty children,' those 'people' who don't know anything about cleanliness and sanitation. Her voice gets cold and hard every time she refers to the Arabs.

I look away. I say nothing. I still want her companionship.

"I think we should go shopping in Algiers tomorrow," Benita suddenly announces. "I want to go to the fish market first thing in the morning." She glances at me to see if I am listening. "We can be back before the men are home from work."

I must have looked unsure because she adds, "Do you think your husband will let you go?"

"I – I think so," I reply. "I'll ask him."

We pull up in front of our apartment building and lift the children out of the car. I set Tarek down on the ground behind me and turn to retrieve his toys.

The children who live in our building gather around us – children of all ages, from toddlers barely able to walk and babies being carried by an older brother or sister to young girls and boys that must be almost twelve or thirteen years old. I lose count of how many when I reach ten. They jockey for position around us in a noisy mob, each one trying to shout *"Bonjour. Bonjour, Madame"* louder than the rest, hoping that he or she will catch the attention of the two foreign women.

My hands now full of the bags I had taken on our outing, I

turn from the car. I smile at the children and they smile back, wonderful smiles set in small grubby faces.

Tarek suddenly dashes up to a little girl about his size and kisses her full on the mouth. He shouts, *"Bebe!"*

The little girl grabs him by his hand, and together, they look up at me, both smiling.

"Bebe nice," Tarek crows, pleased to have found a friend, his little voice clear and self-satisfied.

"Tarek, let go of the little girl," I tell him gently. "We have to get to our apartment." I reach down, take his hand, and unwind his fingers from those of the smiling little dark girl whose eyes get larger as I come close to her. She steps back quickly when I touch her hand and her face contorts in fear, as if she thinks I might hit her.

I smile at her and gently release my son. Taking Zohra's hand with my other hand, I lead both of my unwilling children towards the stairs up to our apartment. I call *Bonjour* over my shoulder, still smiling. "They are so friendly to my children," I think.

I look back to see what Benita is doing. She is still in the car with her son, her blonde hair covering her face, and her head resting on the steering wheel. I make my way back through the crowd of children to the car. I tap on the window and she looks up.

"What's wrong?" I ask, making the words with my mouth rather than speaking them aloud.

She rolls down the window, her face red from crying.

"Can I help?" I ask. "Are you sick?"

She looks at me, rolls her eyes, and then, suddenly opens her car door and roughly yanks Laurant out behind her.

"Am I sick? What kind of a stupid question is that?" she screams at me as she turns away from the car. "Of course, I'm not sick – but I'm going to be – and so are you and your children."

I stand there, speechless. Tarek and Zohra stare at her. Even Laurant stares at his mother.

She waves her hands in the vague direction of the street children, who have ceased their chanting, and seem unsure of whether they should stay or leave.

"Why are you touching these children? They are only filthy

little street urchins," Benita continues her tirade. The entire street is silent around her. One or two Arab men walk by on the other side of the road, also staring at this foreign woman making such a scene.

"You need to stay away from them. They are filled with disease," Benita winds down. Her last salvo is directed right at me. "You are not very smart for being American," she finishes, wiping her hand across her face in an effort to mop up some of the tears. She has exhausted herself.

She picks up Laurant and marches defiantly through the crowd of children knocking a little boy to the ground. She looks down at him, yells, "*Mon Dieu,*" and something in Finnish that I can't understand, and then, she runs up the stairs to her apartment, tears still streaming down her cheeks, her breath ragged. Laurant, looking lost and frightened, clings to her and stares back at us over her shoulder.

"Why is Laurant's mommy so mad?" Zohra asks in the silence that follows.

"I'm not sure, Zohra, but I think she doesn't like the children to gather around."

"Why?" Zohra asks.

"I don't know, honey. Sometimes, it's hard to understand people."

"I think she's just unhappy," Zohra offers.

I smile at her wisdom. "Yes. Maybe she is just unhappy."

I make my way back through the crowd and up the stairs to the apartment. I look back at the children several times. They all stare back at me, clearly not understanding very much of what has just happened. Those staring eyes will haunt me.

These little ones are the children of farm workers who have been assigned apartments in this building. Moe calls them the children of the HLM. He says that HLM stands for *housing at subsidized rates* or *government subsidized housing.*

At five in the morning – every day – when their fathers leave to go to Baba Ali to work – these children are put outside to play, no matter what the weather. They are left out all day long. Only when the sun goes down, and the darkness descends do the locks on the apartment doors click open and the children are permitted back inside.

A few mothers come out onto the balconies at noon to give their children crusts of bread and something to drink. But, mostly, the children all play outside, all day, every day. Most are shoeless. Many have green snot oozing from their noses or large red sores on their faces, arms and legs, and probably also on their bodies under their clothes. These sores are from fly bites. In the summer, flies lay their eggs just under the surface of human skin. When the larvae hatch, they bore up and out through the skin, causing itchy sores. Neglecting the open sores often results in infection. Every single HLM child I have seen so far is scarred by these sores.

The balconies are occupied by a group of women in dirty grey-white veils who sit on the floor. Moe told me about them. "Sometimes, when women are born into a family," he explained. "they have father who never allows them to go to school. Just work at home. The father thinks that is life for women." Moe watched me as he told me about the decisions made for the women. "When they are fourteen or fifteen, they are married off to the man with most to offer – money, position, status in village. When the women make the walk to their husband's house on their wedding day, that may be the last light of day they see. They stay in home. They do women's work – cooking, washing clothes, tending babies. They stay in home until they are carried out for their own funeral." Moe gestures to emphasize that is just how things are.

These particular families are used to living in the countryside. There the children are always free to roam the roads and fields and play. But, since the Algerian war, many families have been forced, for safety reasons, into the cities and villages and confined to these *batiments* or HLMs. Here the children have nothing to do and nowhere to play except on balconies and in stairwells or in the streets. Their fathers make barely enough money to feed them, and year after year their mothers have baby after baby. Some of the apartments have more than eight people living in each unit.

Moe often talks to me about these people. He tells me to be gentle with them for they are uneducated and don't know how to live in modern buildings. Moe says that seeing how these families live is one of the things that makes him heartsick. This inability to live in modern buildings that Moe mentions is evident every-where. When the children need to squat, they simply squat – in a hallway or on a stairway or in the street.

In the evening, when Moe returns home, I tell him about my experience with the children gathering around us at the car and about Benita's breakdown. He frowns and says, "I wish we can help these children but it is only education that will solve this problem. Ignore them. They won't hurt you or Madame Ducont. Our children have to learn to live with them. Maybe their parents can learn from us if we are gentle in our ways."

I ask Moe about going to Algiers with Benita to the fish mar-ket. "That is a good thing to learn about," he says. "The fish mar-ket in Algiers is famous all around the world. Hopefully, you won't hit any roadblocks. I have little money but I give you some. My pay is late again."

As Moe remarks about his paycheque being late, I inadver-tently let out a sigh and a sarcastic grunt.

He frowns at me, and his voice becomes defensive. "Woman, I try to be patient. Do you think it not difficult for me?" He waves his arms. "Yes, sometimes I not get paid for three or four weeks. It is government bureaucracy."

"What do we do if we don't have money? How do we pay the rent?" I ask, against my better judgment. I remember that arguing with Moe is not a good idea.

"Rent is in my pay. It not a problem. Rent and electricity are part of my pay," Moe explains with impatience in his voice. "Food and other stuff is the problem. I borrow from friends and they borrow from me. It is the will of Allah." He looks to the ceiling and down again at me.

I am silent.

The money conversation ends there. I am surprised by the sudden mention of Allah. In America, Moe was always careful to avoid any reference to his religion. I know his beliefs are import-ant to him, but I seldom see him pray. If he goes to the mosque, he never says anything.

I ask, "Moe, do you ever go to the mosque?"

Moe looks at me. He smiles, "Of course, I go to mosque."

"Why don't you ever talk to me about it or about your religion?"

"I not talk to you because I think religion is for you to decide. I think if you see good in my religion you someday come to it by yourself."

"What about the children, will you take them to the mosque?"

"Of course, but I wait for when I not sick and some time passes."

Moe smiles and continues, "You know, if you decide to be in my religion, we must change your name. You should think of name you like."

I smile, too, appreciating his wisdom in waiting to talk about religion. Maybe someday I will change my name.

"Would you be happy if I become a Moslem?" I ask him seriously.

"It not matter. The question is, would it make you happy? Religion is personal thing. I think it make your life here better. People accept you more." He looks at me and at the children playing on the mattress in the other room. He finishes, "But we have much time to decide it. This choice I leave to you. So far none of my friends with American or European wives make this change. Maybe it not matter. I myself don't know the best answer."

The next morning Benita arrives at my door at 6:00 a.m. to go to the fish market. We drive to Algiers in record time. There are no roadblocks or other interruptions. The day is hot and windy and we chat about what Benita will buy for her new house.

"Oh," Benita suddenly says just before we pull into the fish market, "I have some news. In six months, I am having another baby."

Her announcement catches me by surprise. "Are you happy about that?" I ask.

"I am happy about it," she answers, but her voice is sombre. "But, I think Claude is not happy. He is worried that there are no doctors to deliver it here, so he is sending us back to France for the delivery."

"That will be good," I tell her, thinking of her outburst the day before over the children around the car.

"Yes, and we will probably have the new house by the time I return. So we can keep the children away from all the dirtiness of that place." Benita weaves her little car into a tight parking space a few blocks from the market. She attaches her shopping bags to one hand and Laurant to the other. I take Tarek into my arms and make sure that Zohra understands that she has to hold onto my skirt as we walk. The market is so large I cannot see from one end of it to the other. We walk shoulder to shoulder with other shoppers past acres of small stands with buckets and display cases filled to the brim with every size and shape of fish. The air is thick with a salty, fresh fish smell. The market smells like the ocean itself.

On all sides, men call out to us, "Ah, Madame, come and see my fish," or "Buy my fish." Of course what they say is all in Arabic or French so I hear only a cacophony of voices that follow us. Benita knows where she is going in this maze of stalls and after a five minute slippery glide around the main part of the market, she heads for a large corner booth.

"I like this stall," she tells me. "Ali will bargain with me and I always get the freshest catch of the day."

At Ali's stall, I watch as they chatter back and forth in French. I wait until they have made their deal, and Ali has scooped up the fish Benita has bought and packaged them for her. Then, I ask Benita if she will help me buy some, too.

"Of course, go ahead. What do you want?" she asks.

"I love shrimp. I'd like some if he has any."

"Of course he has some, right in front of you, in that bucket."

I peer into a bucket almost full of hundreds of five-inch creatures that look like giant bugs. They are not like any shrimp I have ever seen.

"That's not shrimp," I assert.

"Yes it is. You have to cut the heads off. It's the tails you eat."

Benita laughs at me and says something to Ali who bursts our laughing as well.

"Okay," I say. "But they look weird."

"Of course they do." Benita continues, "They look weird because they are the real thing."

I tell Benita that I want to buy three pounds.

She tells me to buy ten pounds because without the heads and other parts, three pounds isn't very much.

"How much does it cost? I ask her.

She tells me and I translate it into dollars. Twelve cents a pound. I put my *dinars* into Ali's hand. He smiles at me – a huge broad smile and slips the coins into his apron pocket. He wraps my shrimp in newspapers and puts it into my string bag and bows at me. He is still smiling. I feel like I have made the deal of the century.

But, as we walk away, Benita shakes her head. Then she tells me I should learn French – and that I will have to learn to bargain. "You paid a lot for your shrimp," she says.

Benita spends another hour going from stall to stall buying fresh sardines and other fish, mostly things I have never seen before. I am running low on money so I walk with her but I don't buy anything else.

The children begin to whine. I am tired, having carried my thirty-five-pound son most of the way, only putting him down from time to time to rest. Benita suggests we buy some things for lunch from the local confectionary and then head home. "The fish will not last very long in this summer heat," she says, wrinkling her nose.

We tuck the kids into the car and I climb into the front seat. Benita leans into the driver's side. "There's a little store down the street here. I'll be back in a minute," she says, slamming the car door.

I roll down the windows to keep from suffocating in the hot sun and hope she returns soon. The minutes crawl by and the temperature in the car rises. Just as I am about to take the kids out and into the shade of a nearby tree, she returns with a large bag filled to the brim.

"There's a park nearby. I'll drive there and we can eat our lunch," she says, waving the bag by way of explanation.

A few blocks away, she pulls into a lovely treed park. We find an empty table and a bench and sit down. The children and I watch hungrily, as she pulls items from her bag. At the sight of some neatly packaged yogurt, Tarek squeals with delight.

Benita offers thick slices of cheese on Algerian bread to all. She hands me a large bottle of ice-cold *gazoose*, explaining that it is an Algerian version of 7-Up, and opens small bottles of fruit juice for the children. She also has bottled water for everyone. We munch happily on the impromptu picnic. At the end of the meal, she opens Algerian cookies and lets each child choose one. The children jump off the bench and run around the little park. No one bothers them.

I offer Benita some money to help pay for the food, but she refuses. "It's my treat," she tells me.

I thank her and ask, "How did you find this park?"

"Claude used to work not far from here and he pointed it out to me. Not many people come here so it's usually a quiet place to sit in the sun and eat. I come here with children quite often."

I make a note in my head to tell Moe about it. It will be a good place for a picnic the next time we come to Algiers.

We are back in Birtouta before three o'clock. When I get the children and my fish up the stairs to the apartment, I notice that Moe is already home from work. I see him from the kitchen, lying on our mattress. I push the newspaper-wrapped shrimp into the refrigerator and slip into the bedroom. Moe is lying on his stomach with his eyes closed. I am not sure whether he is asleep or not.

I sit down on the mattress and touch his back. "Moe," I ask softly, "Moe, are you alright?"

He rolls over. His eyes are blank and glassy. "I – I want to shleep," he slurs.

I leave the room, shutting the door quietly behind me. My main job for the rest of the afternoon is to keep the children quiet so he can sleep. I start heating water so I can bath the children. When he hasn't stirred by 7:30, I feed the three of us, and take the little ones to the washtub. They like this tub. It is big enough for both of them to fit in at the same time and they like to spend time playing with spoons and pots in the water. I watch them – two cute and funny little kids absorbed in their games, chattering back and forth to each other.

I dress them in their pyjamas, and I have tucked them into their beds for the night before I hear Moe's footsteps in the bathroom. Moe comes in and kisses his son good night. Then he stumbles down the hall to Zohra's room. He bends down clumsily, and kisses her cheek. "*Bon nuit,*" he says in French.

"Good night, Daddy," Zohra smiles at him. "You look funny."

"Daddy funny," he answers and lurches out of the room.

In the living room he slowly lowers his body onto the mattress. His face is red and blotchy. "Moe very funny today." he says, but without laughing. He turns onto his back and drapes one arm across his eyes.

"Why are you home early today?" I ask.

"I go to Algiers today," he tells me, "I have appointment with French psychiatrist doctor."

"Moe, why didn't you tell me? I could have gone with you."

"No, I want to go alone. I see so many doctors these days. This time I am at work and walking along and I faint."

"Moe, this is serious." I sit on the mattress next to him. "What did the doctor say?"

"He says I have extreme nervous tension. He says he is seeing this condition very much in young Algerian men coming from school in other countries. I tell him I cannot sleep and sometimes I cannot breathe. He says it is the symptoms of nervous tension. The fainting is caused by tension in my neck that cut off blood to my brain. I have very high blood pressure."

Moe is silent for a moment. He doesn't move, and when he starts to talk again, his voice is muffled as if it is coming from far away, as if he is about to drift off to sleep again. "Doctor says to go on three-week holiday and sleep for a whole week. He gives me some very strong pills for sleeping so I come home and take one. I take the pills. I go on holiday. Then, I go next month to see him again. I think he is good doctor. He study in Geneva and in France and he very nice." Moe inches his way off the living room mattress and shuffles back to the bedroom.

I spend the night on the mattress in the living room. Maybe Moe will have a better sleep that way.

# Moe on Sick Leave

The summer is hot and very humid. It is difficult to keep the apartment cool so I let the children live in their underwear and I wander around in a short-sleeved blouse and long skirt. Moe takes three weeks off and he sleeps for the first three days. I keep the children entertained with coloring, reading and playing games, but it is difficult to keep them quiet.

I don't know what to do about Moe's condition. He doesn't talk when he is awake. He just keeps taking pills. At the end of three days, I am out of food. I wake him.

Moe looks at me as though he barely recognizes me. He shakes his head slowly from side to side. He says, "I not take any more pills. I not remember anything," He focuses on my face, and asks, "What day is today?" Without waiting for my answer, he continues, "I not like this."

"I don't like it either," I tell him, "but at least you got some sleep."

On the fourth day, early in the morning, I hear a knock at the door. I yank the door open impatiently, expecting to find a child standing there with something to sell. I am surprised to find Aouf, Yarka and their twins. They have come to see Moe. They know he is sick.

I point to the bedroom and Aouf goes in to see him. In my pidgin French, I offer Yarka a seat at the table.

A few minutes later, Aouf returns with Moe, who looks better than he did a few minutes ago. He walks without staggering.

Moe says, "Aouf asks if Zohra can go with them to Algiers for the weekend to play and get some fresh air?" half-asking me if I think she should go, half-telling me it is a good idea.

"What a good idea," I respond, sure she will have more fun there than sitting here cooped up in our apartment with a comatose father, an active younger brother, and me, constantly worried about how to cope with them.

Aouf and Yarka leave with Zohra. Moe drifts back to the bedroom, and I settle Tarek with his trucks in the living room. Then, I hear another knock at the door. When I open it, I find a tall handsome brown-uniformed man accompanied by a beautiful brown-eyed unveiled woman, carrying a baby and accompanied by two toddlers.

"*Bonjour, Madame*," the uniformed man says, clicking his heels together as he talks.

I call out. "Moe, someone in a uniform is here. I don't know him."

Moe comes out of the bedroom. Suddenly, he lets out a loud yell, "Ah, Mustapha!" followed by an excited string of Arabic. The two men enthusiastically kiss cheeks and embrace. The two men hang onto each other, talking excitedly. Then, they realize that their wives are standing silently watching them.

Moe says to me in English, "This is my friend, Mustapha Hushmoui." He gestures at the others. "This is Mustapha's wife, Fatiha. These are their three children. I don't know their names."

The two older children smile shyly at me. Then they catch sight of Tarek playing with his trucks, and immediately run to join him on the floor. Tarek is delighted to have playmates.

Fatiha comes forward, holding her baby against her. Silently, we kiss cheeks. She smiles at me. I look into her large dark eyes and I see a happy and wise woman. I know instantly we will be friends if only we can get past the language barrier. I motion for her to sit down at the table.

She begins speaking to me in French. I run for my French-English dictionary. On my return, I show it to her like it is a link to a better life. She smiles again.

Moe breaks in, "Mustapha and I take children to Baba Ali. Mustapha want oranges. We bring some for us as well."

"Moe," I start to ask, "Are you feeling well enough to –"

He reassures me, "Not to worry. Moe is better." He shakes his head. "I not take more pills."

Fatiha keeps the baby and the men leave with the other children. Babies stay with their mothers. But, Arab men often take small children on short trips. When children are big enough to walk, fathers happily take them where they go. It shows that a man is a good father.

Fatiha chatters at me in rapid French.

I tell her to talk slower so I can understand.

She laughs at my confusion.

At first I have to look up nearly every word, but after an hour or so we get into a way of speaking that is understandable to both of us.

She asks me where my daughter is.

I explain about Aouf and Yarka. Then, with much consultation of my dictionary and gesturing, I ask, "Where is your veil?"

Fatiha laughs and replies, "Mustapha doesn't like veils." She shakes her head. "I wear veil only when I go to village where I was born."

The day passes quickly. Even with our limited vocabulary hampering the conversation, it feels good to talk to someone other than my husband. My voice is hoarse by the time the men return.

Moe half-asks, half-tells me to prepare supper for our guests.

I wince, thinking they might not like my version of their food.

Fatiha seems to understand. "Susie," she says in French, and I somehow understand that she will help me. She opens and closes my cupboard doors and then announces in French, "We eat lamb, couscous and salad." I understand. She rattles off instructions to Moe and Mustapha, who nod in reply.

They take the children and go off to the market.

Three hours later, we sit down to eat. The conversation flows back and forth mostly in Arabic, assisted by much gesturing and even more laughter.

As we finish the last morsels, Mustapha announces that they

must leave because they don't travel at night. He gestures, as if to say, "What can one do?"

The men again embrace enthusiastically, and this time Fatiha and I embrace as well as we say good-bye. I wave at them from the balcony until they are out of sight.

I turn from the window and say, "I enjoyed today. I hope Mustapha and Fatiha will come to visit again."

I continue, "How do you know Mustapha?"

"I meet him in the camps in Tunisia. He is my special friend. Many things happen to us. Some I cannot speak of." A look of sadness crosses Moe's face.

I wonder what it is that he *cannot speak of,* but I don't ask him to tell me. I don't want to break the spell of the day by asking him to recount anything that will make him sad.

When I awake the next morning, I am nauseous and disoriented. I try to drink some tea, but I can't hold it down. After I run to the bathroom to vomit, I go back to bed where I roll up in a ball and beg the universe to let me die.

Moe is feeling okay. He tells me, "People get sick very often in Algeria." He sits on the mattress next to me, saying, "It likely be dirty water or maybe your body not like the change to Algerian food."

I vow to never eat again. I pull the blanket up over my head. In a minute, Moe pats me gently on the shoulder and leaves the bedroom, closing the door quietly behind him.

Partway through the day, I hear Tarek yelling. I drag myself out of bed. Before I even enter his room, the smell makes me gag. I try to get hold of myself.

"Talek bad, Talek kiki," Tarek starts to wail when he sees me, "Owie tummy. Owie kiki."

He is covered in a thick, yellow, stinky, gelatinous muck. Gingerly, I slip my hands under his arms and carry him to the washroom holding him so he doesn't touch me. With every step, I struggle to keep from gagging. I lower him into a tub of cold water. I don't have the energy to heat any.

His crying turns to screaming as I remove his clothes and attempt to wash him.

"Why you make him cry?" Moe demands. He puts his hand into the tub. "That water too cold."

"Fine!" I answer. "You clean him!"

I leave Tarek standing in the tub and storm out of the washroom. My energy deserts me as soon as I get into the hallway. I struggle back to bed, returning to my foetal position and try to shut out the world. "Please let me die," I plead with whatever god might be listening. I really mean it.

I am nearly asleep when I feel Moe sit on the edge of the mattress. "Sit up and take medicine," he commands.

I struggle to a sitting position and open my mouth. The chalky goo that he pours into my mouth makes me gag. "Yuk, what is it?" I mumble.

"Just drink," he commands, his authoritative voice penetrating the fog that surrounds me. "It make you feel better."

I drink. Then I sleep. When I wake up, I feel better. The apartment is quiet and I feel alone. I roll off the bed and make my way to the living room. I find Moe asleep with Tarek on his chest. They look so peaceful. Momentarily, I look for Zohra and then I remember she is still in Algiers. I go back to bed.

Aouf brings Zohra home in the early evening. She chatters about her wonderful day. Mustapha took her to work with him and had his chauffeur drive her around Algiers with the other children. They went to parks and shops. She says she ate ice cream and popsicles all day.

I am not sure I believe the part about the popsicles, but she is so happy I decide it doesn't matter. I am happy to have her back. Tarek is playing with his trucks. Moe is watching him from the mattress where he reclines against a large pillow.

"Moe, you look so tired." I sit down next to him.

He looks at me, pats my hand, and smiles, "Okay. My turn to go to bed."

He walks into the bedroom and closes the door. In a few moments, I hear him snoring.

I play with the children in the living room, making sure they don't get too noisy. In an hour or so, Moe gets up and goes to the bathroom. He comes into the living room. He looks more rested, but his voice is muffled and unclear.

I wonder if he has taken one of his sleeping pills.

Suddenly, there is a knock at the door. I open it to find three dark haired teenagers who might have been triplets had it not been for the difference in their heights. They all carry dishes of hot steaming food. The tallest greets me with *"Bonjour, Madame,"* and the others smile simultaneously.

"Moe," I call, and Moe comes slowly to the door. After a brief conversation in Arabic, Moe shows the young men into the living room where they place the large plates on our table. Their task completed, the boys leave, bowing and smiling all the way out of the door.

"What is this?" I ask.

"This Algerian hospitality," he explains. "I give this family some old clothes I not need. They very grateful. They pay back." Moe looks both pleased and disgusted. He shakes his head, saying, "It is very beautiful food." He gestures at the table. "They not able to feed their children but they feed us."

"Yes, it all smells very good," I agree. I turn away from the table. "Moe, are we going to eat it?" I ask, thinking of the agony I have just been through.

"We have no choice," Moe says. "It is the right thing."

"But Moe, we don't know these people. What if the food isn't safe?"

"No matter," Moe shakes his head again. "We eat. They will know if we not eat and that would be insult." He gets plates for us, sits down at the table and gestures for me to do the same. "I give this worker man his dignity. Now he give me something. It is our custom."

I look at the food – lamb stew with prunes, a large dish of couscous, bread. Dishes for special occasions and for special people. "I feel badly, Moe, especially if his family won't have enough to eat. Can't you explain to him that it is too much for us or something?"

"No, we must eat it." Moe begins to serve himself. Tarek and Zohra come to the table.

Suddenly, there is more banging on the door. I open it to find Mohamed G standing there.

"*Bonjour, Madame.*"

"*Bonjour,*" I answer, surprised. He greets me, and then Moe with hugs and cheek kisses. Moe speaks to him in Arabic and Mohamed G nods, smiles, and heads out the door again.

"He'll be back," Moe says. "Ahmed is downstairs in car. I tell them come for dinner." He grins, "See. This works out."

Moe's smile is weak. He still doesn't feel well. But he is happy to see his friends arrive just in time for a supper prepared by the kindness of the family downstairs.

The smallest of the teenage boys arrives to collect the dishes just as the men finish up the last crumbs. Moe conveys his gratitude while the boy gathers up the dishes. Moe explains that the boy will relay our thankful statements to his father who will then feel at peace with the gift of clothes from Moe.

"Ahmed and Mohamed G want us to stay at their apartment for some coming days. They go to Sahara for work. They have servant. We can have holiday." He continues as he sees my lack of understanding. "They hear I am sick."

"Wow! Word travels fast in this country, doesn't it?" I look at Moe and he just smiles.

"Yes, it is pretty good for no phones. Please go now and pack for few days. It is good idea to go away."

The trip to Algiers is hampered by a roadblock, but when the soldiers recognize the government car and Mohamed G flashes his journalist's pass, they don't detain us. They ask the usual questions about me in the back seat and then smile with their rotten teeth and laugh.

Mohamed G's apartment is an elegant palace located on top of a hill in a suburb of Algiers called *Maison-Carrie.* From the front balcony of the nine-room complex, we see the Mediterranean and from the back balcony, we look over the city. The floors are terrazzo and the walls of the kitchen and bathroom are covered with white marble. I ask how Moe's friends got this apartment, but no one wants to tell me.

The apartment comes with a maid who is also the cook. We

are told to ask her for whatever we want. Tarek asks for yogurt every day, which the maid gladly provides. Every night, for four nights, she makes us wonderful meals – stews made with vegetables and meat, and served over mounds of couscous. Tarek loves the couscous. On the last day, he asks for it at breakfast and we all laugh.

Several times, I ask Moe about who pays for the food. At first, he tells me his friends pay the maid a stipend and she shops for the food.

Finally, he says, "It not your business." He glares at me. "Stop all these questions. It is not for you to know anyway."

On the third day of our little vacation, we walk down the street near the apartment and find a small store that sells household items. Moe picks up a shiny pot with what looks to me like a colander on top.

"This is couscous pot," he announces. "It is called *couscousery*. I buy for us. Now you make real couscous."

We stop at another little shop and Moe buys ten kilos of couscous. No matter what happens to his paycheques – from now on, we will at least have couscous to eat.

On the fifth day, Moe's friends return and take us back home to Birtouta. I am sad to leave. It has been a wonderful holiday. Moe looks rested and happy.

When we return to our apartment, Moe rests and plays with the children. He has two more weeks to rest and visit with people. Zohra, in particular, thrives under his attention. He often takes her with him for walks around the village and conversation with his neighbours at the local coffee shop.

I stay inside, though once in a while I walk with Moe to the market to buy vegetables and meat. People stare at us and I often hear laughter from the children who follow us wherever we go. Sometimes people make comments, but I don't understand what they say.

When I ask Moe to translate, he replies, "It better I not tell you and it better you not ask. Remember these are not educated people."

I stop asking and decide to ignore people when I walk in the street. I don't feel in danger – but I don't feel welcome either.

In the middle of June, a letter from my mother tells me I am not writing to her enough. I realize what she means is that when I write, I don't tell her enough about the children. I have been trying to write something to her every day so that she will be kept up to date, but I have been writing mostly about politics and sickness.

On June 13, 1966, I write her the following:

Dearest Mom and Dad,

I really hadn't meant to neglect the babies so much in my letters and I thought I was doing a pretty good job of including them – well, I shall now attempt a detailed report.

Tarek – He grows into more of a character everyday. He is advanced for his age, I'd say. He understands exactly what you say and because I have a lot of time to spend with the kids, he does a lot of simple tasks, like put away his toys and carry things. He also has mastered the art of shaking hands, which makes him a polite little garçon by the highest French standards. He has begun to talk a lot and it gives him great pride. His newest word is 'Don't.' He says it with a decidedly southern accent. He has also started to say 'kiki.' Of course, he says it after he has filled his pants. Anyway, he is going to the bathroom sometimes successfully, sometimes not – but it's a beginning. Moe thinks that it is great the way Beadies gets around and he is amazed at his personality development.

Zohrie – she has been very upset by this whole move. For a long time she just cried all the time no matter if you kissed her or spanked her. She talks about Mi-Mi's house a lot. Now she is getting much better and adjusting rapidly. Moe has been taking her practically every time he goes to Algiers on business or to visit friends. She loves the extra attention. She runs around the house singing God Bless America in loud clear tones. She is dying for a yellow umbrella. I have been looking here but there are few – and they are so darned expensive. If you want to send one, that would be nice.

She talks a lot about her Mi-Mi and Papa in America. She asks for suckers and birthday cakes and we tell her we don't have any and she says, "At Mi-Mi's house in America."

Don't worry. I have your picture in each of their rooms. They won't forget you.

By the way, thank you for sending all the things you are sending. So far, we have had no problems getting anything through Customs.

Love you a lot,

Sudie

Sudie is a pet name my mother used for me when I was really little. As I write, I am suddenly swept up in tears. I miss my parents. I fold the letter and slide it into an onionskin envelope, hoping that Moe has enough money left for a stamp.

At that moment, Moe bursts through the door full of energy and smiles.

"Wow! You look happy," I observe.

"Moe very happy. Moe get paid," he says, waving some papers in his hand and smiling even more broadly. "It is very happy day also because I get letter from my family. They say they come soon. We need to be ready." He swings his string bag towards me. "Also, I buy you two presents with my paycheque." He finishes with, "You open carefully."

I take the bag and reach inside. The first bundle is light, box-shaped and wrapped in grey butcher paper. As I remove the paper, the smell tells me exactly what it is. Sure enough – six beautiful napoleons, like the ones we had the first day I got to Algiers. I put them in the refrigerator for later.

The second gift is quite heavy. When I pull it out of the paper, I discover an iron.

I look up to find Moe smiling broadly. "Now, you can do ironing for Moe so he looks like business man in white shirts."

I smile less enthusiastically, "Yes, Moe. Now I can do ironing."

Moe wanders into the kitchen, takes an orange off the counter, and wanders back into the living room where I am sitting on the living room mattress. He flops down beside me and reaches into his pocket. He pulls out a small knife and begins to peel the orange.

He stares at me for a moment, and then says, "I not know how much longer we can take things from the farm and not pay. The French complain about it. They say the Arab workers steal food. I tell them if we get paid as much as you French get paid we not have to steal. Claude and others not like that very much."

I look at Moe, surprised, "I'll bet they didn't like that very much. The truth hurts."

"Yes, but I think I maybe should shut up because I am on sick leave. They might throw me out of my job. I am very unhappy with all this situation."

He shakes his head. "I think I am going to see the people higher in the government about this. I think it just wrong. It wrong for my people, wrong for me."

"Won't you get in trouble if you make trouble?" I ask carefully.

"Why you think I am sick?" Moe lashes out. "I am sick because I come back to my own country and I find these stupid people here. They think I am stupid but they are stupid ones."

Moe falls silent and the silence extends between us as he eats the orange section by section.

Suddenly, he declares, "We need car. If we have car, we not need to depend on friends and government drivers. I still have traveler's cheques I not cash yet. I use them only for emergency. Today, I go to see the Renault cars and I ask the price. They say $2,000. They say we can pay $1,000 and then pay each month for the other $1,000. It is much paper work. I only have $450 of traveler's cheques so we need to get more." He continues before I can interrupt. "When I come home, my father promises to help me get car. But, last week I get letter from him and he says my brother is very sick with cancer and he must pay for medicine. So I not ask father for any money." Moe shakes his head and puts the last section of orange into his mouth.

I think of my aunt's stock and of the secret bank account my mother insisted I set up for myself. I decide to tell Moe about some of it. "I have some money back home," I blurt out.

Moe looks at me. "You mean you ask your parents for money?" He shakes his head at me. "No. They already do too much for us. I not ask them again."

"No, Moe. I don't mean to ask my parents." I reach out and touch his arm. "My aunt died. She left me some money. I can get some for the car."

Moe looks at me curiously. "Why you not tell me this before?"

"I was saving it as a surprise for when we really need it." I wonder if he believes me.

He nods and seems to think about it for a moment. Then, he smiles. "Okay." He nods his head rather vigorously. "You get seven hundred more dollars and we buy a car." He sits back and waits for me to speak.

"He doesn't really believe me," I think. "Okay," I tell him. "I will."

# New Friends

Just before dark on the last night of Moe's sick leave, Mohamed G and Ahmed arrive at our door, this time accompanied by an older, heavy-set man I have never seen before. I invite them all into the living room. Moe stumbles sleepily out of the bedroom. He yells loud enough for the whole apartment building to hear and literally leaps from where he is standing into the arms of the heavy-set man. As they hug and kiss each other eagerly, he breathlessly explains, "This is cousin, another Ahmed. This is Ahmed Ben Ahmed."

I smile at Ahmed Ben Ahmed. "How will I keep all these Ahmeds straight?" I think.

"My cousin is Second Secretary of the Algerian Embassy in Damascus, Syria. He is going home to Mascara for a holiday," Moe tells me proudly, slapping Ahmed on the back as he speaks. "He has good education and is good man."

Ahmed Ben Ahmed smiles at me, his fat ruddy cheeks jiggling with his laughter. He speaks to me in French and, with Moe's help, I understand that he wants me to meet his wife, Rashida, when they return from their holiday next weekend. He kisses Tarek and Zohra and tickles them until they scream. Ahmed Ben Ahmed seems as old as a grandfather to me but Moe tells me that he and his wife have two children under two years old.

While the men make themselves comfortable at the table, I cook up the best meal I can, given the small amount of food I have on hand. They seem satisfied. They sit up most of the night telling stories. I hear them laughing and teasing Ahmed Ben Ahmed mercilessly about being a diplomat. I fall asleep after midnight, wondering how Moe will ever find the strength to go to work in the morning.

As it turns out, Moe does well his first week back at work. He arrives home less stressed than I have seen him since I arrived. I relax and look forward to our weekend in Algiers. On Friday night Moe comes home with the news that he has arranged to pick up a government car on Saturday morning and he will be the driver. I know he doesn't have an Algerian driver's license but it doesn't seem to bother him. I hope the roadblock people are as lenient as he thinks they are.

Ahmed Ben Ahmed and his wife are staying with Mohamed G. Moe and I and the other Ahmed are invited for lunch. I complain to Moe about the number of Ahmeds in our lives. He laughs and suggests that I can refer to Ahmed the diplomat, as Little Ahmed. I laugh because Ahmed the diplomat is quite big around, and the other Ahmed, who Moe says I should call Big Ahmed, is skinny but tall.

We leave Birtouta at 9:00 am. Within five miles, we see our first roadblock. Three men are standing in a line across the highway pointing their guns at us. Moe comes to a stop. Tarek yells, "Guns. Guns. Yippee! Yippee!" He jumps up and down on the back seat.

I try to quiet him, but he isn't having any of it. While Moe fusses with our papers, Tarek reaches his little hands out the window trying to touch the nearest soldier's gun. The soldiers' faces slowly soften as they listen to his baby chatter. Soon, they are laughing at his antics. The soldier in charge barks something to Moe, and Moe pulls out his Arizona driver's license and hands it to him. The soldier appears to read it.

He looks inside the car and then walks to my side. He indicates that I should roll down the window. Without saying a word, he reaches inside the car and snatches my passport from my hands and takes it to the first soldier and they examine it together. I ask Moe in English, "What do you think this man is looking for?" I demand indignantly. "If he wants my passport, why didn't he ask me for it?"

Moe calmly answers me in English, "I don't know."

The soldier walks back to my side of the car. He reaches his hand inside and says something in Arabic. Zohra gives him her hand and he holds it for a moment. Then, he speaks to her in Arabic. Zohra answers him without hesitation, and the soldier smiles. He speaks again, and again she answers him. This time her answer is longer and more intricate. Moe and I look at her in astonishment.

Suddenly, that soldier says something to the other soldiers. Immediately, they all step aside, and abruptly wave us on our way.

Mohamed steps on the gas and we leave the roadblock behind. Moe says something to Zohra in Arabic. She answers him and when she finishes speaking, he laughs loudly and proudly declares, "Her Arabic is very good. I ask her why she doesn't speak Arabic at home. She says because you not understand her. Now you have little interpreter. She is fast learner, this little daughter."

"Moe," I wonder, "She's only been here two months. How did she learn that fast?"

"I not know," he replies. "Children sometimes a big surprise. It help to send them to my friend's house."

"What did she say to the soldiers?" I ask.

"The man asks her who she travels with and where she goes. She says she is going to Algiers to play with Mohamed G. She says also that we are her mother and father and brother and her brother loves guns and she loves AMERICA."

"Oh God," I wince. "That could get us in a lot of trouble."

"Yes, but it coming from girl child, so the soldiers think it very funny. I think they see we are just family and not making trouble." He rubs his hand across his forehead. Then he glances at me. "I worry one day we get stopped by bandits who pretend to be soldiers and we be dead."

I stare at Moe. "Could that really happen?"

"Of course. It happen most every day. It is why we not travel at night. It very dangerous."

"Who are these bandits?" I ask.

"No one knows," Moe answers. "Some are bandits and some

just don't like the French or Europeans. Others not like the government and look to make trouble for new regime. Some also thugs."

We arrive at Mohamed G's apartment and again make the elevator journey up to the third floor to the beautiful views of the city and the sea where we find many of Moe's friends.

I am introduced to Ahmed Ben Ahmed's wife, Rashida, a large woman dressed in a beautiful silk chemise with a large red rose pattern. She has a huge bosom that pushes out with every breath she takes. She wears gold ballet shoes and has golden ribbons in her hair. I can't help but count her baubles – fifteen gold bracelets on her round fat arms alone. Five on her wrist and ten more large enough to go around her arms above her elbow. A large gold and ruby necklace around her neck is half-concealed by her many chins. She is wearing thick bright red lipstick and her eyes are outlined with dark thick eye liner. Endless mounds of tightly curled jet-black hair threaded with gold ribbons are accented by a streak of red henna running through the centre. She is a woman to behold.

When she sees me, she leaps to her fat little feet and runs to grab me in her voluptuous embrace. I literally fall into her cleavage. She smells like orange water and lavender. She pulls me even closer to her and then takes my head into her hands and kisses each of my cheeks. I see a woman filled with laughter and energy.

"Ah-h-h. *Americanea*," she exclaims. "*Mon Americanea*," she repeats, half in French and half in Arabic.

I can't help but laugh aloud. I feel as if I have met my sister.

Moe steps forward, looking as if he thinks I need to be rescued.

"Ah, Mohamed," Rashida says as he kisses each of her cheeks. She looks him up and down and then leans over to whisper something personal in his ear. Moe pulls back from her, his face turning red as he grins self-consciously.

Suddenly, she turns back to me and says, "*Bon homme, non?*"

I understand. I nod and smile.

Rashida beckons to me to sit beside her on the blue and gold brocade sofa. Her husband sits on her other side and she takes his hand.

Later, I comment to Moe in English about this public show of affection between a husband and a wife.

"Rashida does what pleases her," he says quietly as the conversation in French and Arabic swirls around us. "She never wear the veil and she says what she wants. Our relatives not like her – but Ahmed not care. He say she is wonderful. She also is from very rich family – so no one talk against her."

At one o'clock, the maid interrupts the laughter and conversations to announce that lunch is served. We sit down to eat. The final course, a fancy dessert, is served at four. Then, someone suggests we walk to a coffee house down the road. With much laughter, everyone agrees.

We arrive at the coffee house. The proprietor stares at us gloomily until he recognizes Mohamed G. Then, he smiles and comes forward to meet us individually. The waiters pull extra tables together for us on the sidewalk and then bring us cups of strong sweet black coffee and plates of pastries. Zohra begs for ice cream. Tarek helps Mohamed G eat a large rich napoleon and the men all laughingly comment that a boy who turns down ice cream in favour of napoleons is sure to grow into a man with rich tastes.

I smile and nod, not quite sure if that is a good thing or not.

Mohamed G and Ahmed beg to keep the children overnight. We are assured they can sleep with Rashida's children and we can pick them up the next day. Zohra is so excited to stay and Moe is happy to let them. I am reluctant, but I eventually give in to their pestering.

At six o'clock, Moe and I head back to Birtouta without incident or roadblock. I fall happily into bed. A few hours later I awake to find Moe gone. I search the apartment but he is not there. I tiptoe out onto the balcony and look through the darkness to the parking lot. The moon is high in the sky and I can see that the government car we have used for the day is not where he parked it.

Back in bed, I picture a willow tree. I picture myself underneath the willow tree, calmly, quietly knitting. The scene helps me push down some of the worry and anger over Moe's disappearance and his refusal to include me in what is going on for him. It is early morning when I finally fall into a restless sleep.

I wake up when Moe returns. The sun is high in the sky. "Are you all right?" I ask in as gentle a voice as I can muster, the image of the willow in the back of my mind.

"Yes," he answers. His voice is weak and tired. "I not sleep so I go for drive to the sea. I listen to water in the darkness."

"Moe, can't you let me know where you're going when you leave like that? I worry about you."

"I know. You sleep. I not want to bother you. I just not feel good and need to go away." He moves restlessly around the apartment, picking up things and putting them down again.

"How will you heal if you don't rest?" I ask. I want to go to him but I know that won't help, and it won't make him tell me anything.

"I not know," he answers. He sits down on the living room mattress, and drops his head into his hands. "I just not know what to do." His voice is muffled. "Sometimes I feel like I not want to live my life. I look at my children and I not know how I care for them." He looks at me. I see anguish in his eyes.

"Moe, you are doing a good job taking care of me and the children. You have to stop worrying so much." I reassure him, and I sit next to him on the mattress. I want him to know that I will be there, right beside him, regardless of what happens.

"Yes, you right, but Moe always worry. Moe promise father and mother I take care of you and I try. Sometimes I am afraid I cannot." He drops his head into his hands again, and sits there slowly shaking his head from side to side and slowly rocking back and forth.

I realize that Moe is struggling as much as I am. Both of us are finding it difficult to adjust to living in Algeria with all of its turmoil and the clash between the old ways of the French and the new ways of the young bureaucracy of the Algerians.

I sigh silently. I expect I will be visiting my willow more often in the coming days.

"Let's go get the children and visit with your friends. You'll feel better if you get out and do things. Okay?" I ask Moe.

"Yes, we go now. It is just before noon. Maybe we miss stupid roadblock."

Moe is right. The trip to Algiers is uneventful and we arrive at the apartment shortly after one o'clock. Eventually the bleary-eyed maid responds to our incessant ringing of the doorbell, and lets us in. We drink coffee until the others wake up. They must have stayed up most of the night.

Mohamed G explains that Rashida and Ahmed went to a hotel for the night, leaving their children with him. We tease him about how he has to stay single so we all have a babysitter when we need one. He laughs and solemnly assures us that he intends to stay single. As he chatters on, Moe translates for me.

"Getting a wife is too expensive and too much trouble." he explains. "Mohamed G meet girl from good family in Algiers. She has a little education so I decide to ask her father to marry her. The father says yes to marriage when Mohamed G has house, car, and furniture. The father also want a car for his own. Mohamed G tells father he not want to buy a wife. The girl's family is very angry and feels insulted that he refuse the price. Mohamed not care. He says he not want to get married right now."

"Mohamed G consider to let his mother pick wife – but she want Mohamed G to follow the old ways. If his mother pick wife, she will be young stupid girl from countryside – and Mohamed G will have to teach her everything."

Moe pauses in the translation. He comments, his voice suddenly abrupt and cold, "You know, like I teach you everything."

I frown at him. "Moe, I taught you things in my country." I want to explain so he understands how I am struggling to understand Algerian ways, just as he struggled in America. "Why does it bother you to teach me in your country?"

"I not bothered," he retorts, his voice now angry. "But I not like it when you make your voice angry in front of my friends. They think I am not a man."

Mohamed G breaks into our argument by announcing that

we are going for a short walking tour of Algiers. As he talks, the children stumble into the room, sleepy-eyed, but smiling.

Rashida and Little Ahmed arrive, looking relaxed after their night in the hotel. In a few minutes, we all are strolling down the street two-by-two, enjoying the view of the white hills of Algiers. Mohamed G leads us down a narrow lane. He waits by a door that is set into the side of the hill, and when we have all gathered close to him, he opens it. Then, he leads us further into the hillside through a long hallway to a large elegant teahouse, decorated with beautiful tiles, carved ceilings and thousands of mirrors. It is a beautiful and unexpected underground palace. We fall silent in the midst of chatter from the other patrons and Algerian classical music playing in the background. A dark little man in a white apron flashes gold teeth as he leads us to a large round low table surrounded by upholstered chairs. Even before we are seated, the tea arrives – traditional Algerian tea with mint, lemon and sugar. The children are thrilled to be served their own special tea, in fancy glass mugs just like the adults.

When the children become bored, Mohamed G suggests a beautiful walk to the sea. We exit the teahouse through a different door and find ourselves on a high flat plateau overlooking the city. Mohamed G heads for the edge of the precipice, and we follow him, discovering hundreds of steps cut into white rock, and winding down and around homes and businesses. We step our way down, down, down to the sea, where we find five little restaurants carved out of the very same white rock. Each restaurant overlooks the sea, colourfully decorated with shells and brightly coloured signs. Mohamed G tells Zohra to choose the restaurant she wants us to visit. Zohra, enchanted by this task, finally picks the one in the middle, which has a huge fish tank in the window. Mohamed G nods his approval and leads us through the door. We are seated at a large round beautifully-tiled table, which holds our party of twelve. Rashida, who has been struggling with the walk in her high heel shoes and tight fitting dress, plops herself down in a chair next to me and with obvious relief, kicks off her shoes.

The fish on the menu are the ones swimming in the large tank at the front door. We are led individually to the tank to select our dinner, which the waiter nets and takes directly to the kitchen. I pick a weird-looking beast with one eye and a flat body that everyone tells me is a bottom feeder. The meal begins with an appetizer of octopus in tomato sauce, our individual selections of the main course – mine is delicious – and ends with thick sweet Arabic coffee. Little Ahmed picks up the tab.

After dinner, we walk by the sea again, taking off our shoes and dipping our toes in the cool water. When the children become cranky and tired, the men carry them on their shoulders to an ice cream parlour called *Fleur du Jour*. Here we are presented with dishes of *Bomb Atomique*, each one a giant ball of ice cream full of nuts and fruit.

Mohamed G calls a taxi and we pile in with Rashida and Little Ahmed, grateful that we don't have to hike back the way we came. Rashida is suffering badly and swears she will never walk again on her swollen feet. The taxi returns us to our borrowed car, and after many good-byes, we leave for home. The children fall asleep as soon as they are in the back seat and we drive towards the outskirts of the city hoping there will be no roadblocks.

A few miles from home, as we pass the turnoff road to Baba Ali, we see men with guns alongside the road. However, no one moves to stop our car. Moe clutches the steering wheel with white-knuckled fingers.

"Bandits for certain," he mutters as he steps on the gas. We speed by them as fast as the government car will go and he doesn't slow down again until we reach Birtouta. I clutch the safety bar on the roof of the car until my hands hurt. We both sigh with relief as we turn onto the street where we live.

As we pull into the apartment parking lot, I am startled to see four people waving at us from our balcony.

"Who's that?" I ask.

"Oh, this Shakiri and his wife. I think her name Jinny." Moe manoeuvres the car into a parking place.

"Jinny?" I ask incredulously.

"Yes," Moe answers, "Jinny. Shakiri is my friend with American wife."

"Jinny?" I say again. "His American wife?" I feel my heart race. "I didn't know you had a friend with an American wife."

Moe explains, "I not mention it. I not sure her husband likes to meet with us. He is high up in oil company, SONATRACH. I think maybe they too good for us."

We make our way up the stairs, each carrying a sleepy child. I hear English – American English. It sounds strange to my ear. I haven't heard my own language for nearly two months.

"How do you do?" I say, putting Tarek on his feet, and holding out my hand to a small wisp of a girl with long brown hair and a large smile. "I'm Susie. Nice to meet you."

Jinny introduces me to her mother and her sister who are visiting from Chicago, and to her children, a boy of three and a girl of six. The children immediately run off to Zohra's bedroom to play.

Jinny explains that she, Shakiri and her family are on their way home from a vacation in Tiarat. "We heard you had arrived and thought we should stop and meet you. Your village is on our way home. We can't stay long this time. It's getting late and my husband doesn't like to travel at night, what with the bandits and such."

I make coffee and serve some sweets. "We saw some men on the highway on our way back from Algiers but they didn't stop us. Maybe you all should stay overnight with us. You are welcome," I offer.

"We'd love to," Jinny responds, "but my mother and sister have to catch a plane first thing in the morning and they still have to pack some things. I promise to come back for a longer visit in a few weeks." I silently envy Jinny being able to have her family come to visit.

When they leave, Moe explains that Jinny has a serious health problem. Moe is not sure what it is but it has something to do with her kidneys. Her mother and sister have come to help her for a while. My envy for Jinny melts away.

All the Beautiful Men

July begins hotter and more humid than June and I wake up to the noise of children playing on the ground below our balcony. I watch them for a moment and then I tiptoe off to the kitchen to make coffee, hoping I don't disturb the rest of the family. I decide to make up a batch of fresh water to have on hand for the day.

Today is the day Moe's father and brothers are coming to visit. I take my coffee to the table and decide to write to my parents. My mother's letters get more frantic every day as she tries to come to terms with the propaganda she hears on American radio and in the papers. I take out the familiar onionskin writing paper and begin.

Dear Mom and Dad,

About the car. Go ahead and sell the 2500 shares of stock and hold the money until I write for you to send it. We really need a car.

In answer to some of your questions in the last letter, let me make it clear. For heaven's sake, Mom. You don't need to worry about us leaving in a hurry or somebody taking our property. Algeria is as safe a place and even safer right now than the U.S. If you're thinking in terms of Communists, forget it. Algeria will never be, and at this point if she were, I wouldn't blame her. She is anti-US, but everybody is at this point, especially after yesterday's horrible fiasco of bombing Hanoi. Doesn't Johnson know he is playing the game the USSR wants him to play? Now they can say the US is the only aggressor in the world. It sounds like propaganda to you, but here the USSR has won a big victory without lifting a finger. All these nations recently independent, associate with the VC because they are fighting for reunification.

> People here identify with revolutions. It makes my heart sad. I
> love the U.S. I know what it is like and what the people are like
> but outside, to admit you are an American is like saying you are
> a Communist back home. It's funny but from these people's point
> of view I can see why.

I put the pen down and wonder how I got off on such a tan-
gent as politics, but my parents go on and on in their letters about
Communists in Algeria. The only Communists I know are those
who studied in Russia and have come back to Algeria brainwashed.
As Moe always points out, Communism has a difficult time in a
Moslem nation.

I pick up the pen and start again. My mother wants to know
why I have so much trouble cashing an American traveler's cheque
at an Algerian bank. She keeps telling me to go to an American
bank or to the American Embassy. Because she lived in Turkey ten
years ago, she thinks Algeria must be the same.

> By the way, giving a cheque on an American Bank isn't going to
> do a damn thing. There is one rate of exchange, period. Whether
> or not you believe it, is beside the point. There are no American
> banks here. Algeria is not in the least like Turkey. It's like living
> in France or Switzerland or any modern European country when it
> comes to money or the law. I have already been to the American
> Embassy – twice. The only people you ever see are French secre-
> taries who are polite and nice and know nothing. Don't tell me to
> stand up for my rights either. That's the way it is. Really though,
> everything is government controlled so the car prices, insurance
> rates etc. are all regulated.
>
> Well, I better get to my housework.
>
> Write soon and take care of your sweet selves.
>
> Love,
>
> Susie

Just as I finish my letter, Moe stumbles sleepily into the
room.

"You up early," he states.

"The kids downstairs woke me up so I decided to write to my
parents. It's hot, isn't it?"

"Yes, it is hot," he agrees. He shuffles off to the kitchen and returns with coffee and a piece of melon.

"I wonder what time my family arrives," Moe says as he sits down at the table with his coffee and melon. "I hope they come today but we just wait. I am excited to see them again. I see them in my first days here, but not again."

"Where will they sleep?" That question has been bothering me since Moe told me they were coming.

"Not worry. My family sleep on floor. They not mind. It is warm. They not need blankets," Moe gestures vaguely in the direction of the living room.

"Well, I guess that is easy," I say, but I wonder how it will all work out. "What do they eat?"

"I hope they are bringing some women to cook. But if not, then you know how to do some things. No?" Moe pauses and looks at me.

It is important to Moe that I entertain his family properly according to Algerian traditions.

"I can try." I tell him, knowing that there's no point letting him know that I feel nervous about cooking for my father-in-law.

Moe's family, expected to arrive on Saturday, doesn't show up until eight o'clock on Sunday evening. We are just getting the children ready for bed when there is a rap at the door. Moe hurries to see who it is and, as soon as the children hear voices, they are out of their beds looking to see what all the fuss is about.

We form a reception line just inside the doorway – Moe first, then me, then Zohra and, last, little Tarek. Abdullah, Moe's father, enters first, wearing a long flowing white robe and a white turban – the clothing of the countryside. He is short, shorter than me, and his skin is golden brown, almost bronze, glowing with good health. He has amazing dark, deep-set eyes and a wonderful sensual smiling mouth. I can't help but gasp when he kisses me on one cheek and then the other. He smiles directly into my eyes and nods as if in approval. I smile at him and then drop my eyes. I wonder if I am allowed to look at my own father-in-law.

Tahar, Moe's younger brother, comes in next. He looks much

older than Moe. The scars from when the FLN thought he was a traitor and cut his throat are visible. Luckily, he was saved by French troops. Moe says he is sometimes difficult to understand because he talks with a croaky animal sound. Tahar moves quickly to embrace his brother. Then he smiles at me and gives me the traditional cheek kisses.

Next is Abdelghani, just sixteen, who has a beautiful smile. He has the same dark Chaabane eyes as his brothers. They twinkle even when he doesn't talk. He is the tallest, long and lanky. By Algerian custom, he is not considered a man until he is eighteen, but he looks like a man to me. He speaks to me in French – and as he talks, he reaches blindly behind him as if trying to catch something.

After a few yanks, another brother appears from behind the door jam. "Djamal," Abdelghani offers, "*Djamal bebe*," indicating that Djamal is the baby of the family, a stepbrother born to Moe's father and stepmother twelve years ago. Djamal looks nothing like the Chaabane brothers. He seems very fragile and sad.

Just as I am about to close the door, another man appears. He is swathed in bandages and walking with crutches.

"Who is this?" I ask, confused. "What happened to him?"

Moe reaches out and carefully helps the injured man inside. The young man smiles weakly at me and says, "Abdel Kader," by way of introduction.

"Why is Abdel Kader covered in cuts and bruises?" I ask Moe in English, curious to know what has happened to this brother.

"He was in big car accident. That is reason they are late," Moe answers me in English, smiling and nodding at his family as he speaks.

I look at Abdel Kader and smile.

Zohra can't get enough of her *grandfodder*. The moment he enters, she takes hold of his hand. When he finally sits down, she climbs immediately onto his lap and hugs him. "My Algerian *grandfodder*," she says in English over and over.

Her Algerian *grandfodder* smiles at her and hugs her close.

"Talk to *grandfodder* in Algerian, Zohra. He not understand English," Moe says to Zohra.

Zohra looks at *grandfodder* and laughs. *Grandfodder* smiles back at her with tilted head and raised eyebrows until Zohra opens her mouth and begins to chatter in his language. His eyes grow large and round, and then fill with tears as he hears her childish words tumbling around him. He suddenly grabs her and hugs her again. It is clear how much it means to this old man to hear his grandchild speak to him in his own language.

Tarek, on the other hand, hangs on to his father tightly through all the introductions and won't go near anyone. Once everyone sits down, Abdelghani reaches out, grabs Tarek and starts to tickle him. Tarek giggles a little and then allows Abdelghani to throw him up in the air. This releases great gaffs of loud laughter. Everyone laughs at his babyish squeals and the ice is broken.

The men begin to talk among themselves and it occurs to me that perhaps I shouldn't be in the room with them. "Moe," I ask, quietly, when there is a break in the conversation. "Is it okay if I sit and talk with your father and brothers? Will I offend them by staying here?"

Moe smiles. "My father says we are your family and he know your customs are different. It is okay."

His father speaks again in Arabic, looking at me as he does.

Moe laughs and then adds, "My father says he is very modern man."

I smile, "I think he is right. He is a very modern man." I smile back at him.

Then I blurt out, "I like your father – and your brothers are very handsome."

The men all pause at my outburst and wait for Moe to translate what I have said.

Moe's look says, "What did you mean by that?" In English, he adds, laughing, "I translate the father part but I not translate the brother part." He translates and his father smiles at me.

"Their faces will be red," Moe indicates his brothers as he switches back to English, "if I say you think they very handsome." He grins at me. "Besides, I am jealous."

"I didn't mean it like that, Moe. I think your family is very beautiful."

"Yes we are," agrees Moe, laughing harder. "Yes, we are."

I listen to the men talk for a few minutes and then I ask Moe if they are hungry. He translates my question to his family and their reaction clearly tells me that it is time to cook something. I have four pieces of lamb's tail and I decide to make a stew. It takes me two hours to chop the vegetables, steam the couscous, work butter into it and simmer everything together.

I call the family to the table. When they have eaten the last morsel and licked the last bit of meat juice from their plates with bread, Moe smiles. I have done a good job. His father keeps nodding his head up and down and smiling. His brothers seem happy.

I get up to clear away the dishes. Abdullah gently touches my arm and shakes his head no. He motions me to sit down. Confused, I sit back down. I ask Moe what is going on. Moe smiles but says nothing as each brother gets up from the table and carries his own dishes to the sink.

"You are queen," Moe, says trying not to laugh. "I tell them it is your custom for men to carry dishes to sink, and if they not do this, you will think they are not men."

"You told them what?" I ask in disbelief.

"Yes, and I never before see a day when my brothers do a woman's work. I try again when we need floor scrubbed." Moe laughs at his joke on his brothers, and they smile broadly as they return to their places at the table, clearly pleased with their efforts to conform to what they think is an American custom.

Now I am the one who can hardly keep from laughing, "Moe, you are so funny."

"Yes, I am," he replies, smiling. "Moe very funny."

Once the kitchen is cleaned up, I retire to the bedroom, leaving Moe to visit with his father and brothers.

"Shall I put the children to bed?" I ask as I leave the room.

"No. Children can stay with us. They soon sleep anyway."

I wake early the next morning when I hear the apartment door open and close. I get up, dress and peer around the corner of the hallway and into the living room. Everyone is spread out on our living room floor sound asleep. Tarek is lying across Abdelghani's chest and Zohra is snuggled up next to Tahar. It is hard to tell where one body stops and another begins.

I can't help but think how my mother would have a heart attack looking at this scene. She would run around trying to be sure that everyone had his own room, a proper bed – and matching linens. I smile and shake my head. It is definitely easier to entertain relatives in this country than it is back in Tucson.

Moe is part of the sea of bodies. He has told me many times how a man and his wife never sleep together when they have guests. "It is old fashioned custom," Moe told me before his family arrived. "But it important to follow it, especially with people from the countryside."

At that point, I realize that Moe's father is not among the sleeping bodies. He must be the one I heard leaving. I wonder where he has gone.

I make coffee, cut up some bread and set out some jam for breakfast. As the water for the coffee boils, Moe tiptoes up behind me and pokes me in the ribs. I jump and turn to face him. "You scared me to death," I whisper.

"Sorry," he whispers back, grinning. "I was thinking I should kiss you, but then I remember my family is here and I not want to make myself embarrassed."

I smile at him. With all the sickness, visitors, and now family, our intimate life has been greatly restricted. I feel a surge of desire, but I push it down, knowing nothing can happen until everyone goes home and we are alone. Moe's eyes meet mine. I know he is thinking the same thing.

"You know, I very proud of you. You try very hard," Moe's voice is very soft. "My father like you very much. He thinks you are good woman."

I smile, pleased that my husband is happy with my efforts to make his family feel welcome in our home. "Thank you for telling me. I think he is a good man. He has kind eyes. I think I will get along well with your family."

"God willing, someday when we get our car, I take you to my village. That will tell the true story of who will approve and who will not. I hear from my father that some of my sisters' husbands not let them visit me any more because I am married to infidel. So, we will see."

"Infidel? What's an infidel?" The mood is broken. These men here in the apartment are only a small part of Moe's large extended family. My triumph is not complete, by any means.

"It is name we have for non-Moslems. Some very religious people in my village think the world is only for Moslems and the rest of people are evil. I think someday it will be big problem in my country."

Moe and I hear the outside door open and watch as Abdullah re-enters the apartment. He is carrying a large yellow plastic cup and a small towel. Moe greets his father and we watch him return the cup and towel to his small suitcase by the door.

"What is he doing with that cup?" I ask, without thinking.

Moe looks at me and his look tells me that I should know why his father had the cup with him.

"No, really. Why did he get up and go outside so early? Is he sick or something?" I press Moe to help me understand.

"No, of course not," Moe tells me. "He went to do bathroom things."

"Bathroom things?" I ask.

"Yes. My father not like western bathroom. He too embarrassed to use our modern toilet because people hear him. In his village, he has bathroom but it is just a hole. It has tiles in it but it is just hole." He shakes his head. "It is very strange to speak about my father's bathroom things."

"Okay. I just wondered." But, I can't get the yellow cup out of my head and I try one more question. "Sorry, Moe. I need to know how this cup thing works."

Moe looks at me again and I feel like he wants to tell me to forget it, but he patiently explains. "He use the cup to fill with water and when he finish – he wash his parts with the water. He has a special towel to dry."

As Moe speaks, I see it clearly in my mind. "Okay, thanks for telling me. I promise not to ask any more questions."

Moe laughs at me and as he does, his brother Tahar appears in the kitchen. He is embarrassed when he sees us laughing together.

He says something to Moe and Moe tells me Tahar needs a towel. Tahar has no problem using our western toilet and his habits seem to be the same as ours. I ask Moe why his brothers would be so different from his father and he tells me his brothers are more modern and that most of them have western plumbing in their homes. He tells me that Tahar has a very nice house and he drives a taxi for a living. He is well off for living in the countryside. Moe also explains that his father and brothers drove to visit us in Tahar's taxi.

The day has already been planned. Moe's father wants to take us swimming in the sea.

As we get into the car, Moe talks with his father, both of them looking at me. His brothers listen intently. When the conversation ends, Moe looks at me and announces in a very serious voice, "My father says you don't have to wear a veil in Algiers. But, he says you can't swim with us in a bathing suit." Moe can hardly keep from laughing as he makes this announcement, though I can tell he is trying to be serious and authoritative.

When he is finished with his speech, I laugh.

"Why you laugh?" Moe demands.

"I am laughing because you are funny. You can hardly keep from laughing. Tell your father that I am happy he doesn't want me to wear a veil in Algiers because I don't own one and even if I wanted to wear a bathing suit, I can't because I don't own one of those either. Guess that makes us all happy." I laugh again.

Moe translates. It takes his brothers about five minutes to stop laughing. Finally, Moe explains, "My brothers think you are great comedienne. I think they like you very much."

I smile at all of them.

We all crowd into Tahar's funny old taxi, which has extra seats that fold down. It is a tight squeeze. The children sit on laps.

Moe, sitting beside me, leans over and whispers in my ear. "It is good we are like sardines in a can and cannot move."

"What do you mean?" I ask, puzzled.

"You know soon enough," Moe answers.

Moe is right. Soon enough, I discover that Tahar doesn't believe in speed limits nor in slowing down for around corners. I put my head down in my lap for most of the trip. My son, obviously braver than his mother, spends the entire trip shouting, "Whee," which seems to act as a stimulus for Tahar to drive even faster. The men laugh and laugh.

Fifteen minutes into the trip Tahar turns off the main highway to Algiers and heads down a narrow gravel road, which he assures us is the way to a quiet little beach that he discovered as a young man. He says it will be a good place to go swimming in the sea.

When I get the courage to look up, the beauty of the countryside and sea together takes my mind off the wild ride. Then, without warning, Tahar drives down a steep gravel embankment, crosses some sand and then bumps over a concrete curb. We come to rest in an asphalt parking lot. After Tahar's description of the isolation of the place, I am startled to see many late model foreign cars, change rooms and various concessions scattered here and there on the beach. Small groups of people in bathing suits accompanied by small children sit in clumps along the sand.

Tahar sputters something and the men all laugh. Moe laughingly explains that Tahar says that the beach has changed since he was a teenager.

Nonetheless, the brothers decide it is a good place to stay. Tahar parks the car and we all troop to an open place on the beach. Moe spreads a blanket and I sit down.

Moe's father unrolls his turban, and drops it near the edge of the blanket. Then, he removes his long white robe under which he is wearing long balloon-style pants and a gray-white shirt that looks like it has never been washed. He strips off these inside clothes and tosses them onto the sand, revealing a small pair of brightly coloured swimming trunks.

He turns to catch me staring at him. Abruptly, he turns and runs as fast as he can for the water. I am surprised. He made no attempt to hide himself as he undressed.

"I think you embarrass my father by staring at him," Moe says with a smile in his voice.

"I'm sorry. I didn't mean to embarrass him. He surprised me

by stripping like that right here on the beach. Why didn't he go into the change room?"

"You forget my father is from countryside. He not understand there is hut for changing."

While we talk, Moe helps Zohra out of her clothes and into her bathing suit. I can tell she likes the feel of this silky suit because she keeps rubbing her hands against her hips and tummy.

"ZsaZsa is pretty today," she says over and over in English.

Tahar asks Moe what she is saying. Zohra translates for herself. All of her uncles laugh loudly and begin to chatter to her in Arabic. Suddenly, I am overwhelmed by both sadness and jealousy. I feel like an outsider because I don't know even one of the commonly-spoken languages. Yet, my three-year-old daughter is already fluent in three languages. She chatters to the Ducont children in French and to her uncles in Arabic – and to me in English.

The minute Tahar is changed, he takes Zohra by the hand and leads her to the water. She puts her toe in and then, suddenly, a large wave rushes at her. She screams. Tahar tries to talk her into going with him further into the water but she only stamps her little feet and yells louder. He leads her back to me. There, he drops down on his knees and begins to dig a hole. Zohra watches warily and then crawls up to it and tries to help him. When he decides that the hole is big enough, he pulls an old piece of blanket out of his pile of belongings and lines the hole. Then, going to the edge of the water he fills a bucket he has brought with him. He carries the water back and pours it into the hole. Tahar carries water until his new little pool is full. He then takes Zohra gently by her hand and helps her climb into the makeshift pool.

She looks at me proudly and declares, "ZsaZsa swim now." She splashes in the little pool for a few minutes, but she is soon bored. She points to the sea and Tahar grabs her up and carries her to the water, laughing.

Moe tries to get Tarek to go into the small hole. Tarek will have nothing to do with it. He clutches his father as if the end is near. When any of his uncles try to pick him up, he wails as if his heart will break. Eventually, they give up trying to coax him away and leave Moe, Tarek and me on the blanket.

Moe looks longingly at the sea. He tells Tarek, "Daddy going to swim. You stay here with Mommy." Moe unhooks Tarek's little hands from his shirt. Then Moe strips down to his bathing trunks and runs to join the others.

 Belonging

"It's okay, Tarek," I tell him softly. "Sit here on the sand and play with your trucks." I pull a small truck out of my bag and offer it to him.

He looks at me with his big brown eyes, and says, "Talek hot."

"It is hot, isn't it? Maybe we should go and see if we can find something to drink or an umbrella or some shade," I mutter half to him and half to myself. I get up and take Tarek by the hand.

We only walk a short distance before I see Abdelghani running towards me from the sea waving his arms, clearly wanting me to stop. I wait for him to reach me. He rushes up breathless, and picks up Tarek. He motions me back to the place where I had been sitting.

I try to explain to him in sign language that I just want a drink or an umbrella.

He shakes his head no and points to the blanket. I go and sit down close to our belongings. Abdelghani puts his clothes on over his swimsuit, picks up Tarek and the two of them disappear over a sand hill.

I wait, getting hotter by the minute, and feeling more and more angry at being told to sit and wait. I can see Moe floating luxuriously on his back in the cool water. "Must be nice," I mutter. "When they come back, they will find me dead from heat stroke. Then, they'll be sorry." I chuckle at my own over-reaction. But I still feel left out, hot and angry.

My frustration mounts until I am about to scream for Moe. I glance at the water to locate him in the sea only to have my line of sight blocked by a group of four women, each with long blond hair and long lean bodies walking up the sand in colourful bikinis, laughing and kicking sand at each other playfully. One of the women is older than the others – they must be a mother and her teenage daughters.

Then I hear the tallest of the group say, "Mom, if you don't decide to sit down soon I'm going to fall down. Pick a place. Put your stuff down and let's swim."

I stare, open-mouthed, my brain slowly registering that these young women are speaking English. They are American.

They pass me, not more than three feet away. I call out, "Hello. Are you American?"

They stop. The older woman comes forward, smiling. "Why yes, we are." She looks at me for a few moments and then asks, "Are you?"

I smile. "Yes, I am." I get up. "I am surprised to find Americans out here."

"So are we," she responds. She introduces herself and her daughters. "I am Margaret and these are my daughters, Lucy, Sally, and Jane." The girls come forward and shake hands with me. "Nice to meet you," they tell me.

Margaret plops herself down and the girls run off down to the water. She glances curiously at all the belongings piled up beside me. "Are you alone?" she asks.

"No, I am here with my husband and his relatives," I tell her.

"Oh. How long have you been in Algeria?"

"Two and a half months," I tell her. "What about you?"

"We have lived here for seven years," she answers. She sits down on the blanket, glances at her daughters playing in the surf, and settles in for a chat.

"Seven years?" I ask in disbelief.

"Yes, my husband works in the oil fields in the Sahara. He travels a lot."

"But I thought Algeria was at war at that time."

"Oh, it was. But nobody ever bothered us. During the war we lived in a small village near my husband's work."

Abdelghani appears bearing a large umbrella. He comes up behind me and pushes the long handle of the umbrella into the sand in such a way that it casts a slice of shade over the spot where Margaret and I are sitting.

I smile over my shoulder at Abdelghani. "*Merci*," I say in French.

"*Gazooze*," he smiles again, and indicates by gestures that he will go and bring some pop.

Tarek runs up to me and throws his little arms around me, saying, "Talek love mommy."

"Mommy loves Tarek," I answer. I hug him and send him off with his uncle.

As I turn back to talk to Margaret, I see she is frowning. Before I can say anything, she gathers up her things and stands.

"You are welcome to sit here," I tell her, confused at the sudden change in her manner.

"No," she says abruptly. "I can see you are busy with your *family*." Her emphasis on family is harsh and she sounds disgusted. She turns without further explanation and heads for a place farther down the beach.

I want to go after her. But I don't.

Shortly after that, Moe and his brothers return. They dress quickly. I try not to watch. Abdelghani brings *gazooze* for everyone and I gratefully down mine in one gulp. They discuss where we should go next, Moe translating the conversation for me so I can follow it.

Still disturbed by Margaret's sudden departure, I tell Moe what happened.

He listens carefully. He shakes his head sadly and gently brushes his fingers against my cheek, saying, "I know what you feel. I feel same when my brother-in-law tell me my sister not visit me because I marry you. There are stupid people everywhere."

We pile back into the taxi and Tahar drives into Algiers. He stops in front of a restaurant that looks more European than Algerian. Almost every table is packed with people in suits and western dress. Tahar speaks to the *maitre'd* in Arabic, but he doesn't seem to understand. Abdelghani steps forward and speaks to him in French. A few moments later, we are led to a large table. People stare. They are obviously shocked to see an American woman with six dark men, one in traditional dress.

After lunch, and a short stop at a department store, Abdullah hands me a package, smiling.

"It is gift," Moe says, "Open now."

I find a set of stainless steel knives and forks.

I smile my thank you and he smiles back.

At an open market we buy groceries for the next day. We arrive back at the apartment in the early evening. The next day, Moe and his family go to Algiers to visit Mohamed G and Big Ahmed who are entertaining Ahmed's brother, home for a visit from Egypt. Moe has known Ahmed's brother since childhood.

I know it can be a bother to keep translating for me. I tell Moe I want to keep the children today. He can go visiting alone with his family.

Three important things occur before the family leaves. First, Moe's father gives us $100,000 Francs, which Moe explains to me is about $200, towards buying a car. His father insists we take it and use it for the tax, insurance and license.

"My father insists we have a car so we can go to Mascara and visit the rest of the family. "I feel guilty to take this money from my father. He supports many of my brothers, but he insist I use this for my car."

Second, the men decide to leave Abdelghani with Moe and me until school starts again in the fall. The plan is that Abdelghani will teach me French and Arabic, and I will teach him English. Moe is happy, saying it will give him a chance to get to know his little brother again after so many years away from him. I am not sure what a teenage boy will do all day around the small apartment, but I say nothing.

The third thing happens the day before the family leaves. In the morning, Moe asks me to wash the men's shirts. "We go to public bath today. They need clean clothes."

I chuckle to myself. "No wonder they don't have much baggage. They come for a week and they each only bring one shirt." I must be getting used to this country. The body smells no longer make me feel nauseous. In fact, I barely notice the thick musky smell of unwashed bodies and garlic that is particularly strong in crowds and even at gatherings of Moe's friends. I am learning that people only bathe once in a while here – when they have money or time to go to the public baths.

"Nobody takes as many baths as Americans do," Moe tells me. Yet, I squeeze into our laundry tub nearly every day. I can't stand to go for more than a few days without a bath.

Moe always laughs at me. I know he washes himself by taking spit baths in the tub, but I also know he goes to the public baths in Birtouta whenever he can. I ask him why he doesn't take me to the baths.

He shrugs, muttering that it is too much trouble to take a foreign woman to the public bath in Birtouta. "The baths are separate and you not know what to do," he explains. He promises me that someday he will take me to the public baths near his village of Mascara. "They have world famous hot springs and a bath for men and women and families together."

"Another occasion for me to be a willow," I think.

When the men leave for the baths, I wash the shirts that belong to the younger men in the little laundry tub and hang them to dry. However, my father-in-law's pyjama-looking top is a large ugly grey-white shirt that hangs to his knees. I wonder if it has ever been washed. When I hold the shirt away from me, the spills almost look like a colourful design deliberately painted there.

To start with, I get out my washboard and wash brush and scrub the shirt as hard as I can. After scrubbing for twenty minutes with little success, I open a container of bleach, pour it into a bucket, add the shirt and sit back to see what it will do. Half an hour later, I pull the shirt out. It is not perfect, but, at least, it is much improved. I rinse it thoroughly and hang it on the balcony to dry. In the heat of the noonday sun, the clothing dries quickly. I get out the iron that Moe gave me and iron all of the shirts. I hang them on hangers in the front room closet.

In the late afternoon the men and the children return, all fresh and clean-smelling, and the men looking for their shirts.

From the kitchen, I hear loud exclamations from my father-in-law. *"La la,"* he says several times. I know that *la* means *no* in Arabic. I step into the hall to see what is going on.

Moe looks at me and says, smiling broadly, "My father not believe this his shirt."

"Well, it's definitely not mine." I joke.

"I know that," Moe grins. "He wants to know how you do this."

"What do you mean, 'how I did it?' I washed it, bleached it, ironed it and hung it up."

Moe looks at me smiling even more broadly than before. "He knows that. He say no one ever iron a shirt for him in his whole life. He is so happy you do that."

"Tell him – of course I wash and iron shirts for him and his sons. They are my family –"

As Moe translates what I have said, I watch Abdullah. His old eyes fill with tears.

He mumbles something to Moe.

Moe smiles as he translates, "He thinks you are a very good woman."

I smile and Abdullah kisses me on each cheek, smiling and nodding.

Later, Abdelghani watches almost mournfully as his father and brothers leave. I wonder if staying behind is his idea or his father's.

On July 13, Moe signs the papers to start the process of buying a car. He discovers that buying a car means several rounds of filling out forms and signing documents, all of them many pages long.

First, we have to file a request to buy a vehicle. Once signed, the papers go to a government tax office where Moe's personal information is investigated to determine if he owes any back taxes. The tax office sends their approval to the Renault dealership. Then, the actual paperwork to order the car begins. The salesman at the Renault office says it will be at least August or even September before we actually have a vehicle. We don't have the option of buying from another dealer, as Renault is the only carmaker in the country that allows customers to put down half the money and pay the rest by the month. Any other carmaker requires the full amount up front and is more expensive. We just have to wait.

The car will be a Renault R-4 family sedan that gets fifty miles to the gallon, or so claims the English version of the advertising brochure. If we lived in France, the Renault would cost $1,100.00, but because of a ridiculous import tax, we pay $1800.00 – and we have to pay for insurance, title, tax, and a lock for the gas tank.

I write to my parents and tell them to sell the mining stock that my great aunt left me and put the money in the bank. If they do that right away, it will be available when we actually have to pay for the car.

Abdelghani spends most of his time playing with Zohra and Tarek, which frees me to do housework and write letters. I feel less lonely. Moe returns to work and is gone from early morning until late in the evening. Abdelghani and I spend a few hours each day with his English school books and I do my best to help him read and understand what they say. I teach him English words and he teaches me French words. After just a week of basic lessons, we start to understand each other a little.

Early one morning I overhear Moe and his brother having a heated conversation. Their voices get loud and they yell back and forth at each other. Abdelghani abruptly stops talking when I enter the room.

"What's wrong?" I ask Moe. "Shouldn't you be going to work?"

"I go now, but my little brother keeps me here to make argument," he answers, curling his lip under like he doesn't know whether to be mad or laugh. "He wants you to wear veil in the village."

This revelation surprises me. "Why? I've never worn a veil before. You take me shopping in the village without one all the time."

"Yes, I know and I tell him that. I also tell him you not own one. He says I must buy you one."

"So, what is he afraid of?"

"He afraid people say bad things about you."

"I go by myself sometimes and nobody bothers me. Mostly, people are nice to me."

Moe looks at me with a sad little grin and then bitterly explains, "Well, you think they nice but you not know what they say. So far, I never hear any bad thing, but people give me respect so maybe they say nothing to my face. With my little brother, they not afraid. You go and see what happen. Abdelghani will tell me if there is problem."

Moe leaves for work and I dress the children for our outing in the village. Zohra has a new summer dress and yellow shoes freshly arrived from my mother so I put them on her and she dances around the room, singing, "Happy Birthday to Mi-Mi and Papa. Happy Birthday to you."

When I open the front door the HLM children crowd around the door, even more closely than usual, as if they were just waiting for us to make our exit. It is impossible for us to get down the stairs.

Abdelghani shouts at them. Some of the children run off and the others back away to let us through. Abdelghani shakes his head disgustedly, picks up Tarek and walks quickly down the stairs.

I run to catch up to him. Abdelghani deliberately walks too fast for me, and Zohra and I have to run to stay close to him, the HLM children strung out behind us like a parade. As we leave the apartment house grounds, the HLM children stop at the edge of the property as if an invisible wall at the edge of the parking lot prevents them from coming any further. They turn back reluctantly. Zohra and I are soon so out of breath that we give up trying to catch Abdelghani. We slow down and continue at our own pace.

Zohra is relieved. "Mommy," she asks. "Why doesn't uncle want to walk with us? He's a brat, huh."

I smile. "Yes, honey. He is definitely a brat today."

We make our way to the little open stalls that serve as the local market. Abdelghani has disappeared. I stop and look at the vegetables. I talk to the man in my usual mixture of French and hand signals about the price of his lettuce and carrots. As I am about to pay for what I bought, Abdelghani appears and says something to the man.

The man smiles and nods.

Abdelghani turns to me and says in English, "Pay too much."

He steps up and takes some of the money from my hand and pays the man, handing the rest of the coins back to me.

The man speaks in Arabic to Abdelghani, a short burst of speech that, to me, sounds abrupt and harsh.

The blood drains out of Abdelghani's face.

"What's wrong?" I ask in English, even though I think he won't understand.

Abdelghani just shakes his head and says nothing.

Zohra and I move on to the meat market, which is located inside a building with an abattoir in the back. Several animal hides hang in the middle of the shop along with the carcasses of several freshly killed animals. The strong smell in this store always catches me off guard.

The villagers seem to know when there will be a kill and they line up to buy a piece of it as soon as it is dead. Today, however, there is no line. I am relieved when the butcher reaches inside a small refrigerator to get the piece of lamb I request. There are days when the butcher simply steps up to a hanging carcass and cuts off whatever I ask for.

While the butcher wraps my meat, I watch Abdelghani and Tarek through the window. A street vendor approaches him and he buys two sweets. Tarek always loves the sticky, fried, multi-armed, honey-dipped treat this vendor sells and reaches out greedily.

I think, "He will be so sticky and dirty after eating that."

The bell in the meat shop tinkles loudly and Abdelghani steps inside to give Zohra her sweet.

The butcher looks at him and says something. Abdelghani frowns and looks at me and says something back to the butcher who looks embarrassed and hands me my package.

Zohra looks at the butcher and barks something in Arabic at him.

Abdelghani grabs her hand and pulls her out of the shop without smiling.

I decide not to ask what is going on. I will find out later.

From the meat market we go to the post office where I mail two letters: One to my parents and one to my uncle Marshall. I indicate to Abdelghani that I want to go to the pharmacy and he nods, frowning and squinting his eyes.

Intuitively, I know that he would rather we head home, but he doesn't say anything.

I look at my children who, after eating their sticky treat, look like a couple of the HLM children. Honey drips down their fronts and, with the dust of the day, they look like they fit with the village children. I have to get over my obsession with keeping them clean.

We step inside the pharmacy and there is a long line up. I take my place at the back of the line but the pharmacist shouts out something and the men in front of me turn and stare at me. Then, silently, and as if in rehearsal for some mysterious dance, they step aside in unison. It reminds me of my experience at the airport where Moe's cousin ordered the line of men to let me go first. Moe explained that this way the uncovered woman would be out of their sight sooner if she was served first.

A few of them indicate with little waves that I should move to the head of the line. The pharmacist talks to me in French and asks what I want. I step forward meekly, careful not to look at the men in line. I hand over one of Moe's prescriptions. I also ask for Tampax. How strange it is that in this little tiny village thirty-six miles south of Algiers, I can't buy toilet paper or Kleenex. However, I can buy Tampax. Benita told me about the Tampax. She said she was rummaging around in the pharmacy one day and came across boxes of Tampax. The pharmacist told her it was left over from the days of the French occupation and the locals don't buy it because they don't know what it is for, and if they did know, they would be horrified. I can't help but wonder how long it will be before Benita and I use up all the Tampax and have to start using rags like the local women.

Benita also told me that the pharmacist has an interesting history. He is from one of the Eastern European countries and has lived in this village for at least forty years. He lives in one of the smaller villas on the outskirts of town and has an Algerian Moslem wife and many children. According to Benita, everyone leaves them alone. When his children reach grade six, he sends them to France to be educated and no one ever sees them again.

Within two minutes the pharmacist has my order ready and wrapped in newspaper. I am glad to get away from the silent staring men.

When I tell Abdelghani that we are going home, I can see his relief. He smiles at me for the first time since we started out. We walk home.

When we arrive back at the apartment, I put the food away and haul both kids into the bathroom to wash the dirt and the stickiness off their faces and change their clothes. As I am running the water, I hear the apartment door open and close and realize that Abdelghani has gone out. I wonder where he is going.

I put the children down for a nap and the afternoon passes quickly. I write to my parents and babble on about politics and how much I hate President Johnson and the war in Viet Nam. I miss them. Moe returns home at 7:00 p.m. and greets his children with a tickling session and kisses. I am in the kitchen when he enters and asks me where Abdelghani is.

"I don't know. We went to the village and I did some shopping. He looked pretty unhappy for most of our walk but he didn't say anything much. He looked grumpy when we came back and then he left."

"I go look for him after dinner. Maybe somebody say something bad."

Zohra immediately pipes up with, "That meat man is not very nice to uncle. He said a bad word."

Just as Moe is about to ask Zohra what the word was, Abdelghani knocks on the door and Moe lets him in. They talk quietly for a few minutes and then Moe tells me that Abdelghani has to leave in a few days. He got a scholarship notice in the mail in Mascara and was talking to his father on the phone today. They want him to take some more tests so he is going home to do that.

"He also says he not go with you to the village again. People call you bad names."

"What kinds of names?" I ask surprised and a little disappointed.

"Just names. You understand I don't care but Abdelghani is young and he want to fight these people. He says you should wear veil." Moe laughs when he says this. "Don't worry," he adds. "I am your husband, not him."

"I'll wear one if you want me to," I offer.

"Not now. But some time you have to. I think if I take you to my father's village you must borrow one. They are very conservative there and my family has to live with these fanatics. I not want to cause them trouble."

I look at Moe and smile. "It's okay. Just tell me what to do and I will do it."

Moe smiles at me and touches my cheek. "Thank you. You try so much. You are doing good job.

"Please excuse my brother," Moe continues. "He is confused. He very young when our mother die. He is taught one thing in school and he is taught another thing by the village fanatics. He get mixed up sometimes."

"I know," I say, "I think your little brother is wonderful. He is helpful and respectful and I like him very much."

"Yes, and he likes you very much too. I watch him watch you. I not like to say this but I think it is the real reason he wants to leave. I think he wants to use his penis on you."

Shocked and mortified, I blurt out. "You are terrible, Moe! I don't think of your brother like that. He's your brother so he's my brother. Why do you say things like that?"

"Maybe he my brother," Moe says in a matter-of-fact tone. "But he still have penis."

In Moe's face, I see seriousness, but also humour. I turn away and shake my head.

"It okay. He is very young and he not ask you anything. But I think it best he go home."

"Okay, Moe. Whatever you say," I realize that I have no choice in the matter, but I still say, "He has helped me a lot with the kids, with French, with housework. No matter what you say, I like him as a brother. He will always be my friend."

Moe smiles at me and leaves the room to talk to his brother.

# The Politics of Employment

On Sunday, July 17, Moe and the kids take Abdelghani to the train. I am sad Abdelghani is leaving and I tell him that in my broken French. He looks at me with embarrassment, kisses my cheeks, and head down, slinks out of the apartment.

"I go to train and then I go to Baba Ali for oranges and milk. I come back in afternoon," Moe announces as he closes the door.

Happy to have some time to myself, I settle down to spend the afternoon writing to my parents and knitting a sweater vest that Moe can wear with his suit. I bought the yarn on a trip to Algiers with Benita and I have been hiding it from Moe. The yarn is soft blue wool from England. Having a project when he is away makes the time go faster.

In my letter to my parents I tell them that we now have all but one of the papers we need to buy the car. The missing document is the one that says we owe no taxes. It has to come from Moussa where Moe was born and it seems to be taking forever for it to be sent. I also tell them that we have finally opened what passes for a bank account. It is a postal account, an account through the post office where you can deposit money. It is supposed to be safer than the regular banks.

The last thing I tell my parents is that Moe is leaving on Wednesday for a mission, which means he is going on an inspection tour of a few nationalized farms in the south. He won't be back until Saturday night. The best part is that Moe says he will be paid a double salary for the trip. I don't tell my parents that I hate being alone for such a long period of time. Neither do I say anything to Moe because I know he has to go. But, I find it lonely and sometimes scary. What if one of the kids gets sick or hurt? I have no way to get in touch with anyone in an emergency. I only hope nothing ever happens.

Moe returns with the children just before dinner. We feed them, put them to bed and curl up together on our mattress. For some reason, Moe is anxious to talk tonight. "Big things happen with job," he says. "I try to work with French but very difficult." He shakes his head, and then pauses. "Now I have big trouble. They not respect me or other workers. They swear at us and call us names. Now it is so bad the workers refuse to do work for French. French tell me to fix this problem. They order me to tell workers what to do. I am too mad to help French."

"What are the French doing that is so bad?" I ask. He tells me so little about what happens at work.

"The French, they sabotage farm. You not believe. I plant research plot and French come and plant over me. They tell me, *Sorry, your plants not important.* They sabotage electrical irrigation system so my plants not have water at proper times."

Once he starts telling me what is happening, the words spill out. He continues, "Two times now I have to stop workers from attacking French because workers know what is going on. I have nervous tension from all this stupid behaviour. I talk to my friends in other places and they have same issues."

He shakes his head, and is silent for a long time. I think that he has decided not to tell me any more when he starts to speak again. "I talk to Mohamed G, my journalist friend, and he is starting to write articles about this. I think I must go meet the big Minister. This whole stupid thing not right."

He looks at me as if he has just remembered that I am there. "I think I look for other job or I be soon crazy."

I hug him. It is all I can do to comfort him. He turns away from me, lost in his own thoughts.

The next morning Moe leaves for his mission to Bone, a city on the Tunisian border, with Claude. Moe's relationship with Claude is strained, but of all the French directors, he gets along the best with him. They have common interests, as Claude is an expert in Animal Science and Moe in forages. Moe tells me he thinks Claude is nice to him because I am the only person his wife can talk to in Birtouta.

Benita is no happier to have her husband away than I am. While Moe and Claude are gone, Benita picks me and the children up every day so we can get out of the apartment. We talk and read while the children play. We avoid talking about our husbands. I don't know what to say to her. We live such different lives.

Zohra hates it when Moe goes away for more than a day. She always gets naughty. One morning, I go into her room to get her ready for the day and discover she has written all over the walls with lipstick. Later the same day, she drops yogurt on the neighbour's balcony below ours and then slaps Tarek across the face, yelling, "Bad Beadies. Bad Beadies." I'll be happy when Moe gets home. She never acts like this when he is around.

Moe returns from his mission a day earlier than expected. "Isn't it small planet? Head of the Bone Experiment Station got degree at the University of Arizona just a few years before Moe," Moe says to me, smiling. "This Bone Station is run only with Algerians and has no problems and nobody to complicate affairs. The Station Director invite me to come and work there in September. I also learn Baba Ali is having two new Algerian Agricultural Engineers, a man and his wife. I am so happy to get this news. Now I have company."

Relieved to find out that Moe is in a good mood, I excitedly unwrap the several newspaper-wrapped gifts that he brought me, only to discover a six-pound leg of lamb and five melons. I smile at how practical he is.

Our lives are accented by hot stuffy days, a shortage of water, ongoing electrical problems and a constant string of uninvited guests. Because there are few phones in this country, people appear on our doorstep without warning. Part of the culture is to extend hospitality to all friends and travelers. However, it is not only friends or travelers that appear at our door.

Yesterday, a man who lives down the hall dropped in just as we were about to eat. Moe invited him to eat with us. Politeness on our part required that we invite him to join us, and politeness on his part demanded that he accept our invitation.

In the afternoon, a friend of Moe's, whom he hasn't seen in six years, stopped by for a visit. He is home after finishing his studies in Yugoslavia. He ate supper and stayed overnight with us. Luckily, people who arrive so unexpectedly usually have low expectations as to what they will be served. This friend got scrambled eggs and canned corned beef.

Today, at noon, another friend of Moe's who studies at Cairo University arrived on a special training mission and ate with us. He got Spanish rice and *gazoose*.

Sometimes we feed people for political reasons. A week ago Moe arrived home with a scruffy and very smelly character that he introduced as the electrician. This electrician has no formal training but gained his knowledge from experimenting on the houses of his relatives throughout the years. He is not only the best, but he is the only electrician in the area. I held my breath when he entered the house and hoped the small white nits that clung to his hair would stay on his head.

Moe instructed me to fix the best meal possible. While I cooked dinner, the man rewired our living room so we could have an overhead light, and he fixed all the plugs that weren't working. I made a lamb stew with couscous. When the man was done, he and Moe ate at the table. I ate in the kitchen with the children. When he left, Moe came out to the kitchen and announced that the electrician wouldn't accept money for his work, but would come back to do our wiring whenever we wanted him. He told Moe we are good people and respect him for his manhood, not his wealth. A lot of things work like that here.

The days pass. Moe works long days and returns home full of frustration. He keeps saying things like "Let's buy a car first and then tickets."

I ask, "What tickets?"

He says, "Tickets for Arizona."

When I press him further and ask if he really means that he wants to leave Algeria, he just says, "Not really."

But, his eyes are sad. I don't think he is telling me everything that is going on at Baba Ali.

Some days, when it is particularly hot, I sit on the balcony with my children to keep cool. I listen to the sounds of the village and the sounds of life from other apartments. I hear the laughter of women and the crying of babies. On occasion, when I gaze out over the unplanted fields behind the apartment building, I see some of the village women collecting wild grains in their colourful skirts, laughing, chatting and nursing, their babies at their breasts, tied there by old rags. I wonder at how strong these women are and how they manage to do so many things at once. Something in the way they work always gives me hope. I want so much to speak to them, but I don't know enough of their language.

Yet, I feel we share a secret. Every afternoon, when the weather permits, when all the men are at work or asleep, the women sneak out of their houses and come to this place below my balcony to gather wheat grains and greens that grow wild there to supplement their evening meals. Here, they remove their cumbersome white veils. They share the company of other women with whom they can laugh. They let the wind blow free against their faces. I envy them their friendships and the wind. I begin to think that my apartment is my veil.

July is also the worst month for water problems. Moe comes home one day from work to let me know that the water to our *batiment* and some of the surrounding houses will be turned off for the next 24 hours. Taking baths and washing clothes is put on hold. Three days later, it is still off. We hear that the mayor of Birtouta lives in Boufarik, two kilometers away, so he doesn't really care if Birtouta has water or not. Moe contracts with numerous small boys in our apartment building to bring water from the town's central tap every day while the water to our *batiment* is off. I spend half my days answering the door to small boys with small containers, their hands out for a reward from the *Americanea*.

At the end of July, Moe gets a letter that says he has to get his Algerian driver's license before he can take possession of our car. Moe goes to Algiers but discovers that the licensing officer is on holidays for ten more days. According to the clerk Moe talks to, there is only one licensing officer in the whole city of Algiers, and that the process of licensing takes two weeks. Moe is also having difficulty getting the necessary insurance. He just mutters about bureaucracy and then resigns himself to the idea that we won't have a car until at least September.

"By the time we get the credit set up, we'll have saved enough money to pay the damn thing off," I tell Moe sarcastically.

All he answers is "*C'est la vie*," and walks away, dejected. These days he takes everything seriously. Most nights, he eats his supper and if there are no visitors to distract him, he goes to bed.

On August 1, I write to my parents.

Dear Mom and Dad.

Here I am again. I have no particular reason to write other than I'm in the mood. I just put the kids to bed. Moe is still at work (It's 8:00 p.m.). Monsieur Shelig is conducting another of his "inspections" so Moe had to go with him to look at sheep, of all things. Monsieur Shelig is the big man, the Director of all the socialized farms in Algeria and head of all research.

In case you are wondering what the weird-looking thing is that I enclose, it is an iris. I was so excited to show you how beautiful they are, but after I pressed it, I found the color had changed. It is not so pretty any more. These irises grow wild on Baba Ali. The real color is yellow – flecked with bright orange.

Well, the fruit season is really upon us now. My kitchen looks like a fruit stand. The other day we took the kids to a different farm near here (The Baba Ali Annex) and we walked through the vineyards. The workers picked us the best of the grapes. In front of me I have 20 pounds of grapes. Moe is teaching me how to cook with these. For dinner, we had hot couscous with fresh butter and sugar with grapes mixed up in. Yummy.

I have been hearing reports here of a black revolution in the States. Keep me posted. We do hear some pretty bad reports about what is going on.

Well, write me when you can. I am unbelievably homesick. I dream I can taste hamburgers and milk shakes, see big cars and clean healthy children without sores and lice. I imagine I can drink out of the tap, take a bath in a bath tub, watch TV, go outside without being stared at, say hi to my neighbour in English, hire a babysitter, go out alone with my husband, read a street sign or a magazine, eat chicken fried in shortening (no shortening here) – and I long for Mama's tuna fish sandwiches. Anyway, there are advantages here, too, but I miss the familiar.

Love to you both,

SUDIE

P.S. We have running water again. Saints be praised.

I carefully fold the letter in half and slip it into an envelope. I wonder what my mother will think of my paragraph about being homesick. I am surprised by it myself. Tears trickle down my face.

I imagine a willow and stop the tears.

A few days later Moe arrives home, and immediately launches into another rant about his job situation. "They are now sending three Frenchmen to France to buy 50 goats with the Algerian government's money! The goats they are going to buy are the same variety the Algerians already have in the Sahara Region!"

I ask, "Moe, have you told your boss about this?"

Moe says, "Yes." He pulls at his hair. "But all the boss say is that he knows it is terrible – but the goats are already paid for." Moe shakes his head. "I wonder if this stupidity and corruption will ever stop," he adds softly.

I wonder at the same time how much more Moe can take.

The next morning Benita walks with me to the police office in Birtouta. I have been notified that the paperwork for my permanent visa has been completed and I can pick it up. The children don't need visas. They belong to their father and are considered citizens.

We walk slowly because she is far along in her pregnancy. I am grateful to have Benita with me. She can translate for me if I run into difficulty. We walk into the dilapidated, bombed-out government building in the centre of Birtouta. I am immediately told I am not eligible for a permanent visa until I have been in Algeria for a whole year. They can only renew my *carte de sejour* – my temporary visa. I pay the man behind the counter the equivalent of one dollar and we leave.

As we get near the apartment on our walk back, Benita tells me that she is leaving the next day for France. Her eyes look tired and sad. "Claude insists I go back to France to live with his mother until our baby is born. Laurant has been so sick these past few weeks. So I guess it is just as well. I am not really happy about it but Claude is insistent. I will return in September. Claude tells me the houses will be finished by then."

"I – I'm sorry you are leaving," I tell her. "I will miss our outings and I know Zohra and Tarek will miss Laurant and playing in the tennis court." I smile at her and give her a hug. In my heart, I will miss having someone to talk English with. But, I won't miss her negative ideas about Arabs. I sigh as she kisses my children goodbye. At least, she will return in September.

There Must Be a Good Doctor Somewhere

I wake up with chills and a high fever. I stumble to the bathroom and look in the mirror. My face is covered in sores and my neck and glands are swollen to twice their size. I drag myself back to bed and fall asleep. Ten hours later I wake up coughing with a sore throat and an aching body.

Moe stands over me, looking worried. He offers me juice and a piece of bread. I eat a few bites but I only want to sleep. He whispers that he will stay home and take care of me.

It turns out to be a good thing he does. I can't do anything for myself for three days. On the morning of the fourth day I feel better. I am still weak but at least I can get up and I can stay awake. Moe goes back to work.

An hour after he is gone, I hear Zohra's bed creaking like there is an earthquake. I make my way to her room and find her curled up in a tight little ball shivering so hard that I worry she is having a seizure. I pick her up. I cover both of us with her blanket. She stops shaking and falls into a deep troubled sleep. I do the same. When I wake, cramped and achy from the weight of her body on mine, I carry her to the living room mattress. She barely stirs. I try to give her some water but she shakes her head and moans. We sleep on and off waiting for Moe to come home.

Tarek sits beside us on the floor and plays with his toys. From time to time, he comes and lies on top of us. "Mommy sick?" he asks and then adds, "Talek hungry boy."

I wonder if the day will ever end. Moe arrives home and finds

Zohra still sleeping and me in the kitchen, attempting to make something for Tarek to eat.

"How are you?" he asks, tiptoeing up behind me and whispering in my ear.

I give him a hug. "I feel better. But, Zohra is really sick."

Moe frowns, "This not good," he says, clearly concerned.

Three days later Zohra is still sick and is getting worse. Her fever returns and her sleep is broken by cries of pain. I rub her down with cool water, which brings her fever down a little. But, it goes right back up when I stop bathing her. I try to give her as much liquid as I can but she refuses everything. At the end of the fourth day, I know we have to find a doctor.

Moe sighs a long loud sigh.

"Why are you sighing? Your daughter needs to go to the doctor. We can't keep going on like this. She is really sick."

"I know she sick," Moe answers in an aggravated voice. "I know she sick," he repeats, and then says, "You not understand. Finding doctor in this backward place difficult. But, I try."

Moe knocks on Claude's door. Claude and Benita have left for France, but Moe goes there anyway. A few minutes later, he returns. "There is French technician staying in apartment," Moe informs me. "He agree to take us to doctor in Boufarik."

"Boufarik? Isn't that the town just north of us on the highway?" I ask.

"Yes," Moe answers, "it very close. But we wait for morning. Doctors go there only in morning."

We take turns sitting with Zohra, listening to the thick grumbling inside her chest and watching as her breathing becomes more and more laboured. I find some old aspirin tablets that I brought from home and we crush them and feed them to her on a spoon. She gags. But, once we get them down her throat, she seems to rest easier. She pulls on her ears and cries out in her sleep.

At 9:00 a.m. the young Frenchman knocks on our door and asks Moe if we are ready to go. Moe wraps Zohra in a blanket and carries her to the car. I follow, dragging Tarek along.

In ten minutes the car pulls up in front of an old rundown bombed-out house. I wonder how it is still standing, let alone being used as a clinic. White veiled women sit on the stairway leading up to the clinic door, and several men sit cross-legged on the ground, smoking and chatting. When we pull up, they all stop talking, and stare.

The Frenchman instructs us to go up the stairs, open the door, and follow the signs. He drives away.

"How will we get home?" I ask Moe, surprised by the Frenchman's quick departure.

"Not worry. He says he comes back in one hour."

I sigh in relief and begin the climb to the top of the stairs, Moe carrying Zohra. I take Tarek by his hand because I don't feel strong enough to carry him today.

The women stare at us with huge round eyes. We weave our way over and around them to reach the door. Moe shakes his head, but he says nothing. I can tell he is struggling under the weight of our daughter.

As we pass by the women, each one reaches out to touch Tarek's blond curls. He sticks his tongue out at them. The women laugh loudly, their toothless mouths gaping like empty holes. I look away from them and continue climbing.

"Hurry up," Moe calls, "or these crazy women will steal our boy."

Not knowing if he is serious or joking, I jerk Tarek's little arm roughly and drag him up the last few steps.

Moe opens the door and we step onto a landing only to find ourselves at the bottom of another staircase. I take a deep breath and follow Moe who is already climbing the steps. I imagine the next door will hold another staircase, and then another...

However, once Moe reaches the door at the top, he is met by a ghostly wisp of a man with a few yellow teeth. He tells Moe that I am the one who has to bring our daughter to the woman's room to wait. He orders Moe to go and sit with the men.

Moe looks at him for a moment and then shakes his head, "No," he tells the man.

Disgusted, the old man looks at me and then at Moe. He leads us to another part of the building where he opens a door and leads us into a room. About ten chairs stand against the peeling walls on one side of the room and three rows of well-worn benches line the other. Most of the chairs are occupied by men. The old man points to an empty bench. Moe sits down abruptly on the bench, red faced.

"You look embarrassed," I state.

"No, I not embarrassed. I mad," Moe mutters. "He says you sit in other room with women but I want to see doctor so I can translate. Also, I think we talk to doctor about your sickness, too. This stupid old man have much power. He says when we get to see doctor. I think now we are waiting very long time."

"We'll wait however long it takes, Moe," I say, keeping my voice quiet even though I know that no one is likely to be able to understand what I am saying. "I just hope this is not a witch doctor."

Moe looks at me curiously. "What is witch doctor?" he asks.

"A doctor that's not really a doctor. You know, a pretend doctor. Someone who says he is a doctor but he never went to school."

"I don't think he witch doctor. The Frenchman says this doctor knows diseases in this town. He say the clinic is dirty. But the doctor is good."

Every few minutes Zohra cries out in pain. I try to sit her up to give her some water but she wants no part of either sitting or drinking. The men in the room murmur to each other every time she cries out. Some of these men are so sick they hold cups to vomit in. Others cough and spit on the floor. They stare at us, mutter to each other and frown. From time to time, the grizzled old man comes in, calls someone's name and leads that person out of the room.

Suddenly, Moe begins to talk to Zohra, not in English, but in Arabic. He doesn't care if she answers him or not. He just wants all these men to know that he understands exactly what they are saying about us. A few of the men look up, surprised. The muttering stops.

An hour later the old man finally calls to us. He leads us up more stairs to another door and tells us to go through to see the doctor. We push open the door and are surprised to find ourselves in a large, clean room with a proper medical examining table and instruments in various stages of sterilization. It smells strongly of disinfectant. I heave a sigh of relief.

"This doesn't look too bad," I tell Moe.

"Yes, not too bad," Moe agrees quietly.

We enter the examining room at the same time as the doctor, who is a man in his fifties dressed in a long white lab coat. He is rather unsteady on his feet. His face is covered by a mask but he removes it when he sees us. His eyes seem strange to me. He looks sick himself. He speaks in French to Moe but switches to Arabic when he realizes Moe's French is not very good. He indicates that we should lay Zohra on the table, quickly examines her stomach and listens to her chest. Then, he sits down on a stool near the examining table, takes out a little white pad of prescription paper and begins to write. Ten minutes later he gives us a stack of papers and tells us to go to the pharmacy down the street to get the prescriptions filled. He tells Moe that she has a big boil inside her ear and an infection in her chest. She needs to have antibiotics.

We weave our way back through the women in white and leave the clinic. Our ride arrives. The Frenchman agrees to stop at the pharmacy to pick up the prescriptions. We find the drug store just a block from the clinic and Moe goes inside, leaving the rest of us in the car. He returns with a box full of vials of liquid and several syringes.

"I don't know how to give a shot," I tell Moe.

"I know that," answers Moe. "The pharmacist says to go to the *Passage St. Augustine*." Moe hands a piece of paper to the Frenchman. I assume it is the address for this *Passage* place.

The Frenchman looks at the paper and says something to Moe.

Moe nods in agreement and turning to me, he says, "We go to this place. It will be adventure for you. You be quiet and follow me. Okay?"

"Okay," I answer. I am curious but I say nothing.

We drive into the heart of the town. The dirt road winds around and the streets get narrower and narrower. People stare at the car and we have to slow down to make our way through a mish-mash of garbage and debris. One or two people grab hold of the door handles and try to hang on as the car moves up the street. Suddenly, the Frenchman stops the car.

"We walk from here," Moe announces.

"We walk here?" I say. I am scared.

"Yes, just follow," Moe answers. I hear the authoritative tone in his voice.

We all get out of the car, Moe picks up Zohra and I take Tarek's hand once again. We follow a path that leads us between two old dilapidated buildings to a walled yard. The men find a gate through the wall, fiddle with the latch and when it opens, we push through. We stumble over some large stones and slowly make our way around them to a large wooden door. The Frenchman heaves on the door handle and it opens wide. We find ourselves in a foyer with rooms on either side. Through an open door I see a room filled with rows of chairs all occupied by men. The door to the other room has the picture of a woman in a veil tacked to it. It is closed.

Moe tells me I have to take Zohra and sit with the women and he will wait in the room for men. I look at him and hesitate. I know better than to argue. When I hesitate, Moe hands me the box with all the medicines in it and tells me to give it to the nurse when it is time.

Moe whispers to Zohra and carefully sets her on the floor pointing at me. I take her hot little hand in mine and open the door of the room marked for women. Inside, I see rows of women in white veils. I find a seat in a corner of the room. I feel naked. When I sit down, Zohra climbs up weakly into my lap and whispers, "Mommy, look at all the *batmans*."

Laughter wells up inside of me. "*Batmans?*" I ask, not sure that I heard her correctly.

"Yes, the ladies look like *batmans*," she explains again, and then scrunches up her nose, grabs her ear and whimpers, "Mommy, my ear hurts so bad."

I hug her and rock her on my lap. I look at the woman sitting nearest to me. She has no shoes. Her feet are covered in such thick callouses that I can easily believe she has spent a lifetime walking in the dirt. I look down the row of women and realize that none of them have shoes. I stare at their hands and find the same thick leathery callouses.

I stare at their children. I can't help it. They all have the deep red round sores that I have seen on the HLM children. I can tell that every woman looks pregnant, even though they all wear dirty, billowing veils. I also can't help but see the lice – or fleas. I still can't tell the difference. But, the little things are hippity-hopping all over their shoulders and the shoulders of their babies and children.

I sit stunned into silence. I feel ashamed that I am here, ashamed that I am clean. But, when I look into their faces, I see them smile at me and some that are close enough reach out to touch my child. I feel both healed and repelled by these gestures.

We wait for twenty minutes, watching the comings and goings of the women. Whenever a new woman joins the group, she walks by me and touches Zohra's head. Zohra smiles. I try not to flinch.

At last, I look up to see a very pretty, clean Arab girl in a white nurse's uniform. She walks up to me and indicates that I should follow her. She leads me through a large set of double doors and into a huge room so shiny and clean that the difference between this and where I have been seated is overwhelming. The girl points to a wooden bench and I sit down, again.

An older woman walks into the room and smiles at me. She is dressed in the white habit of the nursing nuns I once saw in a Catholic hospital when I was a child. She smiles at my look of surprise and tells me she is a Sister of St. Augustine. She speaks to me in English.

"You have medicine and prescription?" she asks.

"Yes," I answer, astonished at hearing her speak in English. I pull out the papers and hand her the box containing the vials of medication.

Preparing a syringe, she smiles and looks at me. "Penicillin," she announces as she plunges the needle into Zohra's arm.

Zohra watches the needle carefully, and even when it enters

her arm she doesn't cry. The nun tells her she is a good little girl. Zohra agrees with her.

As I stand up to leave the nun shakes her head. She isn't finished. We watch again as she prepares another syringe. "This shot is Streptomycin," she tells me and she puts it into Zohra's thigh.

Again, my daughter says nothing.

As we stand again, the sister asks for a donation.

I ask her how much and she mentions a coin the equivalent of ten cents.

She explains, "This is just the first of six shots Zohra will require. But, for the rest of the shots, you can go to the clinic in Birtouta instead of coming to this one."

The nurse leads me out into the corridor and I meet Moe. He is very grateful to her and is also surprised when she speaks English. She is even more surprised when she sees he is Algerian. She asks me if I am a Christian, but I don't answer her.

I follow Moe to the car.

All the way back to Birtouta, Moe and I talk about our experiences. "Moe, I can't get the faces of the women and children out of my mind. Their poverty enveloped me – overwhelmed me. I will always remember the sadness in their faces."

Moe says, "I know how you feel. I was that poverty." Tears fill his eyes and we fall into silence.

The next day as I get ready to take Zohra to the clinic for her shot I mention to Moe that I am not looking forward to taking both children. I am worried about contagious diseases and about having to carry Tarek if he gets too tired. Zohra is doing better after her first shot, but she may not be able to walk the whole way. Moe offers to take Tarek to work with him. I have no idea what he will do with a two year old at work, but I don't ask.

Benita showed me the location of the clinic one day on our way to the market so I find it easily. It is located in a small building built during the time of the French occupation, specifically for the purpose of a community health centre. When I arrive, the path and the stairway to the clinic are packed with veiled village women and their children. I don't know the routine so I make my way through them and they step aside, allowing us to enter.

Inside, I approach a white-uniformed woman who is carrying a clipboard. She isn't wearing a veil. I try to make myself understood in broken French, showing her the vials of medicine. She nods, writes a number on a small piece of paper, hands it to me and motions that I should wait. The number on my paper says 30.

There is no place to sit. I stand holding Zohra by the hand till she gets tired and flops down on the floor. After fifteen minutes, I join her. Zohra curls up in my lap with her head on my shoulder. The women at this clinic seem cleaner and not as poor as the ones we encountered at Boufarik. A few wear sandals, and some wear gold bracelets. The children, healthier and better fed, play with each other quietly. Some don't seem sick at all.

"Mommy," she whispers, "All the *batmans* are staring at us again."

I smile again at her reference to *batmans* and nod. "Yes, they are. It's because I don't have a veil and because you are so beautiful," I tease her gently.

"Mommy, you funny," she answers. Then she says, "I want to go home."

"Soon, honey. Soon, we will go but you have to get your shot so you will feel better."

From time to time, the white-uniformed woman peeks out through the main door and calls a number, first, in French and then, in Arabic. The woman stare at her, and most of the time, no one moves. Then, the nurse comes out and checks the paper each woman holds until she finds the one with the number she has called and motions that woman forward.

Eventually, the number 30 is called and Zohra and I get up off the floor and follow the nurse into the main examining room. I hand over the vials of medication and the nurse prepares the injections. She takes Zohra's little arm and jabs the needle into it. Zohra doesn't react. She speaks to Zohra in Arabic and is surprised when Zohra answers her. The nurse smiles and touches her cheek. Then I hear her ask Zohra another question. Zohra answers and I hear the familiar, "Ah, *Americanea*."

Zohra nods and so do I. We thank the nurse. I try to give her money before I leave but she mutters something in Arabic and Zohra turns to me and says, "She doesn't take money, Mommy."

When I get home, I put Zohra down for a nap while I start lunch, thinking about all the children we have come in contact with over the past few days and happy that there are medically-trained people who work so hard to keep them healthy. I can't get the sight of the little white nuns working in such terrible conditions out of my mind.

Zohra is still asleep when Moe returns home carrying Tarek who is filthy from head to toe. He smells like pigs. I wince when I take him out of Moe's arms. "Where did you take this kid?" I ask.

"I not take him anywhere. One of the French come by the office and ask if Tarek like to see pigs. I not know he play with pigs. I think French do this because I am Moslem. He want to make big point."

Suddenly, Tarek laughs his baby laugh. "Talek see piggies. *Bebe* piggies. *Bebe cochon*."

"Oh, my goodness," I exclaim, "He's already tri-lingual." I laugh with him.

"This is good age," Moe laughs. "This is best age to teach them many languages."

I take Tarek straight to the washtub and give him a bath. He protests, but I prevail and I return to the kitchen with a clean little boy.

"Talek no stink now. Mummy wash," Tarek tells Moe.

We laugh together and Moe and I again marvel at his rapidly expanding vocabulary.

"Where Zohra?" Moe asks when the activity with Tarek dies down.

"She's still asleep, I guess," I answer vaguely. "I put her down as soon as I returned from the clinic. She hasn't made any noise since."

Moe goes to Zohra's bedroom and in a few minutes I hear, "Ew, yukky Daddy."

Moe calls out for me to come and I run to the bedroom. Zohra is sitting on the edge of the bed looking dopey. She wrinkles up her nose and points at her pillow, saying, "Ew, yukky yukky." On her pillow is a huge spot of green slimy puss.

Moe and I look at each other with a sense of relief. The painful boil has burst. I clean her up, change her bed and return to the kitchen.

Moe follows me, chuckling half to me and half to himself, "Just more wonderful Algerian experience."

I can't help but smile.

"Oh, I forget to tell you," Moe says suddenly. "I talk to my friend with the twins today. He say he has a good doctor in Algiers. He is specialist in children. He is Russian. We go there next time. I also find out about doctor we see in Boufarik. Sometimes he good, sometimes he crazy," Moe pauses. "He dope fiend."

I look at Moe and shake my head. What next?

An Ancient Tomb, Dancing Women and a Scared Little Boy

Moe comes home from work on the last day of Zohra's shots and informs me that we are going to visit with Mahmoud, a politician friend of his from Blida. "His wife asks to cook for us and then we will go to big tourist spot up in the mountain. It is beautiful there. I think you like it very much," Moe tells me. "Also, you will like my friend. He is a moderate in his ideas and he is avid patriot. I like him because he try to stop corruption. He is also big war hero with many wounds. I hear that some day, if the circumstances are right, he will be Prime Minister of Algeria."

"Wow. I'm looking forward to meeting him."

At 10:00 a.m. a large black Mercedes with tinted windows pulls into our apartment parking lot. Moe sees it from the balcony and calls out to me. "I think this is Mahmoud. Bring the children and we will meet him at the stairs."

I quickly gather up the children, freshly washed and dressed in their best clothes and scramble out the door in front of Moe. We meet Mahmoud halfway up the stairs. I am greeted with *Madame Chaabane* and a kiss on each cheek. The trip to Blida takes very little time and we pull up to a villa locked behind a large wrought iron fence and electric gate. The car pauses momentarily while the gate swings wide to let us enter. I am instantly entranced by the beautiful thick cascade of full-bloom fuchsias, bougainvillea and other lush greenery surrounding this castle of a house.

The long black car comes to a halt in front of a sprawling marble staircase with pillars that seem to reach the sky. A man in a neat black suit and matching chauffeur's cap opens my car door, smiles and offers his hand to help me get out. We climb the staircase and enter the house through a brass door with thick bars across the front. I see thick black bars on all the windows, and I wonder why there is a need for such hefty fortification.

Mahmoud's wife, Leila, meets us as we come in. She is young and exquisitely beautiful with smiling dark eyes that flash as we are being introduced. She speaks to me in Arabic. Moe and Zohra translate.

Shiny tile floors extend in all directions from the foyer. The sitting room is accented by colourful oriental rugs and thick brocade furniture in beautiful Indo-European patterns and designs. Large tapestries line every wall from floor to ceiling in every room. During our tour of the shiny modern kitchen, Leila tells me she has a cook but, since she is originally from a poor family, she likes to do her own cooking.

She takes us on a tour of their roof top garden where we find a large lush garden of vegetables, a clothes-washing machine and lines to dry the laundry. I see a play area with hand-carved boxes filled to the brim with dolls and other toys. From the rooftop, the view of the city of Blida is expansive, giving a feeling of freedom.

We return to the living room and as we enter, Leila's mother appears carrying her grandson, who is fourteen months old. Leila tells me that she is pregnant again and the new baby is due soon. "*Bebe*," she says, "*Bebe en Novembre.*"

Mahmoud smiles at his wife. We all sit down at a long black highly polished table laden with hand painted china dishes filled with all sorts of condiments from fresh black olives to pickled vegetables. Our meal begins with a salad of eggs, tomatoes and fish followed by roast chicken, homemade bread and a special Algerian spiced lamb barbequed with plums. The fourth course is a large bowl of beautifully laid out fresh shrimp and a yogurt dipping sauce, which is followed by large dishes of fresh green and red grapes and succulent watermelon. Finally, Leila presents us with an array of different types of cheeses and cookies, and the inevitable thick hot sweet tea. It is a feast to remember.

At the end of the meal, though we are barely able to move from our chairs, Mahmoud informs us that our car is waiting.

Leila disappears, and returns wearing a full white veil. I don't recognize her until she speaks to me. I wonder if I should be wearing the same attire.

Mahmoud explains to Moe that his wife is required to wear the veil in the village. Mahmoud hates it, but because he is a politician and a leader in the FLN party, he has to respect some of the more conservative elements in Blida. As soon as the car leaves the town, he tells Leila to take off her veil.

Twenty minutes into our trip through the Algerian countryside, the car begins climbing. The farther we travel, the steeper the climb becomes. Mahmoud's driver gears down several times.

Moe explains, "We go to a special tourist place. In English, it is called *Tomb of the Christian*. It is daughter of Cleopatra and Mark Antony called Cleopatra Selene."

Mahmoud tells us about what we are going to see. Moe translates. He says this place is called *Qabr-er-Rumia* but is known more by its French name, *Tombeau de la Chretienne*. The tomb is near the town of Kolea, seventeen miles southwest of Algiers. This tomb, built 756 feet above the Mediterranean Sea is also the burial place of the Mauritanian King, Juba II, who was the husband of Cleopatra Selene.

The car finally pulls into a paved parking area where we see a large circular stone base. On it rests a pyramid. The base, 198 feet in diameter, is decorated with sixty columns. Mahmoud tells us that it is thought that originally the monument was 130 feet tall, but due to age, and damage caused by weather, people and war, it is now considerably shorter. In the centre of the tomb are two vaulted chambers, reached by a spiral passageway six feet wide.

"We are going to tour the inside passages," Moe announces excitedly. "Mahmoud's wife has agreed to stay outside the tomb with the children while we climb around inside. It will be great adventure for us. You will like this."

I am not so sure I will like this.

It takes us nearly twenty minutes to make our way through all the dirty, narrow little winding passageways. The group consists of the guide, Mahmoud, Moe, me and five other men. At one point, just before we reach a more open cavity in the centre of the pyramid, the passage narrows to the point where we have to crawl on our hands and knees. I wish I had not worn a narrow skirt and high heels.

Eventually, we return to fresher air and we are able to stand up straight. As I exit the tomb, I am amazed to see a 360-degree view, so spectacular that it is more like a painting in a book than a real view. Moe tells me that these plains feed Algeria.

Our trip with Mahmoud and Leila ends with a ride to the sea where we wade in the water and watch the sun go down. The perfect end to a wonderful day.

A few minutes after the big black car brings us home, we hear a rap on the apartment door. I open it to find a small boy with huge black eyes and an ear-to-ear grin. He carries a large basket filled with tomatoes. He tells Moe that they are from the small garden plot his father has at the farm and his father wants us to have them. The tomatoes are about six inches long, red and look like Italian zucchini.

Once again, I am amazed by the generosity of these poor people. Moe accepts the gifts with respect and gratitude. As he closes the door and brings the tomatoes to the kitchen, he explains to me that he spoke a few words to this worker a few days ago, and gave him some advice about some bugs in his garden.

"I think this worker so surprised I talk to him that he bring me gift. You see my people not used to respect. Respect very important thing. If I get respect from French, I be better worker. If I not get respect, I be, what you say in English, *worst dream.*"

"Worst nightmare," I correct. Moe's thoughts always seem to be about the French and their attitudes toward workers. I wonder where it all will end.

On August 26, Moe returns from a trip to Algiers and tells me that he has given $1,200 to the Renault dealer to complete the deal on the car, and the dealer has promised we will have our car by next week. Because Moe paid the whole amount for the car, we have only 4000 Francs (eight dollars) to last us for a whole month.

"We will have car, but no money for gas. No money to go anywhere," Moe quips.

"Well, at least we will have the car for when we do get more money," I say, smiling.

"Our life be easier when we get car. We can go away from this apartment and visit my father and my friends every weekend. It will be good for you and good for me." He talks like he is trying to convince himself as well as me that we have made a good decision.

I look at my husband's sad eyes. He is still staggering under the problems at work. He is tired all the time. He is always taking pills. When I ask him about the pills, he says only that the doctor gives him pills to see if they will help his insomnia and the pain in his chest.

I haven't heard anything about him having chest pain.

When I ask him what he means by chest pain, he says, "Nothing. It will go away."

The next day Moe returns home from the farm with the news that we have been invited to a party by the family that lives below us. Their eight-year-old son is going to be circumcised.

"This will be celebration like in the countryside," Moe says. "It might be strange to you. The first day, the women come together and sing and dance. They bring little boy in and he sit in chair and watch the women dance and celebrate. Then the next day the men have a party, eat and then they bring the little boy in and do the cutting in front of all the men."

"Who does it?" I ask.

"Remember, I tell you this when Tarek was born? You not like it then, I think you not like it now."

I try to recall what Moe told me when we talked about having Tarek circumcised just after he was born. "I remember that these men travel from village to village and they use a knife, but I don't remember what else you told me."

Moe continues, "I remember my own. It is painful – like you cannot believe. All the men gather around and give boy money not to cry. It is hard for young boy. I am happy that Tarek not have to do this. I think it very old-fashioned thing and very dangerous for infection. I remember in the village many got very bad infection.

The young boys also are dressed in white and when they do the cutting, the white cloth sometimes turns red from the blood."

Shivers go up my spine. I am glad my son doesn't have to do this at eight years old. "Do we have to go?" I ask Moe.

"Yes, they especially invite you. You go by yourself. No men can go there. It be interesting for you. Also you will see all your neighbour women with no veils. I will give you money to give to boy. Someone will come from downstairs and tell you when it is time. You go tomorrow night. I go the next night."

"Do I take the children?"

"Yes, all the women bring their children."

At 8:00 the next evening, a little boy knocks on our door and tells Moe that it is time to come to the party. With Zohra dressed in a party dress and bloomers, Tarek in his best pants and little blue T-shirt, and both wearing their shoes and socks and looking like clean little American children, we march bravely out the door and down the stairs. My heart is pounding. As we descend, I can hear a dull roar coming from inside the apartment. I feel a bit dizzy. The little boy leading us points to the door and it suddenly opens. Another child looks at me and then at my children and her shout rises over the noise of the crowd, "*Americanea.*"

I step tentatively into the dimly lit apartment to find a sea of dark-eyed women sitting tightly together in the living room, all suddenly silent, all smiling up at me. I smile back at them and pull my children awkwardly through the door.

I hear a voice call out, "*Americanea, ici, ici,*" and I see several women move, making room for me and the children. I head for the voice. I stumble over several brown legs and finally find a space, where I sit down gratefully, hoping that will make me less conspicuous.

A thick straw matt that is actually comfortable covers the floor. I look around. At least fifty women and about the same number of children are packed in like sardines.

Zohra translates for me what a woman says in Arabic. "Tarek and I have to go play now. They have games and sweets," she says, taking her brother by the hand. They disappear into the darkness of an adjoining room with the other children. I want to tell her not to go – but I know it is because I am the one who is afraid.

As soon as the children are gone, one of the women starts to beat on a small drum. The beat gets louder and louder. A woman in front of me stands up and starts to dance. She dances for a few minutes. When she is finished, another takes her place. The women watch each dancer, clapping to the rhythm of the drum. Every woman seems to know when the one before her is finishing and it is her turn to take the floor.

This is belly dancing like I have never seen before. Their bellies writhe and thrust in such lusty ways that I feel my own body respond and I feel that every women thrills to the sensuous display. Maybe, this is the only time and place where these women have permission to feel alive and wondrous. On the shiny, sweaty faces of the dancers, I see soulful joy. They shout encouragement, telling each other to dance faster – and as they dance faster and faster, their musky smells of unwashed bodies, fresh unadulterated sweat, and the garlic and spice scent of their breath permeates the room. I go deep into myself. I see the heart and soul of womanhood.

The women all have wiry, thick, curly hair. Some tie it back in colourful ribbons while others let it fly free in the wind of their dance. The young women all have thick full luxurious lips the natural color of dark red clay, and their dark eyes are ringed in black, giving them a deeply mysterious look. Some have deeply imbedded blue tattoo lines on their faces, much like the lines that Moe has on his forehead.

The younger women are all at one stage of pregnancy or another. When the women in the late stages of pregnancy dance, their huge round bellies roll and bounce with such celebration. The pride these women feel in their condition – the universal joy of being with child – is transmitted without words. No one wears a bra here. Some of the women dance with no tops at all. Some dance with their young babies at their breasts, attached with strips of material. The small bundles remain attached, even at the height of their twirling. The babies seem to enjoy the dancing as much as their mothers. From time to time, a child of two or three will call out to its mother from the other room and come running to find her. One child climbs onto her mother's lap to nurse from the breast that is not being used by the baby. When the drum pauses, I sometimes hear Zohra's laughter over the noise in the other room.

Suddenly, when there is such a tension in the air that I can barely stand it, the drums stop. The women are all looking at me. One shouts, "*Americanea! Americanea!*" Others take up the chant. The women around me push against me, laughing, until I can do nothing but stand. Once I am on my feet, the drum begins again. It is my turn – but I have no beautiful dance in my repertoire. I start to move to the beat of the drum. The women clap for me just as they clapped for each other. For a moment, I feel at one with them, a free and happy woman dancing and in touch with her soul. Then, another woman stands and begins to dance. I find my place back on the mat. Women around me smile and nod, and for that moment, I feel that I belong here with them. The women insist that I dance for them three times during the evening. By the third time, I am tired and hungry and ready for the drum to stop.

Late in the evening, when the dancing is over, large bowls of food are passed around. One bowl is given to every fifth woman. This woman turns to the women next to her and they all eat out of the same bowl. One of the women sitting next to me takes a bowl that is offered to her and indicates I am in her group. We are each given a large slab of bread. The women use the bread to scoop up gravy and pieces of vegetables. When they pass the bowl to me, I try to do what they do. But, every time I scoop into the stew, my bread comes up empty. The women find this amusing and they laugh uproariously. Finally, one yells out something over the crowd. A few minutes later a woman arrives at my side and hands me a large spoon. I am embarrassed, but they pat my back and encourage me to eat.

The stew is a thick tomato concoction with small pieces of string beans and squash mixed in. It is spicy hot and very greasy. Like the other women, I eat only a few bites. Then, a glass is passed from woman to woman. It is a sweet drink, thick and lukewarm.

When we finish eating and everything has been cleared away, a hush falls over the crowd. Suddenly, there is a commotion at the door. A tall man rushes into the room, grabs one of the women and kisses her on the mouth. All of the women scream and jump up and down. Their eyes seem electric with fear and they rush forward, ripping at the strange man's clothes and hitting at him with their fists. Then, just as suddenly as the screaming started, it stops. The women step back from the man and break into laughter that goes on for about five minutes before I figure out this is all a joke. The man is a woman dressed as a man. The women enjoy this charade so much that their laughter hangs in the air.

It is 11:00 p.m. I wonder when this party will end. I haven't seen my children for the entire evening. Someone pokes me in the back and points to the door. A small group of women lead a little boy dressed in a full-length pure white cotton toga into the room. He seems small for eight years old and he looks scared. The women bring him to the centre of the room and sit him on two beautiful brocade green and white pillows. Two candles are ceremoniously lit and then held behind the boy's head along with an ebony handled hand mirror. One of the women, whom I think is his grandmother, brings a large pot of henna dye and sets it down in front of him. Several women take his hands and carefully place them in the dye. When his hands have absorbed enough of the dye, they tie each of them in red cloth. Then, the rest of the women get to their feet and form a long line that moves past the little boy. As each woman passes him, she drops some money in his lap and then walks out of the room to where the other children are. As I pass by the boy, I smile at him but he is looking down at the money. I drop all the coins that Moe has given me into his lap.

When I find my children in the other room, I am surprised they are both wide awake and still playing. I ask Zohra if she had a good time and she says she likes the children and that they play nicely with her and Tarek.

We make our way out of the party. I nod goodbye and say thank you to the women at the door. They nod back at me and we all smile. Zohra, Tarek and I climb the stairs to our apartment.

The next day Moe attends the party for the men. He stays only a short time. He only says he saw and heard enough and that he didn't feel well. I see the little boy later that day with his white toga spotted with blood. He is playing soccer.

 Abdelghani, Unboiled Water and Our Car

In the last days of August, Moe comes home from work with news. "Abdelghani is coming back to stay with us," he tells me excitedly.

Surprised, I ask Moe why.

Moe looks at me. His voice clearly shows he is annoyed. "My stupid stepmother has left my father. She has gone back to her family in another village. She insists my father cut all of us out of his will and just name her Djamal as first heir."

"She does this all the time," Moe continues, shaking his head disgustedly. "I think it more about getting a trip to see her family than about the will."

He adds, "Also, Abdelghani is mad because my father asks him to quit school and go to work on the farm. Abdelghani wants government to give him money so he can live in the dorm during the week and come here for holidays and weekends. He already apply for a transfer of schools."

"How do you feel about this sudden change with Abdelghani?" I ask.

"I okay. I want my brother to get education." For a minute Moe looks at me sheepishly. Then he blurts out, "Forget about what I say before about him liking you."

I remember Moe's comments about Abdelghani's penis.

He shrugs his shoulders. "I have to help him."

"What about your father and his wife? Can you do anything about that problem?" I ask.

"I stay out of that problem. When we get the car, we go to

Mascara to see what is really going on. This wife has always been trouble for him. She was not good mother to us. She only want her own baby. She have Djamal when she was forty years old. She got crazy after that. My father better off without her, but he not very happy without a wife even if she is crazy. Maybe – if he decide to divorce, he can get a better wife."

I look forward to having Abdelghani stay with us again. Speaking French with him was good for my language skills. He was good company for me and he was really good with the children – and these days I can use some help with Tarek, who has changed lately. In the last batch of packages from the States, he received a ride-on car. He rides all day, going lickety-split all over the apartment. He is into speed and daredevil behaviour. At the moment, he is climbing up and jumping off the dining room table. He thinks this is the best game ever. If I spank him, he responds by hitting me and then telling me off at the top of his lungs in some kind of Tarek language.

Another of his favourite things is to run up to people and yell, "*Itchy-gitchy.*" He sounds like a squealing pig. The other day, he ran up to a drunken man sitting in a restaurant and yelled "*Itchy-gitchy*" at the man. We had to rescue him from the man's clutches.

Yesterday, he ran into my room, carrying his potty and yelling, "*Kiki*, Mama." I reached down to undo his pants so he could sit on the potty. All the familiar noises accompanied what happened next. Tarek looked up at me and said, "Okay, me *kiki* boy, me go." When he finished, he went and stood in the corner. All of these antics make me laugh. I watch him throw himself off the table one more time. He notices that I am staring at him and he runs up to me.

"Me loves Mama. Me want *gang-gang.*" *Gang-gang* means candy.

I laugh out loud. Abdelghani can help me keep Tarek's imagination and energy under control.

Suddenly, a knock at the door brings me out of my reverie. Moe opens the door and I see a large bearded man in a green uniform. My heart drops. Moe's first expression of fear suddenly changes to recognition.

The men hug each other and exchange greetings. Moe introduces him to me. "This is Ahsad. He is one of my far relatives, like second cousin or something. He is member of the Birtouta *gendarmerie.*"

Once, Moe jokingly threatened to sell me to the *gendarmerie* if I wasn't a good wife. I remember that now. I nod to Ahsad. I take the children into the bedroom so that Moe can talk to his cousin.

In a few minutes, five more men dressed in green uniforms appear at the door. Moe lets them in. Several minutes later, Moe pokes his head into the bedroom. He tells me he and the men are going to tour the farm.

"Don't worry," he says. "They want tour of farm because I work there. People are afraid of these men, but I am fine. One is my relative."

I look at the very large men dressed in dark green denim and black leather with motorcycle helmets and guns. I wonder who they really are. Moe gets onto a huge motorcycle behind Ahsad and the other men mount their own motorcycles and kick them into life. They all race off toward the farm.

My imagination starts to work overtime and I wonder if I will ever see Moe again. My rational mind tells me, "Of course, you will see him again. He has just gone to tour the farm."

Once again, I picture the willow.

Just before midnight Moe arrives home, happy and exuberant over his time on the motorcycle and his tour of the farm. The farm workers gathered up boxes of oranges and pails of milk for the men. The group all ended up in a cafe in Blida for dinner.

Abdelghani arrives on September 2, tired after his six-hour bus trip. Though he seems healthier than he did on his last visit, he still looks tired and full of concern. He tells us that a big epidemic wiped out all the horses, sheep and cows on his father's farm and his father had to pay the workers to bury them. He also replays the scenario about how nasty his stepmother has been to everyone, especially his father. As soon as he talks to Moe and finishes a bit of supper, he goes to bed.

Knowing that Moe stopped by the Renault dealer earlier in the day, I ask, "What is happening with the car?"

"More stupid behaviour," Moe spits out the words. "Now they won't accept the traveler's cheques you brought. I go to the British Bank and cash them all. Then, I take the cash to the dealer. I think this whole thing really stupid."

I persist, hoping to get some definite idea about when we might get our car. "Now that we have paid – is there any word on when we can actually get the car?"

"They say next Tuesday. But I not believe it till it happen."

"You should have your driver's license by then. No?"

"I hope so but I even not sure about that." Moe leaves the kitchen and I begin to clear away the dishes from our supper.

My friend, Benita, is due back from France on Monday. Her house on the farm is still not finished. She won't be happy about having to move back into her small apartment – with two children this time. I will be glad to have someone to talk to again. I wonder if I will still find it difficult to relate to her, and I wonder if she will still take me to the farm every week.

I wake up the next day to find I have dysentery again. I want to curl up in a ball and not move. I know it is probably from drinking unboiled water. Usually, I fill two pails with water. One, I boil right away and the other, I set aside to boil later when I do the dishes. This time, I got confused and I accidently drank out of the wrong pail. Thank goodness, Abdelghani is here.

Abdelghani does more than watch the children. He scrubs the floors and does all of the housework. I am unable to eat or drink or do anything for the next three days. When Moe arrives home on the third day, he tells me he is taking me to the doctor.

He also says that he couldn't pick up the car as promised by the car agency. The papers for the credit didn't go through. He told them that if he doesn't get the car within one week, he wants his money back.

On that same day, Abdelghani gets his papers for school in Boufarik, the town where we took Zohra to the clinic. He will live in the school dormitory there when school starts in October. It will cost 10,000 francs a month in tuition and accommodation.

Moe agrees that we will pay for him to go to the school, but if he flunks out, he will make him join the military.

"Why are you so hard on him?" I ask when Abdelghani is out of the room.

"I not hard on him. He is lazy. He is already one year behind. I help him but he have to help himself."

The next day, Abdelghani stays home with the children, and Moe borrows one of the cars from the farm to take me to a doctor in Algiers. This particular doctor has been recommended by the Embassy and his office is located in one of the nicer sections of Algiers. As soon as we arrive, we are ushered into his office. He is a very nice man, he speaks English and his office is clean.

He listens to my symptoms and my explanation of how I drank unboiled water by accident.

He tells me to go on a diet of carrots and milk for two days and hands me a prescription for $10.00 worth of medicine. He charges us $3.00 for the visit. He also reminds me not to drink unboiled water again.

Again, I try to explain to him what happened.

He interrupts my explanation with instructions to change my water regimen so it doesn't happen again. "Water is deadly," he tells me. "You are foolish to tempt fate."

I promise to do what he says and we leave.

Moe finds a pharmacy and picks up my prescription. We drive the whole way home without speaking. When I try to start a conversation, he says he doesn't feel well and doesn't want to talk.

"It's the heat," I think. We are both suffering, especially since there is no air conditioning in the car. The whole country is suffering through the worst heat wave of the century. The trip home takes forever. When we finally arrive at the apartment parking lot, Moe makes no effort to get out of the car.

"Are you coming in?" I ask, curious about his delay.

"No, not coming in," he tells me in a flat matter-of-fact voice. "I go back to Algiers and spend night with friends. I have to take drivering test at 6:00 a.m. tomorrow so I stay in the city for the night."

I am shocked. I blurt out, "Moe, why didn't you tell me this before? I could have stayed with you so you don't have to make another trip up and down the highway to Algiers."

"It better this way," he says. I hear the beginning of aggravation in his voice.

I think, "WILLOW.... Be a willow..."

Silently, I nod and get out of the car, medicine in hand. I head for the apartment as Moe drives out of the parking lot. I am too sick to care, and especially too sick to fight with him.

The next day Moe brings me a huge bottle of some icky-tasting potion from Algiers. He instructs me to take some every day, telling me that it is full of vitamins. He says the doctor told him to buy it for me but he forgot when he first went to the pharmacy. I didn't hear the doctor say anything about this elixir – but I dutifully take it. In a few days, I do feel a lot better. I start to eat normal food again.

At the beginning of September, Abdelghani informs us quite suddenly that he is going back to Mascara to school. The school he wanted to go to in Boufarik is full and the only other school he can get into is Catholic. It is for Arabs and they don't teach religion, but he refuses to go to a Christian school even if it is for Arabs. He will be leaving next week.

On September 13, Moe arrives in Birtouta with our brand new car. It is so fresh neither of us wants to touch it – steel gray color, bone interior, bucket seats, a floor shift. Special locks to keep the kids from opening the back doors. Moe shows me the sheet of instructions that comes with it, telling us how to break it in. We have to get special tune-ups every 500 kilometres up to 5000 kilometres and we have to drive it very slowly for the first 5000 kilometres.

"By the way," Moe suddenly informs me, his face sheepish. "I fail my driver's test – again. They are really stupid there. I hear the testers are on strike and they only pass four from 300 people. I don't care anymore."

These days drivers are getting stopped two or three times at roadblocks on the way to Algiers, first by the army and then by the *gendarmes*. Moe flashes his American driver's license at them. They ask for his occupation and he tells them he is Engineer *Agronome*. At that, they salute him and pass him through. What will happen when his luck runs out?

The heat is still oppressive. The water pump has broken down again. Tarek has a lot of trouble with the heat. He develops eczema on his neck and chest – and he has seven huge boils on his head.

One of Moe's friends tells him that the boils are because of a vitamin deficiency. Moe brings home some children's vitamins. We shave Tarek's head. He cries as his thick curly blond locks fall to the floor. I tell him they will grow back. I don't think he understands.

Following the head shaving, we dab orange-yellow iodine over every inch of his little head. The iodine is supposed to help to draw the poison out of the boils and when they break open, the area around the boils will be disinfected to help prevent infection. In the village, many of the children have their heads shaved and covered with the same orange-yellow stains.

As we finish with Tarek, Moe tells me, "Now that we have our car, I plan for us to go to Mascara. We go on Friday and stay for the weekend. We will need to pack some food."

I ask, "Should I buy a veil before I go?"

He hesitates for a moment and then says, "No, if we need, we can borrow from my relatives. I am always rebel in my family. This village very conservative, but I will do this anyway. I was first in my family to take off traditional head dress and first to wear western clothes, so maybe I am first to have unveiled wife."

He looks at me for a moment longer and then adds, "I think my father will have attack of the heart but we will see."

I am looking forward to this trip, especially to meeting his sisters – Yamina, 28, Fatma, 23, Rakaya, 20 and Khadija, 19. All the years I have known Moe, he has talked about *the soft place* he has in his heart for them. He has told me how he always tried to protect them from beatings by his other brothers.

Finally, the day arrives that Moe has been looking forward to for a long time – the day that he considers my official welcome into his family. From the very first day of our marriage, Moe has drilled into my head that meeting the whole family in the village of Mascara would be the biggest event in our lives. He believes the impression I make on them will either cement our relationship with his family forever or splinter it irreconcilably. Though his father and some of his brothers have already greeted me, still I am filled with apprehension at the thought of our journey to Mascara.

We rise at 6:30 in the morning and dress in our finest clothes. For me, that means a calf-length skirt and long sleeved blouse. For Moe, it means a new three-piece suit and tie. For the children – new outfits brought from the States especially for this occasion. Zohra wears a red velvet dress trimmed with white lace, netted tights, and black patent leather shoes. Tarek wears a red white and blue sailor suit with tiny tennis shoes.

We are hot and uncomfortable before we even leave the apartment – and we have a 500-kilometre trip ahead of us in a car with no air conditioning. We pack the little Renault and hustle our bleary-eyed children into the back seat. With any luck, they will sleep most of the way.

We bring gifts for everyone, our 'leftovers' mostly – a doll that Zohra doesn't like, a half-broken toy car, old shirts, skirts and tops that Moe and I don't wear any more. I am sceptical about the suitability of these gifts, but Moe keeps telling me that they will be appreciated and put to good use.

Both children sleep for the first part of our journey. Moe focuses on driving and watching the highway for the expected interruptions of blockades. I sit in the passenger seat, giving in to the usual drowsiness that comes with getting up so early and the heat in the car. About halfway through the trip, I am startled awake when Moe suddenly slams on the breaks. He stops next to some roadside vendors, throws his door open and jumps out to talk to four scruffy-looking fellows waving a few unidentifiable items in the air and shouting words I don't understand. He disappears behind the stand with one of the men.

An old man comes to the car door and smiles at the children. He says something in Arabic and Zohra answers him. I ask her what he says and she says he wants us to buy some candies. I tell her no. She doesn't argue with me. She just shakes her head back and forth at the man and he returns to his original spot at the side of the road.

A few minutes later, Moe reappears. He is carrying two live chickens tied together with a string. He tosses them into the back seat with the children. I am rather shocked by his cavalier abuse of these poor birds but he assures me they can't feel pain.

I ask him why we are bringing live chickens with us.

"It is custom to bring food when visiting," he explains. "If we kill the chickens, the meat will turn bad before we reach my father's house. If we do reach there with good meat, then my family has no refrigerator. But, if chickens are alive when we get there, then they get killed just before they are cooked and everybody is safe."

I cannot argue with his logic.

By the end of the trip I do learn one lesson: The good thing about chickens tied with a string around their legs is that they cluck happily, entertaining the children for nearly the entire trip. The children are delighted with sharing the back seat with the birds. I wonder if they will be so delighted when it is time to eat chicken stew at *grandfodders*.

I am also reminded, that when travelling the roads of Algeria, *uneventful* is a good thing. I spend most of the drive, clenching the *holy shit* bars on the ceiling with white knuckles. Moe drives at race-car speed, staring into the distance, both of us praying we won't be stopped by any roadblocks, whether manned by army troops, *gendarmes* or bandits.

Towards the end of the day, relieved that the trip is over – and has been uneventful, we arrive at our destination – Mascara. When we finally pull into the village, I see a few dogs and cats, and only one old man sidling along with his sad old under-nourished donkey. The buildings look war-weary and dilapidated, and the only houses I see are shacks of tin or mud that look abandoned. As we proceed farther into the village, I catch sight of some ragged children playing soccer along the street with a strange rather lopsided ball. Moe tells me that, as a child, he used anything he could find in the garbage to make a soccer ball.

Near the centre of the village, the road curves and suddenly, we are on a beautiful wide boulevard that is lined with tall shade trees. Moe explains, "These are the streets and houses where the French *colons* lived before the war. They went back to France, abandoning these places. Now, my people live here. See how many of the houses and gardens look so run down. It make me sad that my own people have no money or knowledge to take care of these houses that are given to them." His voice is angry, as it usually is when he speaks of the problems that he attributes to the French *colons*.

As Moe talks, I roll down the window to escape the heat of the car as much as the heat of what he is saying. The stench of human refuse immediately assaults my nostrils. I wonder if I will ever get used to such smells.

On the far side of the village, Moe pulls up in front of a stark white square cement block building and stops. "This the place," he tells me, the excitement in his voice replacing the anger I heard just a few minutes earlier.

The People and Places of Mascara

I sit in the car while Moe, barely taking time to turn off the car, leaps to the curb and heads for the house. He bangs loudly on the door. It takes a minute or more for any response. At first, Abdullah opens the door a crack and tentatively peeks out to see who it is.

Then, the door swings wide when he discovers it is Moe. He steps outside to embrace his son with kisses and hugs. Even from the car, I can see tears streaming down his sun-browned old face. I am reminded that once there was a time when he thought he would never see this son again. Moe indicates that I should get out of the car and bring the children.

As I approach my father-in-law and look into his face, I am again taken by his amazing dark brown piercing eyes and his kind smile. It is the smile that puts me immediately at ease. I kiss him on both cheeks and he smiles a smile of greeting, saying something in Arabic that sounds like a greeting and a blessing from Allah.

He turns from me to each of his grandchildren, lifting each in turn, kissing them and speaking softly in Arabic. Zohra is delighted to see *grandfodder* again and hugs him eagerly. Even Tarek doesn't struggle against his caresses. Like me, he seems to be in awe of this old man's gentle nature and peaceful countenance.

Grandfodder motions us into the house. The door closes behind us and as my eyes adjust to the light, I follow the group down a hallway with shiny blue-tiled floors flanked by bright white painted walls. On the left, we come to a large room. Moe tells me that this is the eating room and he points to a room off the eating room, which he calls a sleeping room.

The eating room holds one long low table, the top surface only about twelve-inches off the floor – and nothing more. From what I can see, the sleeping room has pillows and blankets stacked halfway up the walls, but no dressers or closets. At the back of the house, we find a large kitchen with a sink, with one tap for running water, and a small stove at one end like a hot plate, but no oven. The floor in the kitchen is dirt. Moe explains that most of the house is unfinished because his father has run out of money.

We keep walking. We are not going to stop in my father-in-law's part of the house. He leads us down a long narrow hallway and we come to another unfinished complex of rooms where all of the floors are dirt. Here Ahmed greets us. Moe explains that Ahmed, his wife, Behia, and their six children live in two of these unfinished rooms. They share their space with at least ten clucking chickens, a mangy dog and two rabbits, all of which have the run of the house. In a far corner of the room, an unmoving figure lies on a mattress and, in spite of the summer heat, is covered with a blanket.

Moe explains, "This is Behia, Ahmed's wife. She must stay in bed because she has a new baby. In the country, the belief is that woman must stay in bed for seven days after birth."

Behia pokes her head out from under the covers, gives me a little wave and beckons me to come over to her mattress. I lean over her and she pulls me close to kiss me on my cheeks. She smells of urine and afterbirth. She smiles, reaches under the covers, and shows me her newborn son. He is wound in grey-white rags so tightly that I can only see a part of his face. I am struck by the beauty of the child and the filth of his surroundings. Behia holds him out to me. I have no choice but to take him in my arms and hold him close to me. He struggles to stretch the way newborns sometimes do. His eyes flicker open and he looks straight into my eyes. I smile back at him, and in an instant he falls into a deep quiet sleep. I smile again, kiss his cheeks, and hand him back to his mother.

I stand, watching Ahmed and Moe talking. Ahmed is tall,

much taller than Moe, and very handsome. I look back at Behia, his wife. She has many lines across what once must have been a lovely sweet face. Her skin is pale and dry and her eyes are sunken and sad. She is rail-thin. Her teeth are yellow and rotten. She can't be older than 24, but in eight years, she has already given birth to seven children, five living and two who died at birth. She smiles and tries to talk to me.

Moe tells her I cannot understand, and she nods sadly.

I wish I knew her language. I have so many questions, but people get tired of translating and the feeling of a conversation gets lost anyway when there is someone in the middle. I hope that time will give me a new language.

I turn to face Ahmed's children who have been waiting patiently while I am introduced to their mother. They are called forward one by one to greet me.

"This is Zohra," whispers Moe. "She is oldest girl and she is eight."

Zohra, the same name as my own daughter. I remember how Moe insisted that his first-born girl be named Zohra, which is Arabic for rose flower, and follows the family custom of naming the first born after a dead relative, his mother. I expect that I will meet many Zohras in this family.

I smile. Eight-year-old Zohra is stunning, even with her long, coarse, rat's-nest-like hair. Her perfectly round dark face and mahogany brown eyes that shine with innocence and joy are spellbinding. She giggles shyly, bows her head and murmurs, "*Bonjour, Madame.*" It is the same French greeting used by the children of the HLM – the polite phrase used to greet foreign women.

I bend down to greet Zohra who purses her lips like a tiny bird anxious to peck the cheeks of her strange new auntie. As I receive her welcome, I am nearly overwhelmed by her smell. It is the musky, organic smell of unwashed body and filthy clothing – the smell of poverty.

"Hel–hello, little one," I manage to stutter.

There are two more little girls to greet. Nadjit is seven and Karima is five. The three girls are like stair-steps, each an inch or so shorter than the others, and each one equally exotic looking and equally unkempt and smelling of unwashed clothing and an unwashed body.

Then, I am introduced to the family's pride and joy, their oldest son. Moe leans over and whispers, "This is little Mohamed. He is six years old."

Little Mohamed struggles towards me on two twisted homemade canes. His legs are cruelly bent and deformed. They are bowed like those of bronco riders I remember from back home. He smiles at me from underneath long black eyelashes. He embraces me with the same birdlike pecks as his sisters and slowly stumbles his way back to his place on the floor by his mother's bed.

"What you think is wrong with our little nephew?" Moe murmurs.

I shake my head. "Why he would ask me such a thing?" He knows I have no medical training.

Moe laughs and I hear bitterness. "You are really smart woman. I think, surely you have seen this before, no?"

"No," I say, "I have never seen this before. I am sure I have never seen this before."

"Then you lucky," Moe says sadly. "This condition common here. I not know the English name, but it happen when mother run out of milk for her baby or when the cow dies, or when one baby is born too fast after another."

Then it dawns on me. "Rickets," I say aloud. "I read about it once. I think it's called Rickets." I wonder why the girls don't have it.

Moe says nothing. He just looks sadly at his nephew and nods his head.

The official greetings from this part of the family are over. Moe motions me to sit down beside Behia on the mattress. I find sitting difficult in my fancy clothes but I do as I am told. Moe is deep in conversation with his brother when I realize that I should find the washroom.

I interrupt his conversation and he laughs in a way that means, "Good luck to you."

"It really better if you can hold it," he says. "Hold it till we can go to my aunt's house. They have inside bathroom."

"I can't. I've already held it as long as I can," I say, giving him a look of desperation.

He sighs, and disappears into another part of the house. When he returns he is carrying a spoon and a small plastic bucket of water.

"Come with me," he says in his *I am the master and you are the slave* voice.

When he uses this voice, I know he means business. I am unsure why he is upset. All I have asked is to use the washroom. The children are laughing behind their hands. Behia is looking a bit sorry for me.

Moe leads me out to the back yard and shows me a plot of cultivated brown smelly dirt about ten feet square. "This is the bathroom," he states, this time in his *I told you so* voice. "Now I will show you how to dig a hole, and squat."

Shocked, I listen to his directions. All the children have followed us out of the house. They stand and stare wide-eyed at me. Moe hands me the spoon and a plastic cup filled with water. Even he stands staring at me to see what I will do. I look at the children and they look at me. I motion for them to go away. They just laugh some more. I turn to Moe and plead with him to make the children go away.

A smirk forms on his lips and he stares at me for a moment before finally turning to say something to the children. Whatever it is, they leave, though reluctantly. Moe then positions himself, face toward the house, between me and the house and any eyes that might still be looking. He stands there until I am finished.

I make a vow to myself never to pee again in this village without an inside toilet. Before I return to the house, I ask Moe, "Why can't we use your father's bathroom in the house?"

"It doesn't work," he says in a tone that tells me he is lying.

"I know it works, Moe. I saw people going there," I challenge.

"Yes, well," he responds self-righteously, "Sometimes you need to listen and learn lessons."

I open my mouth but nothing comes out. I feel the touch of a willow on my cheek.

As we return to the house Moe announces, "I now take Zohra, Tarek, Ahmed and my father and go to find my sisters. I bring them back here to cook for us. You stay here and wait for me."

Before I can say anything, he is gone and I am left with my new sister-in-law and her children. Behia smiles at me. She points to the baby, then leans forward and picks him up, placing him in my arms again. "*Bebe, bebe bien, bebe garcon, bebe garcon,*" she repeats in the French-Algerian dialect that she thinks I might understand.

I nod stupidly and try to acknowledge what she says. "*Oui, bebe garcon bien.*" Yes indeed, a boy baby is good, especially in this country.

I sigh. I feel sad. I feel abandoned. The image of a willow bending in the wind again comes into my mind. "How long till the willow snaps?" I wonder.

I turn back to Behia and Behia's baby. She motions for me to come and sit on her mattress. I move towards her. She moves aside slowly in obvious discomfort, and makes a place for me. I balance the baby on one arm while I slowly lower myself to sit in the space provided. I try to give the baby back to her but she shakes her head no and refuses to take the bundle from me. I decide not to protest and just sit and rock while Behia and I stare at each other, wanting to reach out with words, but each of us locked inside our own language.

Nearly an hour passes before the baby begins to stir and fuss. I happily and forcefully hand him back to his mother. She smiles shyly and puts him to her breast, smiles at him and settles back to feed in the way that mothers all over the world do. He falls asleep again and she hands him back to me smiling. I am not certain what I am supposed to do with him. I look at her with questions in my eyes but she just keeps motioning that I hold him.

The baby sleeps, and he grows heavy in my arms. Somewhere, I find the courage to peer at him through his filthy rag-blankets. I see how small and grey he is. He is wet and smells, not like new babies usually smell, but like old urine, sour milk, and shit. I want to ask Behia to change him but I don't know how. Furthermore, I know they don't use diapers here, just a thick layer of mud against the skin covered with whatever rags they can find.

I look at Behia again. She has fallen into a deep sleep of her own, with that smile still on her face. I can't bring myself to disturb her. Holding her baby is perhaps the only way I can help her. Resigned to this role, I lean back against the wall and wait.

After another hour or more, anxiety floods over me. I can't bear to sit on this dirty mattress another moment with this filthy, sickly baby. Bahia is still sleeping soundly, so balancing the baby in the round of my right arm, and inching myself up off the mattress, I stand up and walk around the small room, stopping from time to time to rock us both back and forth, which may be more for me than for him.

When I finally move the baby enough to look at my watch, I notice that Moe has been gone for more than four hours. What if he never returns?

I keep walking around the room, stopping every so often to rock back and forth. My body starts to shake. Even with my shaking, the baby sleeps on. I am on the verge of tears. I try to suck them back because I know it will be a disgrace to me and to Moe if he arrives and I am crying. I check my watch again. Six hours have now passed since he left.

It must be dark outside. The chickens and other animals are beginning to gather inside the house. Behia's children return from wherever they have been playing. They laugh and talk as they enter the room and their mother stirs from her sleep, smiling.

I no longer have the energy to smile back at her. I am angry. I am hungry. I miss my children. A second before I break into tears, I hear a door open at the front of the house and the sound of familiar footsteps coming towards me. I still want to cry but instead, I hold it all inside. I eat my misery. I remember the willow tree – again.

My children arrive full of energy and kisses and push ahead of their father and their aunties. They nearly knock me over as they scramble to plant their kisses and tell me about their adventure.

"So," I ask weakly, "did you guys have fun with your papa and uncle?"

"We met all our cousins," Zohra chirps. "And *Grandfodder* went with us. Daddy has a lot of sisters." Tarek just bobs his two-year-old head in agreement and beams up at me. It feels like a new day.

Moe steps into the room carrying two of his little nephews in his arms. He smiles at them and they kick their little legs and flail their arms, indicating they want to get down and play. He gingerly sets them down in front of me.

I look over Moe's shoulder and see two young women shyly standing behind him, their eyes lowered but overflowing with giggles. They wear long flowing white veils but somewhere between the door and their meeting with me they have removed the face pieces.

"Are these your sisters?" I ask.

"Yes," he answers proudly. "These are my sisters, Khadija and Fatma."

"Where are the other two? I thought you would bring Rakaya and Yamina as well."

"They not come," Moe tells me sadly. "I try to convince their husbands to come and visit at their father's house but they say I am married to infidel and they not want me in their family." Moe shakes his head. "This situation very difficult for everyone. I think I am sorry that I bring you here so soon. They are just uneducated people and they not understand."

He brushes away the tears forming in his eyes, and quickly turns to introduce me to the two giggling sisters. They look me over and smile and both kiss both my cheeks. I am happy when Khadija takes Behia's baby from me and cuddles him against her own breast. I wonder what these young women think about me.

Fatma is the shyer of the two sisters. The skin on her face is shiny smooth and brown, and she has thick coarsely matted black hair that stands up all around her moon face. She has the Chaabane family eyes. I easily recognize them as they are the eyes of my own children – nearly oriental but a bit rounder and the colour of mahogany with long black lashes that curl up till they almost touch the top of the eye socket.

I am so caught up in looking at her lovely face, that I nearly miss the fact that she is pregnant. From her size, I guess that she is close to giving birth. This will be her third baby in three years. She is married to her first cousin and he has come with her to see this infidel sister-in-law. He is a very old man.

I am introduced to their children. The oldest is a boy of two. His eyes stare straight forward, bulging. His little face is smeared with dried food and he makes little effort to notice the world around him. His stomach is distended and his arms and legs are skeleton-thin. I have seen children like this in the hallways of my apartment. I cannot believe this one is my nephew.

The baby is a little girl about a year old. She cries in a croaky voice, like the bubbly complicated sounds one hears from the dying. No one goes to her aid or even seems to notice. Fatma bends down to set her on the floor. A roach crawls over her little foot. It must tickle because she stops crying suddenly and looks at her little toes. From the laughter of the women, I can tell they find it amusing.

Stunned, I try to smile at these children, but I find I am shaking again. I want to cry. Inwardly, I search for the willow, but I cannot find it to comfort me.

Moe turns from these children and introduces me to Khadija. She seems very different than her sister. She exudes infectious energy that makes the room brighter. She has the same round brown shiny face and family eyes as her sister, but her hair is neatly tied with a ribbon in the back and when she bends over to kiss my cheeks, she smells of soap and rose water. Her three children, all little boys, appear healthy, clean and full of childish mischief.

Moe whispers in English, "This sister has a good husband. He is her age and progressive in his thinking." Maybe this is why his sister is so smiley and healthy.

Both women smile at me again and leave for the kitchen to cook for us. We haven't eaten since the morning. I am hungry. I ask Moe if the children have eaten and he says he fed them at his sister's house. He also fed himself.

We make our way slowly down the hall and into my father-in-law's house. The eating room table is being prepared for a meal and Abdullah offers me a pillow for sitting. Moe, Abdullah and I take our places at the large table. The men chatter to each other and then look at me in silence. I feel awkward. My father-in-law looks at me for a long time and I smile, but I remember to keep my eyes lowered.

Suddenly Abdullah says something to Mohamed and I know that he is talking about me. Moe smiles. He turns to me in English and says, "My father remembers how you iron his shirt. He says thank you again. He also says he will work on his sons-in-law to let my other sisters visit you. Perhaps next time. He thinks you are good woman."

I nod my head at Abdullah and smile.

I hear my sisters-in-law chattering in the kitchen. I wonder if I should be there with them –if I am going to be judged for sitting with the men. I look over at Moe. I try to get comfortable on my lumpy pillow. When there is a break in the conversation, I ask Moe if I should go to the kitchen.

"No, no," Moe replies. "My sisters want to cook for you. They are very excited for this. We let them do this. Besides you just be in the way. When I am at Khadija's house, I make arrangements with her husband to bring her to our house in Birtouta. She come to teach you how to cook."

I look away and smile. It means I will learn to properly cook the food that Moe loves so much. I look forward to this visit.

The children haven't shown their faces in the eating room since they returned to the house after their daylong adventure with their cousins. I ask Moe where they have gone.

"They are in the other room with Behia and her children. Don't worry, they are now everybody's children."

I wonder what he means.

"They are fine," he assures me. "They are with family, which means someone is looking after them."

I am not reassured, but I say nothing. There is no point.

Another hour passes before the food appears from the kitchen. The first dish is carried by a woman I haven't seen before. She is wearing a brightly coloured toga-like dress. Moe tells me her dress is what women in the countryside wear. She seems very old and her back is bent forward so that she walks like she is looking for something on the floor. Moe introduces me to her. She is his stepmother, Aisha. She frowns at me in a disturbing way. I smile at her, but she turns away.

"Don't worry, she doesn't like any of us," explains Moe noticing his stepmother's frown in answer to my smile.

"I thought she left your father. Why is she here?" I ask.

"She is fighting with my father all the time these days and is making us all miserable. She left but I think she is now back. I think it is just so she can see the *Americanea*. I don't know why my father wants her but he does. Just ignore her."

The food is placed on the table in front of me. It consists of one of the largest serving bowls I have ever seen, which holds mounds of freshly steamed couscous covered with a thick stew of lamb and prunes. I recognize it as the dish of celebration – what a family serves to honour the presence of someone special. Moe confirms that this dish is cooked in my honour. I don't know what to say.

Moe's sister, Fatma comes from the kitchen carrying a spoon. She smiles at her brother as she hands it to him. Moe smiles back at her and hands the spoon to me.

"Here" he says. "This will make it easier for you."

I take the spoon and look for some sort of signal to begin eating, but before that comes, a door opens in the hallway and five handsome men of various sizes and ages enter the room. Three of them are dressed just like my father-in-law, though they all have long thick black beards flecked with grey, whereas my father-in-law's beard is short and pure white. They wear the clothing of the countryside – white turbans, long white togas that hang to their knees and white or brown pantaloons that peek through below the hem of the togas. I stare at their thick muscled brown arms. Their sun-toasted faces endow them with an aura of holiness. Moe jumps up to greet them.

He explains that two of these men are his cousins from a neighbouring village. He hasn't seen them for more than ten years. I have met the other two before. They are the husbands of Behia and Khadija. The fifth member of this tribe of beautiful men is Abdelghani. He wears Western clothes and looks like a typical teen-age boy from America or Europe. I think, "I have known you for a very long time and you are my friend." I say nothing aloud, but I smile at him. He looks at me but he doesn't smile back. He looks away and stares at the wall.

As everyone is sitting down again, the children appear. I count them; there are ten, including my own. Each child finds a place on a male lap and looks eagerly at the food in the centre of what has become a large circle of men, children and me. A small boy appears from the kitchen with another bowl of food. He places it next to the first and takes his place on the lap of one of the men. I feel awkward in this place of all men and I ask Moe where the women are.

"The women eat by themselves in the kitchen," he explains.

"What about me?" I ask.

He smiles, "It's okay," he says sarcastically. "You are different. You are *Americanea*. You can eat with the men in this family."

I look at my spoon. Moe whispers to the small boy on his lap, who jumps up, runs to the kitchen and returns quickly with a small plate. Moe takes my spoon and serves me a helping of the lamb stew and couscous. The men smile, almost in unison, and then, as though they have been given some silent signal, they reach out with large chunks of bread to the stew bowls. They all eat from the same bowl, using the bread as their spoons and, at the end of the meal, as their napkins as well.

I remember from the circumcision party how difficult it is to use bread as a spoon and I am grateful for the gift of a regular spoon and plate. When the meal is over, Moe tells me we are going to another village to sleep. His brother, Tahar, lives in Moussa, a short distance from Mascara, and he has a real bed for us.

A Journey Around Mascara

We say our goodbyes for the night, promising to return the next day, and head down the dark road towards Moussa. The children curl up on the back seat and fall asleep even before we are out of the driveway. I spend the ten minutes it takes to drive to Moussa hoping we don't get stopped at any roadblocks. We don't.

When we pull up to Tahar's house, we find him standing in his front yard waiting for us. He is smiling so broadly we can make out his face in the darkness. Tahar drives a taxi and he is married to his first cousin, another Zohra.

We enter the house and are greeted by Zohra, a smiling young woman who greets us in French and makes us feel instantly welcome. Zohra and Tahar have two children who are sleeping and will greet us in the morning.

Moe chats to his brother for a moment and then turns to me. "Tahar and Zohra have painted the whole inside of their house in our honour," he says in English.

I smile and look around, nodding appreciatively. The house is clean and very modern, though it's not large. I feel as though Tahar and Zohra are caught between the old and the new in Algeria – the old coming from the customs and the new from the Western furniture they have chosen for their home.

We sit on the couch in the living room and talk as Zohra prepares tea and cookies. Moe tells me that Tahar does very well for his family. When he isn't driving his taxi, he works on the farm. My Zohra and Tarek try to stay awake, but they both fall asleep on our laps almost as soon as we sit down. Tahar's Zohra motions to bring them to the mattresses she has set up for them on the floor in a back room. They fall asleep as soon as we lay them down and tuck them under the covers. In our honour, Tahar and Zohra have vacated their bedroom where I find a double western-style bed with lovely Algerian quilts and fluffy pillows.

"In this house, I can sleep with my husband," I think in the last moments before I fall asleep. "How strange Algeria is – so many inflexible customs, so many changeable rules.

The laughter of children wakes us up the next morning. We have slept for a long time. I think, "Maybe, the comfort of a real bed in a clean house helped us relax."

We find our children playing happily with their cousins in the middle of the living room. Tahar's Zohra is in the kitchen and motions us to sit at the table. She brings out a familiar break-fast – eggs and hot buttered bread with jam with the usual heavily sweetened tea – not the regular Algerian breakfast. I smile at Zohra's kindness. Tahar has told her what I served when he came to visit our house.

"My brother is a good man, don't you think?" Moe asks me as we finish breakfast.

"Yes, I think he is wonderful. But then I like all your brothers."

Moe gives me a wink and a smile, and mutters, "I know."

I imagine he is thinking something wicked.

While we are waiting for Zohra to finish the breakfast clean-up, Moe announces, "Yesterday my father brought to me interesting document. It is called *Livre de Famille*. It is what we use in this country to record major events in a family. My father tells me he never register my birth until I am eight years old because he think French will put me in army. Then when I need papers, he make me younger. My passport say I am born 1935 but today I find out I am born 1931."

That makes Moe twelve years older than I am. "You really are an old man," I wink at him and whisper just loud enough for him to hear, "My parents will have a heart attack."

Moe looks at me sheepishly, but he is smiling. "No, I think it is good. Maybe now that I am so old and so smart you will listen to me."

Before I can respond to his comment, Moe turns away and enters into some new deep conversation with his brother and sister-in-law. After they exchange a few comments back and forth, Moe asks me, "Would you like to go and visit my sister Rakaya? She has a baby two days ago and yesterday when I saw her, she not in good shape. I want to see her again before we leave. Also I want to visit my older brother, Tohamy. The family tells me he has cancer and is near to die. I like to see him also before we leave." Moe pauses, and then adds, "We also go to visit my mother's grave." I see pain on his face when he mentions her. He hasn't talked about his mother since the night under the canopy back in Arizona when he told me her story. Those days seem so long ago and so far away. The stories seemed like fairy tales to me. Then, I could never have imagined that I would be living in that fairy tale.

Moe takes a deep breath and continues, "There is one thing that you must do. My sister-in-law insist you wear veil." He gestures toward Zohra who is quietly watching me. "She asks me how you feel about this."

I look at Zohra and back to Moe, hesitating. "I will wear one if you say I should," I finally tell him. "I don't know how to put it on. She'll have to show me. Will she lend me one?"

I pause and then ask Moe, "More importantly, how do you feel about me wearing one?"

Moe gestures helplessly, "I not happy – but in this place I think it easier for my family. My family has to live here. I not want to make it difficult for them," He adds, "Also, if you not do this, then everyone will stare and say bad things to insult my family."

I think he is finished and I turn to Zohra, but Moe blurts out what seems to be the most important thing he wants to say, "In fact," he says, "if you not wear one – then you must stay at my cousin's house – and that not be very nice for you."

I nod my understanding. "Okay, I'll wear it. I hate the staring, too."

I notice that Tahar's Zohra is watching my face as Moe talks to me. When Moe turns to tell her what I have said, a look of relief crosses her face. She immediately runs to fetch one of her veils.

I run my hand over the folded material that Zohra hands me.

It is made of a soft and light fabric – wellworn, but good quality cotton. I unfold the fabric, which is about the size of a bed sheet and hold a length of it up to the light, noticing that I can almost see through it.

"What are you doing?" Moe asks me, his voice deep and concerned. He glances at Zohra and Tahar who are quietly watching my movements.

"Oh, I was just wondering why you can see through this material," I tell him, laughing. "I thought you men wanted to cover us up, not tease other men."

"Don't laugh," Moe says sharply. "They will think you are laughing at their customs. They will think you not respect them."

"I'm sorry," I tell him, immediately making my expression as serious as I can. I start to drape the white material around my body in an attempt to arrange it in what I think is the correct way to wear such a garment. Zohra comes towards me, shaking her head back and forth and clicking her tongue to indicate that I haven't got it right at all. She takes the material and wraps it in great folds around my body.

"I didn't know there was such an art to wearing this," I mumble. Moe stares wide-eyed during the whole procedure. "Maybe this is the first time he has ever seen a woman put on one of these things." I think.

Suddenly, my daughter, Zohra comes running in. When she sees me, she stops, and carefully walks a circle around me, staring as if she has never seen me before. Then, out of her mouth pops her four-year-old assessment of the situation, "Wow, Mommy, now you are really a lady."

I laugh. I am also relieved. I thought she might call me *batman* like she calls the veiled women in the village. Then I remember that Moe has just told me that I shouldn't laugh in case Tahar and Zohra think that I don't respect their customs. I clap my hand over my mouth, "I'm sorry, Moe," I say. "I just have to laugh at her."

Moe nods, trying to hold back his own laughter. He loses control, and laughter pours from him in loud hoots of sound. Breathless, he finally manages to stop long enough to tell his

brother and sister-in-law what Zohra has said. It takes a few minutes for all the laughter to subside.

The last piece of the veil that Zohra gives me is a small tri-
angle of lace with two ribbons attached to two of the corners.
The ribbons are long enough so that they can be tied at the back
of the head. It is Zohra's favourite face piece because breathing
through it is easier than through the solid cloth face pieces that
many women wear. She ties the face piece around my head and I
am ready to go. Hurriedly, she dons her own veil, and we all head
for the car.

Zohra and I tumble into the back seat with the four children,
and the men settle into the front. Wearing a veil on this hot sunny
morning makes me feel stifled and I have to swallow my urge to
tear off the face piece. The men roll down the front windows and
the hot breeze on my covered face cools me off a little. As we drive
down the busy streets filled with people, I suddenly feel strange.
For the first time since I came to Algeria, no one is looking at me.
I have disappeared.

In a few minutes, we arrive at a run-down old house in one
of the poorer Arab sections of Mascara. Tahar knocks at the door
and we are invited in by Moe's sister, Yamina. She is looking after
Rakaya. She nervously glances around outside as we enter the
house.

Moe explains, "We come at this time because their husbands
are at work in the fields. They not know we are visiting."

His words remind me of what he has told me before. These are
the husbands who have forbidden their wives to see their brother
and his infidel wife. An image of a willow passes through my mind
and I recognize the danger associated with this visit.

We enter a small room with a high bed made of several mattresses stacked on the floor. I see Rakaya lying there. She is holding a small bundle. She turns towards us as we stand staring at
her and slowly raises herself to a sitting position. She speaks in
squeaky Arabic to her brothers like it is an effort for her to speak
at all.

Moe turns to me, "She seems much better than she was last
night. I am so happy about this."

He quietly introduces her as Rakaya, his nineteen-year-old younger sister with her first baby. I take off the face piece and walk up to her, kissing both her cheeks. She barely smiles at me and I step back quickly, feeling that she is afraid of me. We stare at each other for a moment more and then Moe formally introduces the older sister, Yamina. Moe tells me Yamina is twenty-eight. She looks forty – like Behia, worn out and sad. Yamina has had five babies in five years and is pregnant again. We greet each other with kisses and I smile. She seems friendlier than her younger sister, but both are very shy.

We don't stay long in that house and I am glad. The smell of urine, Rakaya's unwashed body and afterbirth is very strong. Both sisters seem nervous to have us there. Moe was determined to have me meet these women in spite of their husbands, but I wonder if we have caused trouble for them.

As we exit the house, I retie the face piece in place. Moe rambles on about the plight of his sisters and how they are so sweet, yet so poor. In his eyes I see tears.

"It not right they live this way," he says over and over, as we walk back to the car. "I want to help them – but their husbands too conservative. They never accept help from me. They think I betray my family by marriage to you. Ah, they are so stupid, these people. Someday I will show them." By this time, he is glaring at me.

Frightened by the intensity of his voice and his glare, I stutter, "What – what do you mean? What have I done?"

A few seconds pass. Moe takes a deep breath and his expression softens. "Sorry, I know it not your fault."

"I can always become a Moslem," I offer, wishing he would stop frowning at me.

"Yes, you can," he answers, "but then we have to change your name." His smile returns, "One day we discuss this – but not now." He opens the car door and we all crowd back in.

Moe turns his attention to getting us to Tohamy's house, our next destination. Tahar navigates. Tohamy doesn't live far from Rakaya but we twist and turn down back alleys to find his place, a small apartment in a converted garage located behind one of the biggest houses on the main street. Tohamy stumbles out to greet us, his face is yellow, his cheeks sunken, and his eyes protruding, bringing to my mind pictures of holocaust survivors. Before anyone can get out of the car, Tohamy asks Moe to take him with us to his aunt's house. Moe agrees, and Tohamy stuffs himself into the front seat with the other men.

From where I sit in the back seat, I can see Tohamy's face in the car's side mirror as we weave in and out of traffic. When we hit bumps or come to a stop, he tries hard not to grimace.

When we arrive and get out of the car, I find that he towers over me. He is more than six feet tall. "How can this one brother be so tall and the rest of you so short?" I ask Moe, unable to contain my surprise.

Moe appears dumbfounded by my question, but he answers, his tone showing he is disgusted that I am so curious, "I have two brothers and one cousin who look like this. The rest are shorter." He glares at me, "Maybe you could ask me important question, like, *is my brother sick enough to die?* That would be better question. Who care how tall he is? And yes, my brother die soon. His sickness is cancer. Sometimes, you ask stupid things." Abruptly, he turns and walks toward the apartment.

My head down and my face hidden by my veil, I think, "Yes, sometimes I ask stupid things." I follow him and his brothers inside.

As I enter, Moe's aunt barely glances at me in my veil before she starts yelling at Moe, advancing toward him as if she is going to strike him. Moe stands in front of her silently, his eyes on the floor. Then, abruptly she stops her tirade and takes a step backward. When his aunt finishes speaking, Moe says something to her quietly, still not meeting her eyes. She shouts at him again.

The rest of us, adults and children, stand in the entryway staring at this woman. Suddenly, my daughter, who has been frowning at this new relative from the beginning of her rant, yells something in Arabic.

Instantly, Moe's aunt stops her tirade, grabs Zohra, and covers her little face with kisses. Zohra starts to giggle and the tension dissolves.

"Take this stupid veil off," Moe says in his most authoritative voice. "She is very angry at me that I make you wear veil. She call me hypocrite for being educated man and bringing you here in veil. She is very mad. She make me promise I not make you wear this again. She thinks she is very progressive woman in this town."

"Yes, I can tell that. Tell her I agreed to wear it and I didn't mind." I am anxious to smooth over the situation any way I can.

"No, I not tell her anything," Moe states. "She is too angry. Just don't wear this veil when we leave or we both be in big trouble. She thinks you are foolish woman to wear this."

"Okay," I respond, pulling off the face piece and unwrapping myself from the yards of fabric draped around me. I hand the crumpled fabric to Yamina who takes it silently. I can't be certain what I see in her eyes as I give it to her.

Then, to my surprise, Moe's aunt comes forward and addresses me in French, saying, *"Bonjour, Suzanne."* Pointing to herself, she says, *"Miriam,"* and pointing to her short round fuzzy-headed little husband, she says, *"Hassan."*

I smile at Miriam, who has been watching silently as Moe and I speak in English. I decide, "I like her. How strange to find such a progressive woman in village that is so backward in so many ways."

She offers me a seat in the living room right next to her. This house is a lovely villa once occupied by a French family. Miriam and Hassan acquired it simply by moving in and claiming ownership when the French owners fled. It is well cared for and everything inside is modern and clean, smelling pleasantly of orange water and lavender. It is furnished with European style furniture and lace curtains on the windows. The floors are terrazzo like in our apartment. The kitchen has modern appliances. The bathroom has Western plumbing and a bathtub as big as a small swimming pool.

Today, there are many children in the house. Some are cousins and some of the youngest are grandchildren. My children are thrilled and run off to play.

Moe laughs at all of the excitement. "They all come here just to see the *Americanea*," he says quietly to me.

Miriam and four of her grown daughters cook a beautiful mid-day lunch for us with so many courses that I lose count after six. The last course is a bowl of cooked orange peel in a thick sugar syrup – a delicacy in the Algerian countryside. I struggle to finish it all because Moe tells me it is impolite to leave any in my bowl.

By midafternoon, Moe is restless and his face is flushed. During a break in the Arabic conversation that is swirling around me, I ask him what is wrong.

"I not feel well," he says. "I feel tired and my heart beats too fast. I think we leave now."

"O-kay," I respond slowly. I don't quite understand. My mind races trying to sort it all out, "Is Moe physically sick or is he feeling anxious and upset over something? Has our visiting with so many of his family been too stressful for him?" I wish, not for the first time, that I could understand his language and know for certain what is going on around me.

"We go to Oran and visit my uncle. He has nice apartment. If we leave now, we get there before dark." Moe stands up and begins to say goodbye to everyone.

The children are reluctant to leave and Zohra whines loudly. Moe looks at her with his *I am bigger than you* look. Instantly, she sweetly says her goodbyes to everyone. I do the same. As I walk down the sidewalk to the car, I realize I will miss Miriam. I know that is absurd, because I have only just met her. But, she is a light in my valley of darkness, and I am reluctant to leave the spark of brightness that she has created around me.

Moe starts up the little Renault and is just about to pull away from the curb when his father, Abdullah, approaches carrying a small suitcase. He must have walked over from his house. He knocks on the window and Moe rolls it down. They wave their hands back and forth at each other as they talk. Eventually, the argument subsides, and Abdullah opens the back door and swings himself onto the seat next to the children.

"My father insists we pick up Abdelghani and take them both

to Oran with us," Moe explains wearily. "I really have no choice. I would rather not, but he is my father."

The children are delighted to have uncle Abdelghani and *grandfodder* all to themselves for the whole trip. The back seat is full of laughter. We pull into Oran just as the sun is disappearing over the horizon. Moe's father leans forward, pokes Moe, and says something. Moe grunts a response. In a few minutes, he stops the car in front of a large concrete building with a sign in the window. Our passengers get out, taking their bags with them.

"They are going to spend the night in the public bath," Moe explains. "My other brother, Abdelkader, is in town and they want to see him but they think it is too late to call him now. They spend the night here and then go in the morning. My father thinks we should get hotel and go to my uncle's in the morning, too." Moe wipes his hand wearily across his face. "I not doing that. It too difficult to get hotel room in this city with European woman. They want to see all our papers and our *Livre de Famille* to prove we are married." He shrugs. "So I just go to bother my uncle – if I can find his address."

We drive around for half an hour, Moe mumbling to himself. The children fall asleep in the back seat and I reach around to cover them up with a blanket. They look so sweet asleep, curled up together. They have had a long day.

Finally, Moe parks outside a tall modern building with many lights. It looks like a hotel to me. I am too tired to even speak, and I know better than to ask any questions or make any suggestions.

"Stay here. I go to find my uncle," Moe instructs. A few minutes later, he returns. "My cousin answered the buzzer. My aunt and uncle are at the movie." He opens the back door to wake up Zohra and Tarek. "We go up."

Neither child is happy about being disturbed, nor about the idea of visiting more relatives, but we carry them, along with our bags, into the building and take the elevator to the fifteenth floor.

Moe's cousin greets us with smiles at the elevator door. Moe tells me how surprised he is to find his cousin has grown into an adult. He remembers him only as a small child. His cousin leads us into an elegant apartment and immediately takes us on a tour of the ten beautifully decorated rooms filled with artwork and beautiful sculptures of every size and shape. This place has everything anyone could want, even a washer and dryer. I suspect the tour is a way to pass the time until his parents come home.

Moe and his cousin struggle to talk to each other. Moe's French is very poor and his cousin's Arabic is nearly non-existent. The conversation is stilted with much hand waving and many starts and stops. The children of this aunt and uncle have lived most of their lives in France and only recently returned to the city of Oran. We return to the living room to find Zohra and Tarek curled up together in the large lounge chair, both sound asleep.

A few moments later we hear a key in the lock and Amira and Hakim appear with three more of their children. Hakim is curious about who we are, and is amazed when he realizes that his nephew, who he thought was still in America, is actually standing in front of him. Aunt Amira and Uncle Hakim both appear delighted to see us, throwing their arms around our necks, and kissing our cheeks.

Hakim is the brother of Moe's mother. He left their village at an early age and came to Oran for an education. When the war started, he took his family to France. There, he was a very successful businessman. The two youngest children were born there. I wonder why they have come back to Algeria.

Amira wants to know how I liked Mascara. I tell her in my broken French that it was interesting and she laughs abruptly and without humour. She tells me through Moe that she never goes there any more because it breaks her heart to see how they live. Hakim nods in agreement. They both tell me not to go there because I am sure to be sick.

Our children wake up with all the talking. Hakim and Amira's teenage daughter smiles at Zohra and Tarek and they happily follow her to her room and fall into bed. The adults all agree we should go sightseeing in the morning. Moe and I are shown to a lovely bedroom and told to sleep well. As I get ready for bed, I think, "In this family, too, I get to sleep with my husband."

Moe and I sleep until 10:00 the next morning, surprised that no one wakes us up. We hustle out of bed, get dressed and go to the dining room where we find the whole family gathered around a late breakfast. We are introduced to Amira and Hakim's five children. They range in age from thirteen to twenty-five, and all are students in some school or another. Soon, the young people head out in various directions, leaving Amir and Hakim, and Moe, Tarek, Zohra and me eating our breakfast.

Amir, Hakim, Moe and I agree that this is a good opportunity for us to see the city of Oran.

Hakim spends most of the tour telling us not only about what we are seeing, but how it used to be before the war. He explains that Oran is on the Mediterranean Sea and because it used to be a French naval base so there are many more Europeans here than in Algiers.

Moe and I both agree that Oran is much more beautiful than Algiers. Almost every street is lined with palm trees and all along the coast we see white beaches. Hakim points out the government buildings, the three universities, and an 18th century mosque. In the afternoon we stop at a fancy restaurant and have a meal of seafood and vegetables. We sit on a hill overlooking the sea and watch the sun go down, and then we return to the apartment.

"My relatives feel sorry for you going to the village," Moe says that night when we are getting ready for bed. He speaks in a quiet voice that is filled with sadness. "They say it is best if I never take you there again. They say it is bad to look at such sad people. Do you understand what I mean?"

"I understand. But what about you?" I ask, equally quietly, thinking of his sudden desire to leave the village. "I think this visit to the village has hurt you more than me. It must be hard to see your people in such poverty."

Moe's eyes fill with tears. "Yes," he says, "very difficult for me. I think it make me crazy."

Sickness and More Sickness

Sometime in the middle of that night, I get sick. I run down the hall to the wonderful modern bathroom in Amira and Hakim's elegant fifteenth-floor apartment and I am violently ill. The vomiting seems to go on forever. Hours later, I make my way back to the bedroom. I collapse onto the bed, burning with fever. I close my eyes.

I awake to Moe shaking me. My sight is blurry and I can barely make out his face as he bends over me. He has a glass in his hand and he tells me to drink. I push it away. Then, I hear Aunt Amira's voice and she sits down next to me. Moe lifts me to a half-sitting position and I feel something thick and sweet go down my throat. I fall back into a deep sleep.

When I next awaken, the apartment is silent and dark. I don't hear any voices. I don't hear anything. I stumble out of my room and into the hallway to the bathroom. I am dizzy and everything seems far away, but I no longer feel sick. Vaguely, I wonder where I am and I wonder what time it is.

As I re-enter the bedroom, I see a note on the dresser leaning against a large glass of some strange-looking liquid. The handwriting seems familiar. The note says,

Hope you are feeling better. I am walking for an hour if you wake up. Please drink this glass of gazoose. It is good for you. Please do not drink water from tap here. Moe

I drink what is in the glass. Then I crawl back under the covers on the soft mattress and return to a place where dreams and reality meet. Thoughts flit through my mind, "Who is Moe?" "Where am I?" "Who am I?" and again, "Who is Moe?" Then, I remember, "Moe wrote the note." Somehow that thought contents me and I sleep.

Some time later, I wake up again. This time I am clear-headed enough to look around and to realize that I hear voices in the hallway and steps coming towards the door. It opens and Moe's worried face hovers over me.

"Are you finally awake?" he asks, impatiently. "I start to think you sleep forever."

"What?" I answer, trying to make sense of what he is saying, "What time is it?"

"You go to bed two days ago and you not wake up. You sick." Moe's voice is abrupt and harsh, but his hand touches my forehead with gentleness.

"I am so hungry." The words come out of me, but I am not really connected to them. I am still trying to figure out the details of where I am and how two days could have passed without my being aware of them.

"You must be better." Moe says.

I look over his shoulder to see his aunt enter the room. She smiles at me and wipes my face with a soft cloth, speaking to me all the time. I don't understand a word, but I know that whatever she is telling me is full of kindness and sympathy.

"We are here for three days now," Moe tells me, his voice again impatient. "We must go back to Birtouta. I take you to the car and we go now." He motions toward the door.

"I'm so hungry," I say again. "I'm so thirsty."

"No food," Moe says, his authoritative voice taking over. "You are sick. I am sick of watching you be sick. We go home."

Amira says something to Moe and she leaves the room.

"She will bring you something to drink and more medicine," Moe explains. "Then we go. I very embarrassed to stay here so long." He rubs his hand across his face, and his voice drops to a whisper, "I think maybe you die or something."

I look at Moe. I am sorry he is distressed, but I am too tired to say anything.

Suddenly Zohra bursts through the door and throws herself on me. "Mommy," she shouts. Then, she takes my face in her small hands and searches it, clearly looking for something. "You're not sick any more, are you?" she asks.

"Hi honey," I whisper, surprised that I have so little strength. "I think I am better."

"I want to go home," she states firmly. "Can we go home now?"

"Okay. If you want to," I answer. "But, I thought you were having fun."

"I am," Zohra says. Then, her little voice gets very serious and she adds, "But daddy isn't happy."

"Okay," I whisper again. "We'll go home."

Moe helps me up and Amira brings me a large glass of the same thick sweet liquid I remember. I take it from her and greedily down every last drop. I am so thirsty. She takes the glass from me and leaves the room. As I am getting dressed, she returns with another large glass, this time filled with *gazoose*. The watery sweet liquid feels equally good going down. I start to feel better.

I collapse into the front seat of the car and Moe gets our things packed into the trunk and the kids situated in the back seat. I fall asleep as the car pulls out of Oran and I sleep the entire 225 miles back to Algiers. Moe stops only to buy several bottles of *gazooze*, some water, some treats for the children and some crackers for me. I smile at him as he hands me his offerings of food and drink when I awaken near the end of our trip. "You look tired," I tell him.

"I am tired," he agrees, and finishes with, "Tired of taking care of you. I never see you so sick."

"Ah-h, were you worried about me?" I ask teasingly.

"Of course." He keeps his attention on the road and soon we pull into the parking lot outside our building.

"Whatever happened to your father and brothers? We left them at that public bath on the way here. Did you talk to them?" My memory is returning and I wonder what has happened while I was fighting the fever and sleeping away the days.

"Yes, they met with Abdelkader and then they come to my uncle's when you are sick. Abdelkader took them home."

"I'm glad they got home and we didn't have to drive them," I confess.

"I will be so glad to get home I will never want to leave again," I add.

"We sleep when we get home," Moe vows. He pauses, and turns to look at me. His eyes are sad again. "Tonight we sleep and then I go back to work tomorrow."

After his first day back at work, Moe returns home looking weary and thoughtful. The sorrow evident on his face tells me that he is struggling again. Every time we go somewhere for a weekend or a little trip, he seems to get better, and every time he returns to work, he gets anxious and then he gets sick.

He sits down wearily at the table after kissing the kids and telling them to go play in their rooms. He holds his head in his hands and only looks up when I set a plate of food in front of him. We eat together in silence.

Finally, he says, "The Minister of Agriculture is fired."

"Is that a good thing?" I ask, unsure how to interpret what he is telling me and anxious that I don't make him more upset than he is.

"Well, the new one is a *Kabyle*. He may be good and he may be bad. Shelig not liked by the *Kabyles,* so maybe he be replaced. Who knows? One bad rumour is the new Minister wants to lower the salaries of agriculture workers. If this is true, then I not stay here. I get little money for my job now. I not work for less."

"What is the difference between you and a *Kabyle?*" I ask. This question seems like one that won't upset him, and I am curious.

"*Kabyle* are Berber people who live mostly in mountains in north-eastern Algeria. Truth is, 95% of Algerian people have some Berber blood, but nobody talks about this. We think we are Arab – but really, we are also part Berber. Mostly two kinds of people live here, *Kabyle* and Arab – and French colons but they are gone – or going. The *Kabyle* people look more European. You will see them especially in Atlas Mountains. They walk along the roads and many are blond, blue-eyed and very tall. Some very beautiful. Sometimes we don't like each other – I not know why – except for history."

"What is really going on at work?" I ask carefully. I don't want to push him too hard to talk. He is so tired.

He looks at me for a long moment, and then begins. His voice takes on a storytelling quality. "A month ago I write very long letter about all the corruption and nonsense at Baba Ali. I write what is in my heart and what I know to be true for this situation. I send this letter to Vice Director of Research."

He interrupts his story to tell me, "Vice Director is good man and I hope he will be the one who replaces Shelig."

Then he continues. "After I write this letter, I hear nothing. I say in letter that I pay for a sprinkler system one year ago but it never arrive. I tell how I order seed and it never come. I tell many things like how the French engineers plant over my experiments. I tell everything and I hear nothing." He runs his hands through his hair.

"Today, I go to work. I find parts to sprinkler system mysteriously sitting in my office. When I enter my office, the secretary tells me the French engineers want to order some supplies but Shelig tells them Mr. Chaabane now boss of all orders." He shakes his head, and finishes, "French are very mad about this."

"Why are you upset, Moe?" I can't understand. "Aren't you happy about these changes? Isn't that what you wanted – to make the French treat you with more respect?"

"I am happy in one way." He gestures, waving his hands in the air, "But, I am also not liking that no one talks to me about this. I find out from secretary. Not a good sign." Now, he is shaking his head as well as waving his hands.

"There is big meeting planned for Tuesday with all the big people. Maybe things will change." This last part he says, quietly, as if he doesn't really believe what he is saying.

Oh, I forget," Moe adds. "We not get paid – again! I have to borrow more money from Mohamed G."

I think, "Thank goodness for Mohamed G." He has become our personal banker lately and we go to him every time Moe doesn't get his pay on time.

The next day, Moe brings two Arabs guests home for coffee. They have just returned from getting their agricultural engineering degrees in China. The husband is Saleh and the wife is Fahila. They have been working at Baba Ali for a month. After being introduced to them, I ask Moe in English why he took such a long time to bring them to meet me.

Half-laughing, he says, "I wanted to tell you about them. But when I meet them I realize these people are Commie fanatics."

I smile. *Commie fanatics* is something my father would say.

I try to understand something of their conversation, but it is mostly in Arabic, and I only catch a word or two. Through Moe, they make attempts to ask me, "Why is the United States in Viet Nam?"

I tell them I don't know and that I am against the war. They were hoping to engage me in a fight, but they realize that even though I am an American, I agree with them.

When they finally leave, Moe tells me the story of why he invited them for coffee. "As you know, I refuse to wear suit to work. First, because I think it is silly to work on a farm and wear good suit. The French and other Europeans all wear suits. The workers always stare at them. The workers sometimes don't believe I am Engineer because I not wear suit and tie. Anyway, this *Commie* talk to me today. He comes up and put his arm around my shoulders and tells me, 'You good man, Chaabane. You and me, we are different from the others. We are really from the people.' To this guy, anyone 'from the people' is good person."

I laugh at Moe's story and at the fact that he continues to call this couple *Commies*. After the suit encounter, Moe couldn't resist bringing them home for coffee and having a chat.

Silently, I am grateful he didn't invite them for dinner. They eat only Chinese food.

A few days later, we are invited to the *Commies'* apartment for supper. I can't figure out why Moe is excited by the invitation. As soon as we are certain the children are asleep, we climb the stairs to their apartment which is directly above ours. Salah is excited to show us around. He tours us in and out of every room, each of which is painted in a different shade of shiny red paint and decorated with Chinese knickknacks and figurines. The furniture is shiny black. Pictures of Mao Tse-Tung hang on every wall.

Chinese military music thunders through huge speakers in every room, even the bathroom. The living room walls are covered with medals that Saleh received from the government of China for his work with the Communist Party.

When we finally sit down on the Chinese brocade floor cushions they offer us, the music suddenly switches to soft oriental background noise. I am grateful. My head had begun to pound from the other music. The conversation for the evening centres around Algerian and Chinese politics. Occasionally, Moe translates, but mostly I sit on my Chinese cushion and stare at the colourful decorations. My mind wanders back to the other homes I have visited since I came to Algeria – the elegance of Auntie Amir and Uncle Hakar's, the poverty of the homes in the village, the colourful oriental rugs, thick brocade furniture, large tapestries and the rooftop garden in Leila and Mahmoud's mansion, the murals of dancing cherubs on the tiled ceilings of Yarka and Aouf's apartment. Algeria is such a series of contrasts.

When dinner is served, every single morsel of food is Chinese, from the Won Ton soup to the fortune cookies. Moe is in heaven. He particularly likes the twelve different Chinese alcoholic beverages he is offered. He tastes them all. Finally, he is drunk. He raises his glass to his host and announces something in very loud Arabic. I don't understand what he says so I am surprised when we are abruptly and unceremoniously escorted to the door. I thank our hosts as best I can, and help Moe stumble home.

Once back in our apartment, I ask Moe what he said that brought the evening to such a dramatic and unceremonious end.

He laughs. "I just tell them I not like the politics of America or China. I tell them I am Algerian and I want Algeria for the Algerians. I also tell him it is necessary to fix Algeria's problems not the world problems. I tell them we are nationalists and they can take their dogma and *schttuff it up der butts.*" Moe deliberately slurs his words as he exaggerates how he said *schttuff it up der butts.*

I laugh, "You didn't really say that, did you, Moe?"

"Well, I say most of it. I want to say that, but I not say *schtuff it up der butts."* He repeats it and laughs heartily. He repeats it as if he likes the feel of the words on his tongue.

It is good to hear him laugh and to see him get passionate about something again.

Moe stumbles to our bed and passes out – the end of an interesting evening.

I stumble after him.

On Tuesday Moe leaves for work, anxious and nervous about the meeting scheduled for the day. I play with the children and we take a short walk in the village. I write to my parents and tell them about our trip to Mascara but I leave out most of the poverty and sickness. Mom and Dad mostly want to hear about how our children are doing.

I expect Moe to come home at his usual 6:00 p.m. but there is no sign of him. I feed the children and at 7:30 p.m. I put them to bed. Anxious, I try to do some knitting that I have started. I wish I had some music or a radio, but my thoughts are my only company. I asked Moe once about getting a radio for the apartment, but he told me that radios have to be registered with the government and the process to purchase one is very complicated and very expensive. Finally, at 9:30, I hear his key in the lock.

"How did it go?" I ask as I hug him. I turn toward the kitchen to heat up his supper.

"Not worry about food. I have much today," he says to stop me. He throws some papers on the table and falls wearily onto the living room mattress and closes his eyes.

"Hey," I say, walking over and shaking him by the shoulder. "You can't sleep now. I am dying of curiosity. What happened at your meeting?"

Moe opens his eyes and says disgustedly, "It is like the war will never end."

"A war between who?" I ask. "Who is fighting who?"

"I not sure of this," Moe answers. "I not sure who is fighting who. That is the trouble with this. I not trust anyone." He pauses to sit up.

"Okay, I tell you what happen. The meeting not start before 3:00 p.m. and we talk until 9:00 p.m. Three of us Algerian

Engineers, me and the *Commies,* and the *chief de station* and two other Algerian head of workers tell Shelig everything we know. We tell him about corruption and sabotage. The workers ask to get the Frenchman, Giovanni, fired or moved. The workers hate him. They say he is former French SS officer and they think he murdered two men in Blida during the war," He shakes his head and tells me in an aside, "I not know if this is true – but it is what the worker's believe."

He continues, "Then I talk and tell him how these French always dig out my experiments. Early yesterday, they do this for third time, so I go and pull out their plants. Then I tell how Ducont and Giovanni come after me screaming and yelling like children. I ask how they can do it to me, but I cannot do it to them." He shakes his head from side to side as he remembers. "I tell them I don't care anymore and that I am not a slave to them anymore and that I am going to go straight to the Minister."

"When I finish telling Shelig this story, he looks at me and says, 'Why you didn't tell me this before?'"

I tell him I did, but he says he not remember. This whole thing insanity. Shelig is Director of Research for Baba Ali, but he has two jobs. He is also Director of Research for the whole area. I get idea that Shelig is more worried for his job with this new Minister than about us. I think he is playing both ends to the middle. You know what I mean?" Moe's headshaking is slower now as if he is accepting that nothing will change.

Moe shrugs his shoulders, "When I finish my story I am told they will have another meeting tomorrow. I don't care anymore." He closes his eyes again.

"Wow, Moe! Did you really say all that to everyone?" I try to be encouraging, to let him know that I am on his side, that I think he did a courageous thing.

"Yes, I say it all. I not care." Moe lies there with his eyes closed, not moving.

"Moe, don't get discouraged. I think it's a good thing you are doing."

Wearily, he opens his eye and repeats, "I have nothing to lose now. This has to stop."

Later, Moe falls into bed after taking a handful of pills. When I ask him what they are, he stares at me sullenly and says nothing.

The next day the only thing I hear about the second meeting is that Shelig is working on a plan and one of the Frenchmen is going to Europe for an extended period of time. When I press for more information, Moe just changes the subject, saying, "I want to invite Mahmoud and his wife Leila to dinner on Sunday. It is good to have friends when things not good." Mahmoud is Moe's friend who is a political leader in the FLN party.

"Okay," I answer, surprised that he wants to have guests. "I will be happy to see them again. They're very nice people."

On Sunday Mahmoud and his wife arrive, bringing a beautiful cake for me and candy for the children. We have a wonderful evening together and our children play happily with theirs.

After they leave, Moe tells me we are not the only people having trouble with the government. There is trouble at the very top of the regime. Mahmoud has been told that the government ministers are not happy with President Boumedienne who is in Yugoslavia at the moment. When he returns home, the FLN is going to force him to call a convention of the party to sort things out. Discontent is increasing everywhere.

Maybe Paris, Revenge by Donkey, and Thoughts of Becoming a Second Wife

It is October 13, 1966 my kids are fed and Moe is off to work by 8 am. I have been in Algeria for four months and 24 days. A total of 148 days. I sit down and write the following:

Dear Marvellous Mommy and Darling Daddy:

I have some news to tell you. Better sit down and relax and get comfortable first. Try not to faint. In the last letter I told you there was a chance we would be moving. Well, it's definite. We are moving to Paris! (Please faint later.) Moe is being sent on a "stagge." In English, it means a training tour and all of us get to go. We will be in France for two years. Moe will be working on a farm there and also going to school at the Sorbonne to learn French. They are going to ship our car for us. We are leaving very soon and will have to leave special forwarding instructions for the Christmas boxes. I am rather worried about it. Within the next two or three days we should know the exact date of departure. It will be great for the kids. At least, I will be able to take them out for walks and play without finding ourselves in the middle of a demonstration.

I stare at the words on the fine onionskin paper. I can barely believe what I have written.

Moe arrived home last night with the news. He didn't have any more details, but he is so sure. I decide not to send my letter right away. I will wait for more details which Moe assures me will come by tomorrow.

The next day, October 14, I pick up my pen to finish the letter I started.

> Somehow I was interrupted. Moe has gone to Algiers today to write his 'commitment.' A 'commitment' means we have to agree to work in Algeria for five years when we return from Paris. The papers are sent to Paris and we leave in two to four weeks. Anyway, I will let you know the minute-by-minute details. We get to keep this apartment here. All we take with us is our clothes. Moe will get paid in a funny way. Now, he is getting 140,000 francs per month. When he is in France, he will get 70,000 francs from the Algerian government paid to us in France and the other 70,000 francs will automatically go into our account here. In addition, the French government will also pay us 3,000 francs. So, on the whole, we get 100,000 in France while our bank account grows here in Algeria. In two years we should have a nice pile of money. Of course, 33,000 a month will go out of the account for the car, but that's only for one year. As well, Moe gets two months paid vacation. Our friends from 'the people' are going too. Well, got to run. Write soon.
>
> Love, Susie

I fold the letter and slide it into an envelope, gather up the kids and walk to the post office. My parents will be so happy to get this particular news.

Moe is so excited about all of this news. He talks so fast I can barely understand him. He keeps telling me over and over again that, maybe if we go away for a little while, things will change. The news, however, doesn't help his sleep. He rolls all over the bed and is up and down all night. At one point, I get up to see if I can do something for him, and catch him just as he downs a handful of pills. I go back to bed without saying anything.

Returning to the apartment after my walk to the post office, I see our car parked in the spot nearest to the door. I look up to our balcony and our apartment door is open. I tell the children, "Hurry up. The door is open. Daddy must be home."

We hurry up the stairs as fast as Tarek's fat little legs will carry him and as fast as we can get through the HLM children without hurting someone. As we enter the apartment, Moe is packing a suitcase in the middle of the living room floor.

"Moe," I ask, out of breath. "What are you doing?"

"I am packing. What you think I am doing?" he snaps. "Where have you been?"

"We just went for a walk to the post office. Why are you packing? Is it about work?"

Moe looks at me glassy-eyed, and blurts out, "No, it not for work. My stupid bossman tell me today I not have to work any more until we go to France." He shakes his head and pushes at the clothing that threatens to spill out of the suitcase. "So, I go to Orleanville with my friends."

"Orleanville? Isn't that where all those people just got killed in the floods?"

"Yes."

"Why would you go there?" I ask, wondering what is really going on.

"My cousin is getting married and I have to go. It is family thing." He looks at me, waiting for me to speak again.

I plough on. "Well, can we all go with you?"

"We have to drive a long way and then we have to park the car and go on by donkey. It is too dangerous and difficult for you and kids. I be back in a few days. I return by Saturday," he says, all of the words tumbling out one over the other. He pauses. "I promise," he finishes lamely.

"By Saturday? That's not fair," I wail. My words tumble out of my mouth before I can stop them. "You are never home now, you just work all the time – and now you are going to leave me here in the village where I can't talk to anyone for five days! That's not right."

I am shocked by the force of my reaction. Anger, hurt and abandonment overwhelm me, and inside, I stagger under the weight of these emotions. I shake my head to dispel them.

Moe says nothing for a few minutes. When he speaks, his voice is quiet, but he is close to losing control. He pronounces, "I go. I be back in a few days."

He goes into the bedroom and kisses the children goodbye.

Without another word to any of us, he picks up his suitcase, and strides out the door, slamming it shut behind him.

The sound of the door slamming brings Zohra and Tarek running into the living room. They are full of questions, their small eyes round with anxiety, "Why is Daddy so mad? Why did he slam the door? Where did he go? Mommy, why are you crying?"

I haven't any answers for them. I sit there on the mattress, rocking back and forth, staring at the door. Sometimes it is difficult to find my willow.

We keep ourselves busy while Moe is gone. I play with Zohra and Tarek and I read to them. I finish knitting one sweater and start another one. I write daily letters to my parents telling them how mad at Moe I am – but I don't mail them. I can't have Mom and Dad worrying about me. I walk in the village with the children and try to ignore the people that stare and mumble behind our backs.

On the third day, a small boy knocks on my door. It is the butcher's son. This little boy and I have become friendly through the few months I have lived here. We communicate through hand signals and bits of French. Sometimes Zohra translates. He always knocks at my door when there is a fresh kill at the butcher shop and I always agree to buy the liver. He asks me if I want the liver of the cow his father is butchering today.

"Yes," I tell him." I think, "Why not? At least, I will have something tasty to eat while Moe is gone." I chop the liver into meal-sized pieces for the three of us. I offer to share the fresh liver with Benita and her family, but she says they don't eat liver. I put the rest into the small freezer space at the top of the refrigerator.

Benita tells me that she is moving into her new house on the farm tomorrow. I try to imagine the swaying branches of my willow as I force myself to cook a special evening meal of onions, liver and fresh bread for Zohra and Tarek. They are happy to join me for supper and we make a little party of it.

I wake up on Saturday morning, the day Moe has promised to return. I have convinced myself he will be back like he promised. Both kids come running into the bedroom and jump into bed with me. They ask me when daddy will be home.

"Soon," I tell them. "Daddy will be home soon."

But as I help the kids into their pyjamas after supper that evening, he is still not home. Tarek is sniffling and feels hot to the touch. He is probably coming down with a cold. I tuck the kids into their beds, but neither wants to sleep alone. I relent and put them in my bed. We snuggle together and it isn't long before they are sound asleep. I leave them in my bed and lay down on the living room mattress. I can't sleep. I am too worried.

I watch the sun come up on Sunday morning through the glass in my balcony door. The days are warm for October, but the nights are getting cold. I try to picture where Moe might be. Orleanville is only forty miles east of Algiers. It's not like he is a thousand miles away. "Why is it taking him so long to come home?" I cry until I can't cry any more. I drift into a restless sleep, dreaming in bits and pieces of something coming towards me. As it gets closer, I see that it is a large willow swaying in the wind. The willow disappears just as I am close enough to touch it.

At 9 p.m. on Sunday night, I hear a key in the front door and my heart jumps.

"God, I hope it's really Moe and not some HLM child fooling around," I think. I stay on my mattress until the door swings open and I see that it is Moe. I roll off the mattress and go to him. He smiles at me in a distracted way. He looks weary. I notice that his pant legs are muddy and he smells of horses. He sets his suitcase down, goes into the washroom and turns on the water. He asks me to heat water for him. He wants to take a bath in our small tub. I do as he says.

"Are you hungry?" I ask. I keep my voice gentle and quiet.

"No, I just dirty," he replies, the tone of his voice reflecting mine.

I heat the water and he joins me in the kitchen when the first pot is boiling.

"It was very bad trip," he says, looking hard into my eyes, daring me to protest. "Are you happy for that?"

"I nearly wreck car," he continues, ignoring that I haven't answered his question. "I take it over ten miles in big flood, with roads under the water. Then, we walk for many miles. Then, my cousin brings me donkey to ride for last ten miles. It very uncomfortable."

I turn away to tend to the water and to hide the small smile on my face. Maybe I am happy it went so badly.

The next day Moe goes to Baba Ali to talk to his boss. When he returns he says, "We will be leaving for Paris in fifteen days. We will go by boat with the car to Marseilles and then drive to Paris."

While I stand there wondering if I should start packing right away, Moe says, "We not wait here doing nothing for fifteen days. We go for another trip to Mascara to say goodbye to my family. I make visit to Tiaret to visit my old school friend, Abdullah. We also need to pay respect to our friend, Mohamed G. I hear just today his father die last week. His family live very close to Abdullah so this work out good."

"I am sorry about Mohamed G's father," I say, remembering the old man from when we visited Mohamed G in Algiers.

The next day we load the car with enough clothes to last for a week and head down the highway toward Tiaret. I feel apprehensive about going, but neither do I want to stay behind. Moe really seems to want me to be with him. "I want you to meet Abdullah and his wife. She is known for her cooking." Winking, he continues, "Maybe, you learn some recipes from her."

The road to Tiaret is beautiful. Moe chats as we travel along. Tiaret is 95 miles from the seacoast and lies southwest of Algiers. It is called the Gateway to the Sahara. As we get further south, the countryside begins to change. With each passing mile, the land looks more desert-like. Suddenly, we come up over a low hill and find ourselves driving alongside a herd of camels. The children squeal in delight. They ask a hundred questions about the tall bumps on the camel's backs and Moe dutifully answers them.

"I didn't know you knew so much about camels," I say, surprised at his knowledge.

"I did not know either," he says, smiling. "I guess it's just something I know as an Arab." He laughs at this remark, like it tickles him somehow.

I relax, more than I have in a long time. It is nice to have Moe in such good humour.

When we finally enter Tiaret, it is noon and Moe drives around for half an hour looking for the house. He eventually pulls up in front of a stone-walled yard and pushes a button on the front of the iron gate. A voice calls out and he answers. The gate slowly swings open for us. The house and adjoining courtyard sit at the end of a long drive. It is lovely, surrounded by thick bright red bougainvillea vines and tall stately palm trees. Moe stops the car at the front door and a man wearing a black suit comes out to greet us. Moe gives him the car keys and we walk up the steep steps to a large door that swings open and a little girl about Zohra's age peers out, shyly smiling.

"You must be Moona," Moe says to her in Arabic and she nods at us.

"Zohra, this is Moona."

"I know that, Daddy," Zohra answers, impatience in her voice, "I speak your language."

Moe laughs. "Yes, I know that, my little princess. I am speaking in English so your mother can understand."

Zohra looks at me with understanding, but little compassion. "Oh, I forgot," she snaps.

Moe and I laugh, and hear our laughter echoed by a man and woman descending a long staircase at the back of the large entryway. They are obviously our hosts. They greet us with the usual cheek kisses and hugs.

Abdullah is very handsome. He looks to be in is fifties, and looks like a very distinguished and professional man. He wears a soft blue silk lounging suit with a high collar, something I have never seen before. He seems extraordinarily comfortable in it.

His wife's name is Isha and when she smiles at me, her eyes sparkle. She has long black hair that falls in smooth shiny waves down her back, and she wears a long skirt and a peasant blouse. She looks to be older than me, but not by many years.

The house is extravagant – more like a palace than a house and more lavish than anything I have seen – even in America. The floors are solid terrazzo tiles with intricate designs. In some rooms, these tiles go halfway up the walls. The four bathrooms have beautiful gold fixtures and oversized bathtubs. The house has ten bedrooms, all elaborately furnished with elegant oriental furnishing, silver accessories, and red and black velvet and satin curtains. Isha shows us where we will sleep. I imagine what it would be like to live there. Moe and I sleep in a very large double bed outfitted with royal blue silk bedding and fluffy pillows.

The children are given a separate room. Zohra has her own single bed and Tarek is assigned to a large solid oak crib with stuffed animals and little trucks. We stare until Moe pokes me in the side and tells me my gawking is rude.

I close my mouth and smile. "Sorry," I mumble, "I just find everything so beautiful."

"I know," Moe remarks, his voice soft and his tone gentle. "I too feel like we are being in fairyland. No one is sure how Abdullah keep this place in the war. I am sure it is a big story."

Our hosts lead us to a large dining room that contains mahogany tables and enough chairs for fifty people. A small table has been set and we arrange ourselves around it, our family on one side and theirs on the other.

Isha has cooked the entire meal. It is served in the traditional course style, one dish at a time, starting with salad made of tomatoes, onions and feta cheese followed by a thick tomato based soup called *shorba* that has chickpeas and pieces of beef in it. Next, we are served a fish fried with various vegetables and spiced with lots of lemon and garlic. The meat course is a wonderful lamb stew with prunes and vegetables laced with hot peppers that we are warned about. Moe chomps down on them gleefully but I know about these hot peppers and I push mine to the side of my plate. Unless you are born to these spicy peppers, you are better off having nothing to do with them.

I like this way of eating one dish at a time. I have a chance to really taste each dish without mixing many tastes together. When we finish eating, I have counted seven courses. I am so full I can barely move. The last courses flow into one another, a tray overflowing with French cheeses, a huge bowl of exotic fruit – bananas, pineapple, a cactus fruit I don't know the name of, and a

large bowl of the usual orange skins boiled in syrup. Abdullah and
Isha are devout Moslems. They don't serve alcohol.

Moe and Abdullah adjourn to the living room to talk and I
stay behind at the table using my fragmented French to communicate with Isha. Zohra translates for me for a while but she gets
bored and goes to play games with her new friends.

Isha and I babble at each other, pretending that we understand what the other is saying, but most of the time we don't. We
talk anyway and smile and laugh with each other. She is such a
warm woman and I enjoy her company whether I can understand
or not. A servant girl clears the table. Isha and I wander into the
room where the men are making plans for the next day.

Moe agrees to stay one more day so we can see the countryside
and so he can pay his respects to Mohamed G's family who live
close by. Abdullah suggests that he and Moe take his large limo
to visit Mohamed G and that I stay behind with the children. The
children are delighted that they can stay and play all day with
their new friends. I am delighted as well.

At the end of the day, when Moe and Abdullah return, Moe
says he is ready to head for Mascara in the morning.

I remember how our last trip to his family's village ended.
"Moe, I love it here with Isha and Abdullah. I could stay forever,"
I tell him mournfully, hoping he will understand my reluctance to
go again to visit his family.

He laughs at me for a minute, and then says very seriously,
"Abdullah doesn't need another wife. He can only satisfy the one
he has."

I look at Moe. Is he serious? "What do you mean?" I ask.

"Well," Moe explains, "If I let you stay here, you have to marry
Abdullah. You couldn't just stay here without...."

"Moe," I interrupt, "I was making a joke. I don't really want
to stay here, nor do I have any wish to marry Abdullah."

"Oh," says Moe, a twinkle in his eye. "Sometimes I really not
know when you are serious and when you are joking. I think that
maybe, now that you see how good this life can be, you want to
leave Moe and marry his rich friend."

"You know," I tell him, straight-faced, "maybe I will do that."

His mouth falls open, and then it closes. He smiles wickedly at me and walks away.

The next morning we head for Mascara.

 Roadblocks, More Roadblocks, Public Baths and Craziness

I see the row of automatic weapons glinting in the sun before I notice the cadre of men in green and brown camouflage motioning us to stop. Our trip to Tiaret was so free of any unpleasant events that I expected that this trip would be the same. The car jerks to a stop and three dirt-smeared, greasy, leering men come forward with guns pointed at us. Suddenly, I wish I was wearing a veil.

The leader of the group says something to Moe in Arabic and Moe tells me to give him my passport. I take it out of my purse and hand it to Moe and he hands it to the man along with his American driver's license. Pointing the barrel of his gun directly at me, the leader says *"Americanea,"* to the other two men.

"Ah," says the second man in the group, his gun also pointed in the general direction of our car. This man says something further to the leader, and the leader, abruptly and unexpectedly, waves us on.

Moe guns the engine and we fly down the road.

A few minutes later, the roadblock out of sight behind us, I glance at the speedometer. It reads 120 kilometres per hour.

"It's okay to slow down now, Moe," I say, though I am still frozen with fear.

"Oh," says Moe. He is shaking.

"They make me have nervous breakup," he says, spitting out the words with anger and frustration.

"It's nervous breakdown," I correct him.

"I don't care – breakup, breakdown – make no difference. I hate this." He mutters as much to himself as to me.

Then, glancing ahead, he exclaims, his voice showing his disbelief, "Oh, shit. Another."

I look up. In front of us is another roadblock, much more elaborate than the last. Three army trucks packed with soldiers block the road. A few oddly dressed men stand in the middle of the road. This time, several cars are stopped ahead of us. The soldiers have one man from the lead car out and up against his car. One soldier is checking his pockets and running his hands over the man's body, obviously looking for something.

"Shit for this," says Moe. His face turns red.

I grip the holy-shit bar tightly and I don't let go until I lose the feeling in my fingers.

"What are those men doing to that man?" Zohra asks, the innocence in her little-girl voice underlining the danger of our situation.

"Nothing!" Moe yells at her, his voice vibrating with vehemence. "Sit down and be quiet unless you want me to go to jail!"

Zohra looks at Moe's face in the mirror and immediately breaks into a loud scream. Tarek immediately does the same. I turn around in my seat and try to comfort them with soft words but they will have none of it. They scream and scream.

Two men from the side of the road walk up to the car and say something that I can't hear. Moe tells me to give him my passport. I hand it to him and he hands it to a man in a green uniform.

"*Americanea,*" that man says loudly. He says something further to Moe and Moe shakes his head and reaches into his pocket for his American driver's license. The man looks at it and looks at me and then at our screaming children. He hesitates, and I think he would like to say more, but the children's screaming is too loud for him to be easily heard. Abruptly, he waves us through the roadblock.

Moe drives around the army trucks and gets back onto the road.

The children quit screaming. "I don't like those scary men," Zohra says in a loud voice.

"Nice screaming," Moe says to her in English. "You too, Tarek."

"You're funny, Daddy," Zohra says back. "Daddy funny."

I look at Moe and shake my head. "Did you tell the kids to scream like that?"

Moe looks at me and smiles. "No, but they did good job, no?"

An hour later, we round a long curve and ahead of us is yet another roadblock.

"I not believe this," Moe says in his most disgusted way. "This just stupid." I watch his hands start to shake and his face again turn red.

Three men with guns, but no uniforms, come towards the car.

"I think these are bandits," Moe informs me quietly as they approach.

I forget to breathe until Zohra asks if she should start screaming.

"Not this time, sweetie," I tell her. "Let's wait and see what the nice man wants."

Moe glares at me like I have lost my mind.

The largest of the three comes up to the car and Moe rolls down the window. The man sticks his gun inside the car and up against the side of Moe's head.

"Are you an idiot or just stupid?" Moe yells at him in English. "Why do you insist on harassing Algerian citizens? I am sick of you people."

The man with the gun bends down and looks inside the car. He looks at me. Then, he smiles.

You speak English," he says to Moe. "I speak English too."

Moe doesn't back down. He says, "Well, if you speak English, then you can tell me why are you harassing my family?"

The bandit removes the gun from the side of Moe's head. "You go now," he says. "You speak English, I speak English. You go now." He steps back and waves us on.

As Moe steps on the accelerator, the sweat trickles down his forehead and runs off the end of his nose. I take a handkerchief from my purse and blot his face. Again, the speedometer reads 120 kilometres per hour.

"How many more times do you think this will happen?" I ask, speaking to no one in particular.

"Who care?" Moe says, great bravado in his voice and tears streaming down his face. He laughs a little crazily, and adds, "Moe is saved by screaming children. Moe is saved by American wife. Moe is saved by English." He pounds his fist against the steering wheel. "What this be like if I just simple Algerian workerman? I drive along road – I get put in jail by police. My wife get taken for sex by soldiers. I get shot and left dead by bandits. My country is crazy! Soon, I will be crazy, too!"

Now, he is driving more slowly, but he is crying harder. I ache in sympathy for his pain.

"Why does Daddy cry?" Zohra asks. "Why does Daddy cry all the time?"

"He's not crying, Zohra," I say, sure that Moe won't want the children to know that he is crying. "Daddy just has something in his eyes."

Moe suddenly explodes, "Not tell her that!" He glares at me.

He catches Zohra's eye in the rear view mirror and tells her, "I cry for my country, Zohra. I cry so that someday you not have to cry."

Zohra stares at her daddy. "Here, Daddy," she says. She tosses her doll into the front. It lands on the seat beside Moe. "You can play with my dolly. She will make you feel better."

He looks into the rear view mirror at his daughter again, and the trace of a smile appears on his lips. "Yes, my little one," he says. "Your dolly makes me feel much better."

We drive on to Mascara without another roadblock.

The situation in Mascara is better in some ways than it was when we visited two months ago. Moe's sisters are all pregnant again, but they seem to be in good health. Moe's stepmother is back with his father, which means none of Moe's brothers visit their father any more, but his father seems happier. If he wants to visit his sons, he goes to their homes, alone.

The day after we arrive in Mascara, Moe's father asks to be taken to Bou Hanifia. "Bou Hanifia," Moe explains, "is a famous natural spring where people go to heal aches and pains. People come from all over the world to soak in these baths. The water comes boiling from the ground. There are many types of baths. My father says you and I can go to the bath for men and women, but that the water is too hot for very young children and so Tarek should stay home with Abdelghani. Abdullah will go to the public bath for men and Aisha, his wife, will go to the public bath for women and she can take Zohra."

I am confused. "Why can't we take Zohra with us?" I ask.

"My father says that children cannot go into the place where there are men and women together. There are no baths for families."

Because Moe is so anxious to show me the baths, I agree. I don't like the idea of leaving my son in the village with Abdelghani, but Moe assures me Tarek will be fine. We wave at Tarek as we leave and he starts to scream. Seeing his unhappy little face makes me feel worse.

Bou Hanifia is located 25 miles from Mascara and the road is quite bumpy and slow. When we finally arrive, nearly an hour later, we begin by dropping Abdullah off first at the bath for men only. Then, we drive a few doors down and drop off Aisha and Zohra at the bath for women only. Zohra isn't sure she wants to go without us, but like we did with Tarek, we drive off quickly, leaving her yelling in the dust as Aisha pulls on her arm, and drags her through the door of the bathhouse.

Moe and I finally find our way to a building that looks more like the entrance to a hotel than a bath. After waiting in line for a few moments, we are directed into a room where we wait again, until a man comes to take our money. He gives us towels.

The rules are written on the walls of the bathhouse. Moe reads them to me. "We have an hour to stay inside the baths, and then, a buzzer will go off, and we have to come out." We walk down a long hallway and into a white tiled room with a tub the size of a small swimming pool. Once the door clicks shut and is locked, we strip off our clothes, soap ourselves and jump in. The water comes naturally hot from the ground and it is so deep I can just barely touch the bottom. The water smells like clay and feels like sand against my skin, even though it is as clear as glass. We spend the hour soaking and washing each other. I am disappointed when the buzzer goes off. Moe tells me we have to get out right away and get dressed before the next buzzer sounds or we will have to pay double. I dress as fast as I can.

I feel so relaxed and I tell Moe, "That was so wonderful. I would like to do that everyday."

He laughs. "Yes, that is one thing I miss about my village. Too bad it is almost the only thing I miss."

"How do you know when and where to pick everybody up?" I ask as Moe starts the little Renault.

"I'll drive around and pretty soon they come out and stand on the street looking for us.

Forty-five minutes later, we have collected everybody. Zohra is happy to see us and squeals in delight as we stop the car to pick her up. Her skin is all red, like it has been rubbed raw, and she is wearing a new dress – full length and very fancy like a christening gown, like I have seen dresses on little girls during the moslem holidays when all children get new clothes. I ask Moe about it.

"My stepmother, Aisha, buy her the dress. She try to be nice sometimes," Moe says, and then shakes his head, "but mostly she is just crazy. She also say that she paid for Zohra's bath." Again, he shakes his head with disgust, adding, "I know bath is free for children." He dismisses Aisha with a wave of his hand. "I just ignore her. She too strange."

"I think it was very nice of her to buy Zohra a dress," I tell Moe. "Would you tell her that?"

Moe frowns at me and shakes his head, "I hate even to talk to this woman." Then, he holds up his hand to prevent me from protesting. "But – I will tell her."

Moe turns to Aisha and gives her my message.

She leans forward and pats my arm as if to say that's okay, dear.

I nod and smile quickly at her and look away again.

I agree with Moe that it is difficult to look at this woman. Moe doesn't want to look at her because he doesn't like her. I am reluctant to look at her because she has such bad teeth – all broken, chipped and yellow. Her eyes are sunken into her head. She looks sick to me.

It seems to me that she got a raw deal when she married her brother-in-law and took on the raising of his fourteen children. I have tried to tell this to Moe, but he always shrugs it off. He tells me she was nasty and mean to all the children when they were growing up – and she isn't nice to his father. I can't help but think maybe she has reasons for her behaviour. But, I keep all of these thoughts to myself.

Early the next morning, after a night on a lumpy mattress in Abdullah's house, Moe shakes me awake. "My father asks me to go to a meeting with him to help my cousin who is involved in a dispute about land. The mullahs will be there and many of the town's people. We must help my cousin discuss important matters and be witnesses for him. This cousin is ignorant man with no one to help him. My father wants you to come with us. You can watch the children with the other women in the women's room."

We arrive at 9 a.m. The community hall is a large square, fairly new concrete building. Moe directs me to the women's entrance, and then disappears into a sea of men merging into the building at another entrance. I herd the children forward and step inside. Inside, the building is one large room divided in half with blankets hung from the ceiling, One side is for the women and children, and the other side is for the men. The women are all squatting in small groups, chattering away with each other. I look around. There are no chairs. I carefully lower myself down to the cold terrazzo and lean up against a wall. Zohra and Tarek sit beside me.

Once I am seated, the noise surrounds me and settles in on top of me like an oppressive cloud. I try to focus on a specific sound to see if I can make some sense out of it all. But, the voices come back at me in a jumble of discordant noise – the high sounds of the women and children chattering, the low sounds of the men's voices, some so loud that they all seem to be talking at once, some angry, some soft, some shouting. Above the din, I recognize the piercing screaming of babies and young children as they try to make their needs known. My head begins to throb.

I reach into my diaper bag for toys to entertain Zohra and Tarek, wondering how long I will have to stay here with little to do and no one to talk to. The women stare at me for a few moments and titter to each other, obviously talking about me, but it isn't very long before they turn back to each other, leaving me feeling even more alone.

Slowly, a few of the local children come forward and talk to Zohra in Arabic. She answers them and when they realize she can speak their language, they accept her. She offers to share a few of her toys and their faces light up at the sight of her dollies and their dresses. Tarek plays contentedly with one particularly dirty little boy.

I sigh. Why can't it be that easy for adults? I watch their children's games. When I look at my watch again, four hours have gone by. I am numb in some places and stiff and sore in others.

Tarek wanders by and asks for something to eat. I have a few pieces of cheese and some dried bread left from a meal on the road, which I offer him along with a bottle of water and he seems content. At two o'clock, large trays of sweet and juicy watermelon are passed among the crowd.

The bathroom becomes an issue for me and for Zohra. I tell her to ask one of the ladies where we can go. She looks around at the many groups in the hall and then skips over to a woman sitting by herself at the other end of the hall. I see her little head nod up and down and pretty soon she comes skipping back.

"It's outside, Mommy. I'll take you there," she gallantly declares. I get to my feet and clutching my belongings, I follow her out the door and down a short path to a tree-protected area behind the building.

The toilet is another *dig your own hole and dump your own waste* place. I find a number of woman and children there all engaged in various stages of waste deposit. The smell is overwhelm-

ing. Zohra tells me where to go as part of the yard is *used* and part
of it is *new*. It takes me a moment to understand the concept.

I choose a spot in the *new* area and I squat. A piece of old used
Kleenex, found in my pocket, becomes my toilet paper. No water
in a cup here.

As I stand up again, my daughter declares, "Mommy, your
shoes are poopy."

She is right. They are, and it isn't my poop. I try to clean it off
the best I can with a paper napkin I find in my purse. I make my
way back into the building and find my seat again, up against the
cold wall. I wait. All I can think is that I need to get out of here
soon.

The other women in the room seem quite happy. Most are engaged in sometimes heated conversations about who-knows-what
and others are knitting. Some are breastfeeding.

I watch roaches and ants scurry across the floor gathering up
any morsel or crumb they can find. I look up once or twice to see
where Zohra and Tarek are, but they seem content to play some
game with the filthy little boy they first encountered. When I look
at my watch again, it is six o'clock.

Suddenly, a loud argument breaks out in the middle of the
room. Two women, one young and the other old, start yelling at
each other. Tarek comes running towards me and flings himself
into my arms, frightened by the shouting. All the women look
towards the noise. A few start to chant something I don't understand. They stand up facing each other. A loud crack echoes across
the room as the older woman slaps the younger one hard across
her face. The whole room goes silent. The young woman runs to
the other side of the building and holding her face sits on the floor
with her head buried in her hands. The older woman sits down,
triumphant.

"Why are these people so mean?" my daughter asks, her face
white with fear. Unaccountably, at my daughter's question, I am
aware of much sadness in the room. Feeling abandoned and overwhelmed by exhaustion, I burst into tears. I reach inside to find
my willow. But, it is nowhere to be found.

My head throbs unbearably. I hear loud sobs, not realizing for a moment that they are coming from me. The voices nearby me fall silent and I can feel everyone staring at me. I feel that I can't stay in this room another minute. I fight to stop the tears and as they subside and the sobbing stops, one of the women comes near and talks to Zohra.

Zohra asks me, "Are you sick, Mommy? The lady wants to know if you are sick."

I shake my head. "No, I'm not sick."

"She wants to know why you are crying."

"Tell her I don't know."

Zohra relays my reply to the woman.

The woman frowns at me. She speaks harshly to Zohra. Then, she fastens her veil across her face and leaves the building.

My tears are stopped for the moment, but I am barely in control of them. Zohra comes to me and gives me a hug. "That nasty lady said you are crazy and she is going to bring Daddy."

A few minutes later, the woman returns and tells us to leave. I gather up my children and my things and stumble out the door, coming face to face with Moe, who is red-faced and barely coherent with anger.

"Why are you crying? I told you women don't cry here. All these people think I beat you or I am bad to you. Why are you doing this to me?" Moe shouts at me in English as I emerge from the building.

"I-I-I am tired," I stutter. My voice is soft at first. Then I hear it get louder, " – and the women in there are fighting. I have nothing to do, and nothing to eat and I have shit on my shoes." I look at Moe and the dam inside me bursts. "I want you to take me away from here. I want to go home, and if you don't take me, I will scream at the top of my lungs until you do." I thrust my face at him and I scream, "How can you leave me here with nothing for a whole day? I am not the one who is crazy! You are the crazy one!" I hear myself screaming and feel the tears streaming down my face.

The rage builds up inside Moe, the redness travelling up from his neck and slowly making its way to the top of his head. "You embarrass me," he starts, quietly. "I am shamed by you." His voice grows louder until he is shouting at me. "If I have the heart, I would beat you."

"I don't care what you do anymore, Moe! Just get me out of this rat, roach, ant-infested place and do it now! I won't stay here another moment!" I stand, defiant, in front of him.

By now, both children are crying, not understanding why we are screaming at each other. People on the street and from inside the hall stare at us. Many of them are muttering about my behaviour. I try to stop my tirade, but I can't. I blubber a few more sentences, and then break down into sobbing, sure that I want to die.

Moe yells at Zohra to follow him and he picks up Tarek. Then, he grabs hold of my arm and pulls me, stumbling and blubbering, along the sidewalk to the car. He opens the car door and shoves the children into the back seat, at the same time ordering me to get into the front. He gets in behind the wheel.

Through my tears, I see Moe's father come out of the building and walk towards us. He says something I cannot hear. Moe shakes his head back and forth vigorously as he slams the door and starts the engine. He drives us away from the building and all the way to the edge of town where he pulls the car to a stop and turns to me.

His face is still fiery red and full of rage. His voice is hard and cold. "We go home. I never bring you here again. It is very dangerous to travel now. There are many bandits. If we get shot dead, it is your doing. My father very upset with me. He thinks I do something to you to make you cry like this. I cannot even talk to you until I am home."

Moe barks at Tarek and Zohra to lie down on the seat and go to sleep. He puts on the lights and guns the engine. We fly silently through the night. I don't dare look at the speedometer. We are on the road for more than an hour when the car rounds a curve and careens across the road. It jolts as we go into the ditch on the other side of the road, up and out of the ditch and back onto the road. Moe hits the brake and we come to an abrupt stop.

I start to scream, a long high-pitched scream that cuts through the night like the sound of a wild animal. It stops only when I feel

Moe's fist connect with my chin. The blood pours from my mouth and down my front. The children sit in stunned silence.

We drive on through the night. Motionless, I watch the blood drip down my face onto my clothes. Maybe I will bleed to death and make the whole world happy by my leaving it. I am devastated. I have no resources left. For the past three years, the image of a willow bending with the wind has been my mainstay, my line of defense when I was overwhelmed with sadness or anger, when I didn't understand the customs, when Moe demanded something that I didn't feel ready or capable of giving over to him. Today, for the first time, my willow has failed me – and I have failed everyone.

As we climb the stairs to our apartment, Claude comes out of his. He is about to speak, but catches sight of my face and is stunned into silence. I look away and keep walking. As I enter, I hear him say to Moe, "We are finally moved into the house on Baba Ali and I am getting the last of our things out of the apartment. While you were gone, twenty directors from the Ministry of Agriculture were thrown in jail for economic sabotage." Then he adds, his voice quiet, controlled and dripping with sarcasm. "I thought you would want to know that,"

Moe shakes his head. "Good. I am having meeting with the minister and five other engineers next week so maybe more will be in jail by that time."

Claude frowns, adding, "I heard your trip to Paris is cancelled." He leaves.

"That man is trouble," Moe says as he enters the apartment. "My life is like very bad movie."

# What Does It Take to Drive a Man Crazy?

November starts out cold. The humid wind off the Mediterranean chills me to the bone. Grateful that my mother shipped my big white woolly coat that I wore when I visited my grandmother in Utah, I discover that there is winter in Algeria.

Moe hasn't been paid for months. He is running out of people to borrow from and his benefactors are themselves running low on cash. I write home to get money from my bank account and my mother does her best to send it as fast as possible.

On November 8 a cheque arrives and Moe drives into Algiers to get it cashed at the French Bank, the *Credit Lyonnaise*. Previously, they have cashed our cheques in American dollars with no problems. This time, they refuse. The teller informs him that last time the bank had to wait six weeks for the Southern Arizona Bank to send the money. Politely, the lady informs him that the bank does not like to wait such a long time to get their money back. This time the bank insists on a document called the Order of Payment up front. The teller instructs him that he has to wire the Arizona bank to send the Order of Payment to the Algiers branch. Moe doesn't have the twelve dollars it costs to wire Arizona. He walks out of the bank with nothing. He arrives home furious – angry at the bank, and livid that he made a trip all the way to Algiers for nothing. In frustration, I write to my mother, demanding that she go into the stupid American bank and tell them to stop fooling around with our money. I don't know what else to do. I am disheartened. Why does everything have to be so difficult?

Before we go to bed I ask Moe if he has heard anything definite about our move to Paris.

He mumbles something about not having received any official word either way. Then he adds, "But I hear today also that University of Algiers refuse to give me credit for my American degree. I cannot believe this. But I should expect this, no?" He shakes his head. "What next?" he mumbles, "What next?"

The answer to, *What next,* turns out to be sickness. Tarek and Moe both wake up early in the morning with severe diarrhoea. I feel fine, but when I wake Zohra, she is feverish and shaky. I spend my morning cleaning up after them. They are all miserable, cranky and demanding.

The prospect of looking after a sick family day after day affects my mood. I find myself thinking, "Maybe living in Algeria is too much for me. Everyone is always sick. No matter how hard I try, Moe is never happy. If I try to cheer him up, he yells at me." The events of the past few days run through my head over and over, and the stress of our visit to the village and the nightmare ride home threatens to overwhelm me again.

Moe's eyes are glassy again this morning. "Moe, what's wrong?" I ask him.

"I told you, I am sick today. I have diarrhoea," He stumbles back to bed.

"But, diarrhoea shouldn't give you glassy eyes," I say to myself.

The next day, I wake up early and start my chores, heating water to wash more bedding and clothing, boiling water for drinking, trying to figure out what I can feed them that won't go right through their bodies. I hear Zohra cough hard and begin to cry. I go to her room to comfort her.

"Mommy, my throat hurts," she whispers. "It really hurts." I go to get her some water. Moe is standing in the kitchen staring straight ahead with a handful of pink and yellow pills in his one hand and a glass of water in the other. He is about to swallow all of the pills.

"What are you doing?" I shout, grabbing his hand.

"Huh?" he answers. "W-what you mean 'what's I doing?'" he slurs. "I need shomthing for this diarrhoea."

"Those pills are not for diarrhoea, Moe. Those are the pills the psychiatrist gave you – " I take the water glass out of his hand and reach for the pills. "– and I can tell by your glassy eyes that you have already taken too many of them. You will kill yourself if you take all those."

Moe stares at me. He appears stunned by my words. Abruptly, he throws all the pills on the floor and stumbles back to bed.

I stand in the kitchen, the pink and yellow pills all around me. Was Moe aware of what he was doing? Was he about to deliberately take an overdose? Or was he just confused because he was tired and sick?

A few hours later, I search the mostly empty cupboards trying to find something to prepare for lunch. Moe wanders into the kitchen.

Ignoring the episode with the pills, I attempt to joke about our lack of food choices. I begin, "Moe, I'm deciding what to make for lunch. All we have is some lowly chick peas and rice."

Moe's answers, his voice agitated, slurring his words, "I knows we neegs money. Kids not do good on s-shick peas and rith." His eyes tear up and he stumbles around the kitchen, grabbing the counter to maintain his balance.

"I go to farm and get shom milk," he says groggily.

I hate to see him like this, sick, disheartened, nearly incoherent. "Okay, Moe and while you're out, Zohra really needs some medicine for her chest. I am worried she will get pneumonia."

"She should see doctor in Algiers. Maybe I go." He moves unsteadily toward the door.

As he passes me, I see that his eyes are now not only glassy, but also blood shot.

I interrupt his movement toward the door by stepping in front of him, "Moe," I say quietly. "I'm not sure that's a good idea. You seem really tired." I want to avoid a confrontation.

He says nothing, just sways his way into Zohra's room. He tells her to change her clothes and get ready to go to the *Algerthian* doctor. I hold my breath, and continue to work at getting a meal ready. The minutes tick by. I don't hear any more talking.

Then, Zohra, disgusted, stomps into the kitchen with her little fists clenched on her hips.

"What's the matter, honey?" I ask.

"Daddy told me to get dressed and now he's sleeping in the living room. I tried to wake him up, but he just told me to go away. He's a poop," she shakes her head.

I explain to her that Daddy is tired and that he is not a poop. "At least, he won't be driving," I think with relief.

She follows me into the living room where we both watch Moe, lying on his stomach in a deep sleep, snoring. Moe sleeps on through lunch. I don't bother to wake him.

Late in the afternoon, I hear an unexpected knock on the apartment door. Moe doesn't stir, so I open the door to see who is there. It is Chekiri, who has the American wife named Jinny. He is a petroleum engineer who got his degree from the University of Oklahoma, a wonderful tall handsome man with black eyes, tight curly hair and a beautiful smile. I welcome him and invite him in. I chatter away for several minutes in English before telling him that Moe is asleep on the mattress.

"That's okay," Chekiri says. "I'll surprise him."

In two long strides, he is at the edge of the mattress, bending down and whispering something in Moe's ear.

Moe stirs and suddenly sits straight up in surprise. "Chekiri," he shouts, scrambling to stand up, a bit unsteady on his feet.

Chekiri looks at him curiously. They hug in the man-to-man way that Arab men do when they haven't seen each other for a long time. Then, they pull up chairs and sit down to talk, first in Arabic and then, when they continue in English, I pull up a chair and join them.

Moe launches into the story of his troubles at work. He looks sad and so fragile. His speech is clearer now and he isn't slurring his words, but as he talks, his eyes glisten with tears. After a few minutes, Moe slows down and then he falls silent.

Chekiri tells him gently, "I know what you mean, my friend." He touches Moe's arm in empathy. "I work for a French oil company in the Sahara. I make a lot of money. I go to the desert for three weeks. Then they fly me to Algiers for a week and pay for everything. This might sound good but the truth is, I do nothing. The truth is there is no job. The French workers do everything and we are just tokens to appease the government's worthless quota system. In this job, I am wasting my education. I am looking for another job. I am seriously considering going back to the States or to Canada to start over. Half my friends have already left and they intend to never come back."

The sadness returns to Moe's face. He shakes his head.

Chekiri eats chickpeas and rice with us in the late afternoon and then drives home to Algiers.

"I am happy for his visit. I know now I am not alone in my thinking. I feel better," Moe tells me after Chekiri leaves.

The next morning Moe gets out of bed in a good mood, filled with positive ideas about what can be done to solve some of these heart-wrenching problems. But, when he returns in the evening, he is in another rage. He thrusts a letter at me. It is from the Office of the Agriculture Minister, informing him that he can go to France but he must attend the Agricultural Institute in Paris to work towards a degree.

"A degree," he screams at the top of his lungs. "I have a stupid degree. I'm not going to go back to school to get what I already have. This is a stupid government." Pacing back and forth, he continues to rant. He met with the agricultural engineers who studied in Russia and they told him the government has told them they also must go back to school.

"We are victims, all of us! That is what we are. This stupid government refuse to recognize any foreign degrees! It not possible to get degree here during war so where they expect us to go?" Shaking his head, he finally stops pacing and sits down. He puts his head in his hands and falls silent.

I try to comfort him, but he just shakes his head. After a few minutes of staring at the floor, he announces that he and six of his friends have made an appointment to meet with the Minister. "I think he won't even see us," Moe adds sadly, "I think he will say we not important."

Slowly, he gets up and tells me he doesn't want to eat tonight. He just wants to sleep. I watch him walk slowly into the bedroom and collapse on the bed. His sadness permeates everything.

The next day just a few minutes after Moe goes to work, I hear a knock at my door and find Benita Ducont standing there, smiling. She asks me if I would like to go to Baba Ali and to the market this morning.

"I would love to get away today," I say, smiling back at her. It has been a long time since I have seen her. I invite her in but she says she will meet me at the car. I hurry to get the children dressed and pack a few toys and snacks. Zohra and Tarek are excited to see Laurant again and to meet the new baby.

"We'll go to the market when I take you home," Benita begins once we are on the road. "That way, whatever we buy won't go bad. We'll go to Baba Ali so you can see our new house," She rattles on as she drives, happily telling me all the details. "It is quite nice. There are some problems, but I assume they will work themselves out."

We park near the new house and she takes me on a tour. The villas are lovely inside. All the furniture is brand new. The floors are the usual terrazzo tile and the walls are painted in soft pastels. Benita even has a washing machine and dryer and other brand new appliances. I am stunned by the size of the house. Each child has his own room and bathroom. I love the look of the bathtub, round and tall with large claw feet and deep sides.

"You like your new house?" I ask.

"I like it just fine," she smiles. Then she frowns, "Except that we can't flush the toilets and there is never any water or any electricity. These Arab workers are just too stupid to do anything right!" She stops abruptly, and turns red, realizing what she has said. "I get frustrated sometimes," she finishes lamely, almost apologizing.

I say nothing.

She continues with her rant. "Did you know that the third house is empty because Monsieur Siban refuses to live in it? He won't tell us why. He says he'd rather live in the apartments. Can you believe it? He'd rather live in those horrible apartments with all those horrible children than live in a new villa! I think he must be crazy!"

I still say nothing. I have no idea what I could say. I wonder what Moe would have to say about the villas. He hasn't said anything to me about them for a long time.

Zohra and Tarek are excited about the new house but I think it is mostly because of all the toys. Zohra and Laurant play well together these days, but Tarek still prefers to run one truck up and down the floor muttering to himself in some alien language. Sometimes he stops and just stares out the window and sucks his thumb while twirling a blond curl on the top of this head.

Benita tells Tarek twice to stop sucking his thumb. The third time, she yells at him, making him cry. He stops sucking for a minute each time she says something, but then goes back to it. It is almost three o'clock when Benita drives us home. She tells me that she doesn't have time for us to stop at the market. It is later than she thought and she needs to get home.

I tell her that it is okay, there is nothing left at the market at three o'clock anyway.

That evening I tell Moe about my day and ask him what is going on with the villas of Baba Ali.

He smiles at me with some satisfaction and then laughs loud and long. "Well, I guess I tell you what I think is happening at Baba Ali villas, but maybe you not find it funny as Moe does."

"Try me," I challenge him, remembering Benita's attitude toward the Algerian workers and my discomfort over her calling them stupid.

"Okay. The houses are made for Duconts and Mr. Giovani. The other house is truly empty. It assigned to the Chef de Statione who is Mr. Siban," Moe looks at me to see if I am following his explanation.

I nod to indicate he should continue.

Moe says, "Mr. Siban is Algerian. It seems Mr. Siban refuse on principle to live in his house. He says it wrong to give houses to French, so he not want to live there. The farm workers also mad about the houses for French people. They make life for the Duconts difficult. I think it is on purpose. I know farm workers cause the electricity generator to burn out four times since they move in. I also hear from some workers that they attach water pipes to the house so they can turn water off to house when they want to. They do this many times since French move in. I also hear the sewer to the toilet goes up instead of down so all the shit stays in the back yard."

As Moe finishes this story, he laughs. Behind his laughter, I hear anger and indignation. "I not know if all this true or not but the workers sometimes talk and I hear them. I know it not nice to laugh, but I can't help it. Sometimes, these *colons* be so ignorant to the workers. Sometimes, I think they deserve this treatment."

When I hear Moe's story, I am happy we have our apartment. Nobody bothers us here and we only do without water and electricity one day out of five. It is better than life on the farm in fancy villas with brand new furniture and rooms for each child.

A few days later Moe comes home from work at noon. He announces that we are all going to Algiers. He vows that he is going to go to the bank and make them cash his cheque, no matter what. And then, we are going to visit Little Ahmed and Rashida.

I am happy to be going to visit Rashida, but I am dubious about the bank. This is our third attempt at cashing the cheque. Why should today be any different?

We stay in the car while Moe enters the bank. I settle in for a long wait. However, barely ten minutes pass before he reappears. He throws open the car door and tosses a handful of red, green and blue bills at me. He offers no explanation except to mutter that it just depends on the mood of the damn bank teller. I say nothing. I just gather up the bills, fold them in half, and hand them back to Moe. He grins and puts them into his wallet.

Little Ahmed and Rashida are happy to see us and greet us with kisses and hugs. I really like Rashida. In private, Moe calls her a cow, but I find her funny. She is very loud and very large. She has big, fuzzy, backcombed hair, and her huge body covers half of the couch. She tells us immediately that she is pregnant and about to give birth again.

However, to me, she looks no different than the last time we met. Even though I don't understand French very well, I can understand Rashida without knowing her language and she makes me laugh. I relax and enjoy her company.

Rashida's children are the same age as Zohra and Tarek and they always have wonderful new European toys to play with. A full-time nanny oversees their play but doesn't get in the way of it. They have a real playroom, big enough so the children can run and chase each other without annoying the adults.

Several hours later, Rashida and I are talking and laughing together when Zohra appears and asks, "Where's Tarek?"

"He's with you, isn't he?" I answer with a question. I have always felt the children were safe with the nanny.

"No, he isn't in the playroom. I thought maybe he came out here." Zohra looks around as she speaks.

Moe overhears our conversation and asks in Arabic, "What do you mean Tarek's not in the playroom?"

Ahmed jumps up and goes to the playroom. He returns and asks Rashida where the nanny is.

"I sent her to the store," Rashida answers, her voice concerned, "– a long time ago," she finishes.

We all run to the front door, which is wide open. Everyone tries to go through the doorway at once, looking up and down the hallway.

Suddenly, we hear the sound of a child's steps running and Tarek's voice, screaming, "The *bebe!* The *bebe!*" He runs out of an apartment down the hall, and as fast as his little chubby legs can carry him, he rushes straight into his father's arms.

We look down the hall at the place where Tarek was first seen. A little European boy stands there looking curiously at all of us. He smiles shyly, and then disappears inside his apartment. Moe, Ahmed and Rashida look at each other. They cannot contain their laughter. They laugh so hard they can barely find the breath to explain. Rashida laughs till she cries and her mascara runs down her face.

I don't find it funny that someone left the door open and my son wandered out. He could have been lost or taken away, or hurt – it could have been dangerous. I am not laughing.

Finally, they all calm down and the laughter subsides. I ask

Moe to explain. With much interruption by more laughter, the big joke is relayed to me.

"Tarek runs yelling, 'The *bebe*. The *bebe*.' We know he is saying 'the baby', and that he means the little boy at the end of the hall. In Arabic, the *bebe* is a huge black horsefly. It sounds like little Tarek is running as fast as he can from a giant black horsefly."

I smile to be polite, but I am not sure it is all that funny.

On our way home from Algiers, Moe decides to stop at INRA, *Institute Nationale Research de Agronomique,* the government department that he works for to check on the status of our Paris assignment. We park the car and walk to a small garden on the grounds of INRA. I find a bench to sit on while we wait for Moe. When he returns, I learn that his boss is writing a letter for him requesting that he be allowed to do his Masters Degree, instead of the degree he already has.

Moe is still mad. "Don't hold your breath for this," he tells me.

He also brings the news that his back pay has been released. He has been assured he will find it in his account when he gets home.

An American Thanksgiving and an Algerian Christmas

My mother's latest letter tells me her plans for Thanksgiving. I picture my family back home sitting down to a turkey dinner and homesickness floods over me. "I love this holiday," I think. "How will I get through it without some sort of celebration? Maybe Moe would consider having a party. I could prepare a real American Thanksgiving dinner." My mind races ahead. "All our new friends could come. It could be a thank you to all the people who have been so welcoming to me."

Just thinking about it makes me feel better. However, making dinner and getting the kids ready for bed drives the idea out of my head so I don't mention it to Moe.

That's why I am completely surprised when he looks at me over dinner and suddenly announces, "I think we should have a party. So many people who help us these days. Maybe we invite them all together."

I stare in amazement and then burst out laughing.

"What so funny?" he asks.

"Moe," I chuckle. "I had the same idea this afternoon – but I didn't know if you would like it. Next week is American Thanksgiving. I was thinking maybe we could make a real American Thanksgiving dinner and share it with our friends."

For a moment or two, he doesn't say anything. Then a smile breaks across his face and he nods, "I think it a good idea. It not for religion this holiday. I think my friends will understand Thanksgiving. So, when is the real date of Thanksgiving?"

"On Thursday," I answer excitedly.

"Thursday is work day. Let us make invitation for Saturday afternoon. We have time to talk to people and buy food."

I want to make the dinner as American as possible with roast turkey and all the trimmings. Moe says he will take care of the bird and not to worry about it. I make a list of who to invite.

On Friday, Moe walks into the house with the turkey walking beside him tied to a small piece of rope. Moe and the turkey walk through the living room and out onto the balcony where he carefully secures the rope to the balcony rail. "Now," he says, smiling broadly, "if you want turkey, you kill." He chuckles and walks out of the apartment, leaving me alone with the turkey.

I am speechless. I look at the poor pathetic bird and shake my head. "This party is doomed," I think. "There is no way I can kill this creature."

The bird on the balcony stares back at me. Suddenly, it lets out a loud squawk. In my head, the squawk sounds like the bird is saying, "Save me! Please save me!"

I back away from the turkey.

Tarek comes up behind me. "Pretty bird, pretty bird," he repeats. "Birdie talk?" I grab Tarek before he can go out onto the balcony. I slam the door.

"Even my son can hear the damn thing talk!" I think. "What am I going to do?" I plunk myself down on the living room mattress to think about what to do.

I hear the key in the lock and Moe enters with a strange man who is wearing a long white apron, carrying a large knife in one hand and a bag and some wire in the other.

Laughing, Moe says, "I bring rescuer. This Ali, the butcher from the local shop. He will take care of turkey and make him ready for your pan."

"You planned this all along, didn't you?" I yell at Moe.

Moe just laughs heartily, opens the balcony door for the butcher and closes it behind him. After much flapping of wings and words that sound like swearing in Arabic, the butcher opens the doors and, grinning broadly at Moe, hands me the now heavy bag, which is dripping blood and other bodily fluids.

Reluctantly, I take hold of it and run to the kitchen where I heave it into the sink, muttering to myself, "Why couldn't he, at least, carry this dead and dripping bird into the kitchen for me?" Trying to dismiss it all as part of Moe's great joke that I don't really understand, I think, "At least, I have the centrepiece of my quintessential American Thanksgiving dinner. Now, all I have to do is figure out how to cook it – and before that, I have to figure out how to fit it into my tiny little oven."

I gingerly open the bag and take the bird out only to discover that it is still covered with feathers. Dismayed, I call to Moe, "How do I get the feathers off this bird?"

Moe stops laughing long enough to say something to the butcher and they both laugh again as they enter the kitchen. "Your rescuer has agreed, for money, to take the bird away and fix feathers for you," Moe finally says.

I gratefully stuff the bird back into the bag and hand it, still dripping blood, to the butcher. He and Moe exchange a last chuckle as he leaves. Several hours later, the turkey is returned to me, naked.

I carefully wash the bird and set it in a large roasting pan that I borrowed from Benita. I have never cooked a turkey before. But I am sure that I can. I have watched my mother do it many times. I mix the stuffing made with Algerian bread and whatever spices I think might make it taste American.

It is not until I am ready to put the stuffing into the turkey that it dawns on me that there isn't any place to put it. I look between the legs where the stomach cavity is supposed to be. But there is no cavity.

"Moe," I call into the living room where he is playing with Tarek and Zohra.

Moe comes into the kitchen, looks at the turkey in the pan, the stuffing in a dish beside it. He shakes his head, and again, bursts out laughing. When he can control himself, he says, "You are such silly woman. Doesn't your mother teach you anything?"

"What do you mean?" I ask.

His voice disgusted and cold, the laughter gone, he explains what he obviously thinks I should already know. "You have to take out the guts."

"Guts?" I ask, appalled.

"Guts," he repeats and turns away, shaking his head at the stupidity of American mothers.

I mutter to his back, "Why didn't the butcher do this?"

"Because we not ask him," Moe says, leaving me alone with the problem.

Eventually, I figure it out. Awkwardly, I use a sharp knife to make the necessary incision. Then, holding my head as far away as I can, I reach inside and take hold of whatever is in there, pulling hard and feeling the organs rip away from the stomach walls. I hold my breath – the smell coming out of the bird is overwhelming. Once I have pulled out everything I can, I wash out the cavity.

From time to time, Moe pokes his head in the door and makes some comment. When I am finished pulling out all of the organs, he shows me what parts I should save and what parts I should throw away. He doesn't know the names of all of the parts in English. He just points them out and tells me to boil them and chop them up for the gravy.

I only recognize the neck, the liver and the heart, but I do what he says. When the turkey is in the pan and ready for cooking the next day, I search through my grandmother's cookbook – the only cookbook that I brought with me – looking for instructions on how long it will take to cook the turkey. The book says I should cook it for 4 1/2 hours. But, I know that the bottled gas that heats my oven is really not very hot – definitely not as hot as an American oven. I pick a number out of the air – I decide I will cook the bird for twelve hours.

Shaking my head, I mutter, "The way this party is shaping up, the food is either going to be really good or really terrible."

Saturday morning, I wake up early, both excited and anxious by the prospects of my Thanksgiving party. Moe has done the inviting and he hasn't told me how many people will be coming, but I assume there will only be six or seven. Our apartment isn't very big.

To complete my menu, I cut up sweet potatoes, boil them and mash them with butter, almonds and honey. I top this dish off with the marshmallows my mother sent for the kids in one of her last packages. I cook regular potatoes and mash them – something I have never seen done in Algeria. I make salads, using lettuce, parsley, tomatoes and lemons.

Finally, in a last-ditch effort to make a special dessert, I remember that my mother has mailed me an angel food cake mix. I decide to bake it – in my slow oven – with no tube pan. I have no mixer. So I use a spoon, beating as fast as I can till my arm is so tired I can hardly move it. I scrape the raw dough into a stew pot and put it in the oven. I cook it for two hours alongside the turkey.

I don't read the box instructions until after the cake is in the oven. When I read them, they confirm that I have done everything I could possibly do to make the cake fail. "But, I can't help it," I complain to myself. "I have no special pan. No electric mixer. No temperature of 325°F." I lean against the table, staring at the oven. "Maybe the cake gods will take pity on me. Maybe I will get lucky." I gesture futilely at the ceiling, thinking, "That's all the help I have – the cake gods."

At 12:30, friends and family start to arrive. Zohra and Tarek are delighted with the children their age, and take them to play in their rooms. In the end, twenty adults and half as many children crowd into our little apartment.

They want to see if it is possible that the *Americanea* can, indeed, cook. I wince at that thought and hope that it turns out that I can cook. I am not really sure that it will.

It is 2:00 before we finally eat. I put all the serving dishes on the table and pile up the plates buffet style. This way of eating is not unknown to our friends, but it is uncommon. They all gather around the table, and I explain what Thanksgiving means in America. I describe what is in each dish and why it is served at Thanksgiving. Moe translates, and they all smile and nod.

We fill our plates and they find places to sit. I watch closely as they eat my food. At first, they are inquisitive about the stuffing made with Algerian bread, a concoction barely recognizable to them. Algerian stuffing is made with ground beef, rice, spices and raisins.

Several women ask about how I made the mashed potatoes, and they are fascinated by the ingredients in the sweet potato dish. The desert turns out to the biggest hit of all! It tastes nothing at all like an angel food cake – but it is delicious. I try to explain that I made it from a mix that came in a box, but they want to know how to make it without a box. I promise to get them a recipe. No one leaves until late afternoon. The dinner has been a huge success.

Moe tells me that our guests like the idea of having a holiday to be thankful and that being thankful for one's blessings is a very important idea in the Moslem faith. He even tells me that it was a good meal.

I am happy that my party has been a success. I look forward to Christmas.

In early December when we go to Algiers on a shopping trip, I discover that the big department stores are all beautifully decorated for Christmas. Trees in all shapes and sizes, decorated in tinsel and elegant ornaments from all parts of the world, adorn the windows of the large stores and some of the smaller French boutiques on the major streets.

When Zohra and I see the trees, we immediately begin to search for Santa Claus. No matter how hard we look, however, we can't find any semblance of the round jolly fat man. Moe tells us, to our dismay, that European Christians, including the French that live in Algeria, celebrate with St. Nick, not Santa Claus. Moe points to a picture of a tall thin man with a funny scraggly beard in one of the store windows and says, "That St. Nick."

Zohra and I look at each other, both confounded and disappointed. We chant, "We want Santa Claus," the rest of the way down the street to the car. Moe shakes his head at our antics. Tarek doesn't know what to think. He is too young to remember Santa and he isn't sure what this whole Christmas thing is about anyway.

On the way home, we talk about celebrating Christmas, a holiday Moe loved when he was in Tucson. For the five Christmases that we celebrated together, he always said how much he loved the surprise of the presents and the idea of Santa Claus handing out presents to little children. He knows how much my mother and my grandmother love the holiday and how they do it up in such a big way. He knows what it means to me.

"I know it will be difficult for you this year. You are not with family. I think it is okay if we have a little Christmas, me, you and our children. They can have a few presents and we will make special food. We just not tell anybody. It is our family secret."

He continues, "I think, one day soon we should discuss about the religion. I think you should study the Koran. We have English copy in my bookshelf and you can read it. If you like it, I can help you. The children will go to mosque when they are older and understand more. I think it is good for them to have Allah. Also, you should think about how to name yourself with an Arab name. This very important if you stay here in this country."

"If I stay in this country?" I ask. "Why do you say *if I stay in this country?* Of course I will stay in this country." I am indignant that Moe would even suggest that I wouldn't stay. He smiles at the passion of my indignity. "You say that now. But, only Allah knows what is ahead for both of us in this crazy place. I think nothing is for certain, and nothing is forever." He falls silent.

A shiver runs through my body, from the top of my head and down the full length of my back. I wonder if there is more in what he says than what I understand. I look into his eyes, searching for what he might really be saying. But his eyes look back at me, only with what might be pity – and a deep sadness that, even in the worst of times, I haven't seen before.

An image of a large weeping willow creeps into my mind. It is not the willow I usually imagine when I need solace and I shake my head to dispel the sadness it brings. I have no need for any willow right now. But, the image persists. After a few moments, I wonder if this particular willow is meant for me or if it belongs to Moe. Another shiver passes through my body.

Moe comes home from work the next day and announces that his boss, Mr. Shelig, has spent his entire department's budget for the year. There is no money for salaries for anyone until after January first or even later than that. Moe delivers this information without his usual anger or frustration. He states it in a dead flat voice like it means nothing at all.

He pauses and the colour slowly rises in his face. "There is no money for toys for our Christmas," he mutters softly. "It is also Ramadan starting on December 15 and I need money for this. My father is coming to visit. What he will think if I cannot even feed him?"

Abruptly, he jumps up from the table, grabs a chair with both hands and hurls it across the living room. The chair smashes against the far wall, barely missing the glass door to the balcony, and falls to the floor. Moe appears shocked by his own behaviour and flings himself onto the living room mattress. He buries his face in the soft covering and goes totally silent.

I pick up my knitting just to hear the clicking of the needles. The children peek out of their bedroom doors as if to say, "What is going on that would make daddy throw a chair?" But, they are silent and their eyes are wide with fear.

"It's okay," I tell them, keeping my voice soft and quiet. "Mommy is going to fix dinner. Daddy is tired so let's let him sleep. Come into the kitchen and help me make something nice for Daddy."

Moe lifts his head. "No, no, it okay. I play with kids. You cook," he says. "Moe okay now," he reassures me. He smiles at Tarek and Zohra and beckons to them.

Relieved, the children run to the mattress and jump on him. As they wrestle, I go to the kitchen to find something for supper. My mind is racing, "This is the first time I have heard that his family is coming and the first he has mentioned that Ramadan starts on December15th." Then, it hits me, "Today is Moe's birthday. How did I forget?"

After his outburst, our life returns to normal. Moe stumbles off to work every day and says little about anything that is happening. His family doesn't show up for the promised visit. We fall into a routine where I take the children for a walk every day in the village and Moe takes us somewhere for an outing on the weekends.

A week before Christmas, Moe arrives with a huge box from

the post office that has Customs stamps all over it. I am surprised that it came through without being opened at any of the stations along the way. It has been our experience that when a box is large and worth more than $100 we have to pick it up at the main Customs depot in Algiers. For some reason, this particular box was sent directly to us in Birtouta and to the local Birtouta station. The postal system is always a curiosity because we never know what is going to happen with either incoming or outgoing mail.

Moe struggles through the door with the box and puts it down carefully on the living room floor. We are all excited, and the children jump up and down. Of course, it is from my parents and I am certain that it is the Christmas box. Their timing is perfect. The children want to open it right away, but we explain to them that they have to wait for Christmas. Disappointment fills their faces, even though we assure them they don't have to wait too many more days.

That night, after we put the children to bed, Moe and I make plans for when we will celebrate our little family Christmas. It really doesn't matter when we celebrate. There aren't many Christians in our lives, and the children won't know the difference between one day and another. He wants to celebrate on December 23 instead of the 25th because he wants to go to Mascara to see his family for part of Ramadan.

One of the first things we pull out of the box is a two-foot-high white-sprayed Christmas tree. Just looking at it makes me happy. I have no ornaments to put on it, but I solve that dilemma by tying 30 foil-covered hard candies onto the tree using the red ribbon my mother has included in her gifts to us. When I am finished with the decorating job, I tell Moe, "This is the most beautiful Christmas tree in the whole wide world."

He laughs. "You probably right," he says. "I think the kids for sure like it."

The next morning Moe and I wake up the children and bring them out to see our surprise for them. They rub their eyes sleepily. We tell them Santa has brought them some presents because it is a special time of year.

When they see the tree and all the packages, Tarek immediately jumps as high as his little legs can jump and squeals in delight, "Pretty, pretty, see, see."

Zohra surveys the room quietly, and using her prim and proper voice, asks, "Where are all MY presents?"

One by one, we hand out the gifts. Even Tarek opens each of his by himself. His favourite is a large, colourful, five-foot rubber clown. Moe blows it up for him. We show him how it works. It is heavy on the bottom and light on the top, which means that it can be used as a punching bag that won't stay down. It keeps bouncing back to an upright position. Tarek will have nothing to do with punching it. He jumps on the clown and covers its face with kisses, especially its funny rubber nose. We laugh at his antics.

Tarek's other two gifts are little boy toys, one a truck and the other a bus. Late in the afternoon, we find Tarek sound asleep curled up with the blue bus in his arms as if he was cuddling a baby doll.

Zohra is delighted with all her gifts. She tries on all three of the little outfits that my mother has picked out for her. They fit perfectly. She parades around the room showing them off and telling us how pretty she is. Her favourite gift, besides the clothes, is an umbrella. "Now I am a lady with my own *umbella*," she tells us in her self-important voice.

When the children have their gifts and are busy playing, Moe looks inside the box again and pulls out a large Christmas-wrapped package with a card that reads, "To Moe" in huge letters. Carefully, childlike, he opens it and finds inside, a whole new wardrobe – four shirts, two ties, some underwear, a pair of long brown dress slacks and a matching sweater. He puts everything on at least six times, admiring himself in our long bedroom mirror. He is speechless. His eyes fill with tears when he tries to express himself.

"Moe," I say. "You know my mother – she loves Christmas. I'm sure she enjoyed shopping for you."

"I love your mother too much," he repeats over and over. "I love your mother too much. She a good woman."

I eventually open all my gifts. I unwrap them very slowly, with great care and deliberation., wanting to prolong the feeling of excitement as long as possible. I find a beautiful blue turtleneck sweater with knitted pockets. It will feel so good in the cold of this humid climate. I unwrap a package containing several bras – items that I am too embarrassed to buy here. Another package contains half a dozen pairs of underpants. In yet another, I find a photo album. And, in another, a xylophone. I can't quite figure out why my mother would send me a xylophone. In the end, though, the best Christmas gift of all is for me to see Moe so happy.

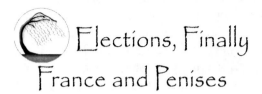

Elections, Finally
France and Penises

On Christmas Day, we are ten days into Moe's big holiday of Ramadan. I ask him if I can fast and he laughs. "Sure, if you can do it. It not easy. Remember, it mean you have no food or water from sun-up to sun-down."

"Maybe I'll lose weight," I tell him. I am determined to share his holiday with him as he allowed me to share mine with him and the kids.

"And maybe you won't," he retorts. "It not that we not eat. It's that we only eat at certain time of day."

A week into my so-called fast, I end it. I have never eaten so much in my life. I cook big meals for Moe. I am so hungry that I eat twice as much as I normally would. Moe laughs at me and then tells me my motivation is all wrong.

"Wait until you understand my religion before you try. It not work, if you not understand why you do something."

It seems he is right. I go back to eating regular meals with the children, leaving him to fast on his own.

Our plans to visit his family in Mascara to celebrate the end of Ramadan never materialize. He goes to work every day and comes home with endless tales of doom about the present regime in control in Algiers. The gossip around the farm says that the end of the Boumedienne regime is near. Moe explains, "Boumedienne is the second President of Algeria since the war for independence. He take over from Ben Bella in a coup in 1965."

Moe's journalist friend enlists Moe's help in a campaign to expose some of the issues in agriculture, like workers not getting paid. They write stories that are published in *El Moujahid*, the local newspaper. Moe is also still trying to meet with the Minister to discuss the ongoing corruption. These meetings don't happen and it adds to his frustration. Some days he talks about learning more French and other days he rejects that idea.

At the end of January he applies for an American-based scholarship, and for a few days it seems that he might have a good chance to return to the U.S. But, somewhere there is a glitch in the system. When he enquires about the status of his application, he is told he never applied.

This event confuses and overwhelms him. He misses many workdays and his moods are like a roller coaster. In the middle of it all, he finds another doctor. This doctor pronounces the diagnosis of Moe's trouble to be rheumatism. He gives Moe more pills.

I have a difficult time trying to figure out how a diagnosis of rheumatism can come from Moe's symptoms. He no longer sleeps unless he takes pills.

He doesn't listen to me. I am lucky if he talks to me.

His symptoms become worse. This new doctor asks him to try another regime, which involves Moe going to Algiers every day for injections. Moe agrees. After a week of daily injections, he starts to feel better. He looks brighter, his face is a healthy pink color and he seems happier than he has been in a long time.

As Moe is beginning to feel better, one of the workers at Baba Ali asks him if he will run for a seat on the new Council of Birtouta. The election is part of a new program called the Communal Reform that has been set up by the government. Villages are expected to elect their own councils and mayors. The central government wants the local people to take responsibility for local problems. The election is at the end of February. While there is only one political party, the FLN, there are eleven other candidates. All but two are illiterate.

After considering for a few days, Moe decides he will try for the position. "This is a form of socialism but at least they try to deal with local issues," he says when he has made his decision.

To me, it sounds like it will be just something else to add to his frustration. But, he is so wound up at the idea of actually running a campaign, I decide not to say anything. According to Moe, the other candidates are very conservative. They have lived their whole lives in the village and either run businesses or are ex-FLN soldiers. He says he feels like an outsider. Yet, he is adamant that somebody on the council should be able to read and write. Occasionally, when I am out walking in the village, I hear his name on the one local radio station that booms out over the village square all day every day. I see his name in the Algiers newspaper on a weekly basis.

In early February, Moe, along with all the other candidates, are required to attend two separate gatherings of government officials. One is for training purposes and one is so the radio stations and newspapers can take photos of the candidates. Throughout the whole process, Moe seems lucid and happy. He is sleeping better and he looks forward to the vote. If he wins, the term of office is four years and he will be paid a small salary.

The night before the election, we notice many men streaming into Birtouta from the countryside. The roads are full of people walking in the streets, laughing and buying food from the local shops. They are coming to vote in the election. The event seems to be important to everyone. The town takes on a festive air. For the village people, it is the first opportunity to vote in a local election that is meaningful to their lives. Moe believes this is a good sign and goes down to the town square to talk to the visitors. He returns happy and relaxed and full of information. All the votes will be counted by hand. It will take at least two days to get the results.

The next morning Moe goes out to vote. When he returns, I ask if there are any women voting. He looks at me, cocks his head quizzically, and answers, "I not see any."

I push the question, "Are women allowed to vote in this election?"

Hesitating, he answers, "I think they allowed, but I not see any."

At the end of the second day, Moe comes home from work and sits with a borrowed portable radio on his lap until all the voting results in all the villages are announced.

"Well, I not on council." he announces abruptly. "Only two damn people on council can read or write. Stupid people. They get what they deserve."

For a moment, he puts his head in his hands. Then abruptly, he gets to his feet. He goes to Tarek's room where he spends the rest of the evening playing trucks with his son. Not only do I feel Moe's disappointment, but I feel responsible for his losing. It is difficult for people to vote for a man with an infidel wife.

A few days later, when Moe tells me that he is leaving for France and will be gone for ten days, I collapse in tears. He glowers at me while I sputter and spit and wipe my eyes on my sleeves, but he says nothing further except that he needs some clothes washed for the trip.

"How can you go away and leave me here alone again?" I wail. "What if something happens to you – or to one of the kids?"

"You know what to do," he answers, impassive. "You do this many times and you can do again. Why you always behave like crazy woman?"

"Moe," I try again to explain to him why I feel so abandoned when he leaves for days and days. "I don't know the language. I can't leave the house without being chased down the street by a horde of dirty children. I have no one to talk to, except a two-year-old and a four-year-old."

He continues packing.

"What if someone breaks into the house?" I finally ask him, grasping at anything that will keep him here.

Moe looks at me with the last of his patience and says, "If someone dares to break into this house, then me and my brothers will kill them when I return." He walks into the bedroom, shaking his head. "You are becoming like crazy woman," he repeats, "just a crazy woman."

"He's right," I think. But I have a bad feeling about this trip, so I persist. "Why are you going to be gone for ten days when you are visiting only two farms?" I ask. I know I sound childish, but I try to keep the conversation going.

"I not plan this trip," he retorts. "This is for work, not pleasure.

I am going with some new engineer guy who was world famous professional soccer player, Djibalis."

The name means nothing to me. We go to bed angry, not talking, unable to resolve our differences. He doesn't understand my feeling of abandonment.

He leaves in the morning without speaking a single word to me. I feel sad – and sick and tired of everything, of this place that I wanted to love so much. Looking for more excuses for my unhappiness, I decide it is because I have had diarrhoea for six months and am just now beginning to recover. "Yes," I decide. "That is why I am so unreasonable."

I spend the rest of the day with Tarek and Zohra, watching them be silly, playing and having fun. In the late afternoon we go to the market, more for something to do than to buy anything. Aside from being hounded by the usual horde of HLM children as we leave the building, no one bothers us.

The weather has changed and become milder and even though it is only the end of February, it feels as though winter is nearly over. I return to the apartment, refreshed.

The next day, a young boy brings a big box from my mother to my door. I offer the boy a few coins for his kindness. He refuses my offer, mumbling something about Moe and dashing off down the stairs like a frightened rabbit. As I shut the door, I realize that this young boy knew that I would need someone to carry this package from the post office, that he knew I was alone. The whole town must know. I am not sure whether that makes me feel safer or more vulnerable.

The following day, a young girl about eight years old knocks on my door and thrusts a bowl at me containing six dirty brown eggs. She smiles and says, "*Bonjour, Madame.*"

I send Zohra to get a container for the eggs and carefully count them out from her bowl to mine.

"*Combien?* How much?" I ask her in French. She shakes her matted thick coarse hair and flashes her beautiful eyes, smiling, "*Non, Madame. Pour vous,*" she says in broken French and then mumbles something in Arabic.

Zohra, who has been watching the girl curiously, turns to me and says, "Her father brought the eggs from the farm. They are a present."

The thinness of the girl contrasts sharply with her generous offer of this precious gift, sending chills up my back. I tell my daughter to thank her and especially to thank her father. The girl nods at Zohra's remarks, and smiles. She stands rigid in the hallway as though she is waiting for something.

Suddenly, Zohra runs back into the apartment and returns with a few pieces of the brightly coloured foil-wrapped candy that we used as Christmas tree decorations. She plunks them into the bottom of the girl's bowl. The girl looks at the candies, smiles and runs quickly towards her own apartment downstairs.

"How did you know what she wanted?" I ask.

"I dunno, I just thought she would like candy," Zohra answers.

"Well, you are a smart girl." I tell her, smiling.

"Of course, Zohra smart girl, I have a smart mommy." She smiles at me and then reaches up to give me a hug.

I love this daughter of mine.

On the eighth day of Moe's absence, I am ironing in the living room when I hear a loud knock. I open the door to findAhmed Ben Freha (Big Ahmed) and Mohamed G with their arms full of packages and bags.

I am surprised to see them and unsure how to tell them that Moe is not here.

They smile at me. Mohamed G asks me in broken English-French how I am.

"*Bien*," I answer nervously.

Zohra hears Mohamed G's voice and runs out of her room. She leaps up in an attempt to jump into his arms, but stops short when she sees he is carrying many packages. "Where's my present?" she yells.

Tarek is right behind her and screeches at the sight of both men. "Uncle, uncle-man," he suddenly squeals.

I have to laugh.

The men step inside the apartment and take their many packages and bags to the kitchen. They then each grab a child to hug.

"Nice uncles," my children keep repeating as they hang on tight.

I look at both men as they embrace my children and I smile. I am, however, nervous to be alone with these men. I stand by the door to the apartment and make sure it remains open. I also make sure I can be seen from the front balcony by anybody passing by. It is what Moe has told me to do.

His voice is firmly planted in my head, "If any of my friends ever stop by and I am not at home, never shut the door. The neighbours will think you are whore if you shut the door. It is also a reminder to my friends."

The two men gently set the children down on the floor and smile at me again. They stay only a few minutes and inquire if I need anything.

I thank them for their gifts and tell them I am fine.

Then, they bow awkwardly, but respectfully and leave.

As soon as they have cleared the threshold, I shut the door. I feel uneasy, even though I suspect that Moe told them to come by and check on me. I know they mean well but I wonder if they will report to him and what they will say. I hope I get the chance to report to Moe first.

The children and I go to the kitchen to see what goodies they have left us. The first bag contains boxed pastries, napoleons – the expensive kind that I like so much. I can already taste them. The second bag contains two jars of strawberry jelly, a fresh loaf of French bread and a large hunk of fresh butter. Two packages wrapped in white butcher paper appear next, so I let each child have one to open. Zohra's contains a wonderful smelling yellow cheese and Tarek's some smoked meat. What wonderful treats. We will feast tonight. Tarek licks the entire length of the salty meat and then wrinkles up his funny little nose. We all laugh.

Moe returns a day early and in good spirits. "I enjoy myself very much in France," he tells me grinning ear to ear. "I not realize that Djibalis is such famous person in France. Everywhere we go, we get everything free. It work out good. I get money from government to eat and live in France but I not need it. Instead, I spend it on clothes."

He walks over to his suitcases and throws them open wide. One is brand new and bulging with unfamiliar items. He pulls things out, one by one, explaining as he goes. First, he pulls out two hangers holding two complete suits of clothes. He feels the material and explains that it is called *Tergal*, a material that never needs ironing. He carefully carries the suits over to the closet and hangs them up side by side. He lingers there as the children and I watch him again finger the material and smile.

Next he pulls out a pair of wide-legged trousers and three beautiful jackets. "These the best of Paris," he tells me proudly.

"Paris? I thought you were going to the countryside to look at farms," I say before I can stop myself.

"Yes," he answers sheepishly. "We did and then we go to Paris to buy clothes and visit Djibalis' friends. Good trip," he repeats.

From his other suitcase, he pulls out a year's supply of hard candies for the children and a new dress, which he presents to me with a long explanation. "This is special dress," he says. "The sales lady calls it, *Mini robe*." He holds up a teal green straight-skirted dress made of some kind of knitted jersey material.

"If I can even fit into it," I think, "it will be at least three inches above my knees."

Moe insists I try it on immediately.

I pull it over my head and turn to look into the mirror. I am pleasantly surprised by what I see. I have worn nothing but long skirts and long-sleeved blouses or sweaters for so long and I have lost a lot of weight with all my sicknesses. I return to the living room and parade in front of Moe and the kids.

He looks me up and down appreciatively and winks at me. Then, he promptly informs me that I can wear it, but only for doing work around the house.

I shake my head, smiling, and imagining myself doing housework in a dress that is three inches above my knees.

Tarek and Zohra both like my new look. "Mommy pretty lady," Zohra tells me and copies my exaggerated walk around the room. We all laugh together.

"What about the work portion of this trip? Did you get any work done?" I inquire once I have changed out of my new outfit.

"Yes," Moe answers. "I talk to the people at French plant breeding station in Memes. They say I should come to work there." He pauses, reflecting for a moment whether he should continue. "They also say it is very bad what is happening in Algeria."

"What do they mean by that? How would they know anything about this?" I ask.

"I think they know and understand. I am just surprised and confused by this because they are all French." Moe shakes his head, unable to understand how some Frenchmen can be sympathetic when others are so mean.

"By the way," I break in to change the subject, "Mohamed G and Ahmed stopped by and dropped off some treats while you were away."

"Oh?" he says, surprised. "I hear they both gone for a trip these days."

"Really? I thought you sent them to spy on me. Don't worry, I left the door open like you always told me."

Moe frowns for a moment, and then smiles, "I not spy on you, and I not worry about Ahmed or Mohamed G. They are good men."

"Yes, Moe, but remember what you told me before? All men have penises, no?"

His eyebrows rise until they point straight up. "You are sometimes very silly woman."

# Side Trips of All Sorts

Because Moe is back from his trip early, he doesn't have to return to work for a couple of days. It is a good opportunity to take a short trip and get away from Birtouta. He wants to drive up into the mountains between Blida and Medea. The kids are very excited when they find out that we are going away for the day with Daddy. I dress them in comfortable clothes and we pack a few things for snacks. Carrying coats and hats, prepared for whatever the mountains may bring, we set off.

Moe takes the turnoff at Blida. There are no roadblocks to upset our little outing. From here, the road is full of steep curves, and we meander back and forth up into the mountains. Halfway up, we come to a switchback where we discover a coffee house built into the mountainside. With waterfalls on either side, it is so breathtaking that Moe pulls into the parking lot so we can take a closer look and explore. We pile out of the car and enter the large wooden doors of the coffee house. It is a spacious building with little tables decorated with white linen tablecloths and lovely brocade chairs. We can't see any people, though we can hear voices. No one seems to be in the main part of the coffee house. Moe tells us to stay there and he will go and find out what is going on.

He disappears around the rear of the building following the noises and the voices. Zohra huddles up against me as soon as Moe disappears and whispers, "Do you think this place has ghosts?" she asks.

"No, honey. I don't think there are ghosts. We will wait until Daddy comes back."

Moe returns smiling and waving at us to join him in the back. I herd the reluctant children ahead of me following Moe to a large glass window. Through it, we can see at least fifty people outside on a wooden platform, staring at a dozen or more men standing in the tall grass, feeding hundreds of small grey and brown monkeys. We watch transfixed as these little critters rise up on their back legs and eagerly take food from the outstretched hands of the men.

Tarek squeals in delight. He runs to the door to go out to the platform but a tall, dark man dressed like a soldier stands in the doorway and won't let him pass. He scoops Tarek up and places him in Moe's arms, smiling and chatting to him.

Moe explains, "He says no children can go on the platform because the monkeys like to bite little ones."

"The monkeys bite?" Zohra asks, disappointed.

"Yes, honey. I guess they do." I respond. "We'll watch them eat from here."

Reluctantly, Zohra stands at the window and watches. When the monkeys have finished all the food in the large buckets, they turn and run back into the hillside forests and the people trickle back into the coffee house.

A waiter offers to seat us at a table close by. We accept his invitation and when we are seated, we are served thick Algerian sweet coffee and triple-layered pastries. The children drink watered down sweet tea out of real teacups and happily eat two pastries each.

The waiter tells us that the monkeys come down to feed every day about this time. They usually come down in small family groups. He estimates that at least 100 come back day after day. This place is called Monkey Rock and the monkeys are Barbary Macaques, a tail-less social monkey native to Northern Algeria and Morocco, and the only macaques found in Africa.

When we suggest it is time to leave and go home, both children balk at the idea.

"We like it here," Zohra tells us. "We like the monkeys and the tea."

Moe and I smile at each other. It has been a wonderful day. We are all reluctant to leave. That night while getting ready for bed, Moe and I agree that it would be nice if all our Algerian experiences could be like today. He tells me he will work harder to find other adventures for us.

February moves into March, and the weather gets better, but, unfortunately, Moe gets sicker. In early March, he throws his back out and can't get out of bed for two weeks. Mostly, I just look after him as he struggles with a sore back, no sleep and more pills. By the end of March he seems better. He stops taking the pills and goes back to work.

We get another invitation to visit Moe's politician friend, Mahmoud, in Blida. I am happy to get out of the house and relieved that Moe is able to drive again. I like visiting with Mahmoud and Leila. This trip is to pay our respects to their new baby who is now three weeks old. We buy a few presents and put money in an envelope for the baby. We spend a wonderful evening in their beautiful house.

When Moe returns to work, he finds many changes at Baba Ali. Shelig, the number one boss, has fired his general secretary who was working on Moe's scholarship application. No one can find the forms anywhere. They don't know if they were sent on or not.

Moe decides not to pursue working or studying in France. He tells me he will just keep working at Baba Ali until something else comes along.

At the end of March, my grandmother sends me a box of special chocolates from See Candies in Salt Lake City, Utah for my birthday. It arrives exactly on the day, March, 29th. I bring it out as a surprise for dessert.

Moe apologizes for forgetting my birthday.

I tell him it is okay because I forgot myself and it is not really the custom to celebrate birthdays in Algeria.

Zohra is obsessed with the chocolate. For three days afterwards, she asks me every day, "Mommy, what smells?"

"I don't smell anything," I tell her every time.

"Yes," she insists, "I smell the candy Mi-Mi and Papa and Granny sent. You better look at it and see if it's okay."

By the third day the candy is gone, but it takes another two days to convince her she has eaten all of it.

"Everybody ate MY candy," she cries over and over again, heart broken.

Tarek says his first long sentence and it turns out to be about chickens. He calls them *wickens*. On a trip to the market, he sees a dozen or so chickens scratching in the dirt near the market place. He stops and watches them a long time. When Moe arrives home from work for lunch, he is greeted at the door by an excited child.

"Talek see *wicken* today."

Moe looks at him astonished, not understanding.

Tarek suddenly jumps up and down, flapping his little arms and clucking in a perfect imitation of a chicken.

We all laugh so hard we have trouble finishing our lunches. Moe goes back to work mumbling something about how funny Tarek is. I am happy to see Moe smiling.

A few days after my birthday, Moe drives into Algiers and buys me a present. My mother's most recent cheque has finally been cleared by the bank and they release our money. Moe hasn't had a paycheque for three months. My present is a 40-piece china coffee set with an old-fashioned red and white rose pattern. The set includes a coffee pot, milk pitcher, twelve cups and saucers, and twelve dessert plates and a sugar bowl.

The first people to use the new coffee set are Moe's brothers, Abdelghani and Tahar, Tahar's wife, Zohra and their two children, Beheda, a boy of five, and Haceba, a girl of three. They stay for four days. Zohra, my sister-in-law, and I communicate through a combination of French and a few fractured words of Arabic.

I love going to her house in Moussa because they have a real bed and always make an extra effort to make us feel welcome and comfortable. On this visit, however, she is very pregnant and can't stand to sleep in a bed. She requests a quilt for the floor and curls up in the living room each night with her children and a blanket.

I want to give her my bed the way she gave hers to me, but she insists otherwise. Each morning she gets up early and washes my floors and does the cooking. She teaches me some new couscous recipes and how to make the pastry for little Algerian meat pies.

A few days into their visit, Tarek comes to me crying in the night with a high fever. He is having a difficult time breathing. He coughs so hard that he gags. As the light of morning brightens the room, I shake Moe awake.

"I take him to the doctor. Tahar can drive me. You stay here. It too much trouble if you go," Moe snaps at me, as if I am somehow responsible for the reactions of his countrymen.

Tarek tries to scream when Moe takes him from my arms but he is so sick that no sound comes out. Moe holds him tightly against his chest.

My sister-in-law, Zohra, puts her arm across my back in a soft and sympathetic way as I watch the men carry Tarek out the door to the car.

I burst into tears.

Zohra tells me not to cry but I can't help it. She wipes my eyes with her fingers. She smells of orange water.

It stops my tears. I want to be strong. I wonder if the doctor will know what to do.

I wait anxiously for the men to return. Zohra fusses in the kitchen and I know she is cooking something special. I feel bad that she is standing up doing all the work in her condition. She rejects my offer of help, however, and I realize she really wants to do this.

I sit down at the table and write a letter to my father about the deterioration of the American-Algerian political relationship.

Hours later, the men return and I notice that Tarek already looks better. As soon as the men enter the house, he reaches out for me. I take him from Moe and hug him tight. I can still hear the rattle in his chest.

"Yuk, he sounds awful. What happened?" I ask.

"He has pneumonia. The doctor gave him big shot with penicillin. We go to clinic for more shots tomorrow but he already better. Good thing I have money these days," he adds.

"Talek get owie," Tarek tells me in his little voice as he shows me the place in his bottom where the needle went in.

"Ah, poor Tarkie," I tell him as I rock him back and forth. "It will make you feel better." I hold him until he falls asleep and then

I slip him into his bed, wrapping him in a warm blanket and closing the door as I leave. I don't like the deep rattle in his chest.

Early the next day, Moe takes his brothers and Zohra to Algiers to do some sightseeing. The men take Tarek to the clinic for his next shot before they leave. I stay home. Tarek sleeps most of the day and by the time the family returns, he is better. The rattle in his chest is slowly disappearing.

A few days later, just as Moe's family is leaving to return to Mascara, I come down with a carbon copy of what Tarek has been fighting. I visit the doctor and he gives me a shot of penicillin and tells me to stay in bed for three days. I try to do what I am told but I still have to wash and cook and look after my children while Moe is at work. The following day, Tarek is sick again. Again, the doctor says it is pneumonia. We start the shots again and within a few days, he is better again. I am tired of all the sickness. It seems endless.

On the last day of my scheduled shots, Moe comes home for lunch with the news he is leaving for the desert. He will be back on Saturday. He will be gone for the next four days. It doesn't leave much time to pack his bag and fix his lunch, but I manage.

I also manage not to yell or make any comments about him leaving while Tarek and I are both sick. Why bother? Maybe it is just as well. I will be able to rest and not have to make his meals or entertain his friends.

Moe returns early from the desert. He seems anxious as he chatters about his trip. The first thing he says is that he is going to resign from Baba Ali in June. It takes three months for a resignation to take effect. We will be able to leave in September.

"Where are we going?" I ask, surprised at another turn of events that I didn't see coming.

"We are going to Tiaret. I am going to work for my friend who is in control of agriculture in that region. I think you like to live there. It has good schools. It is very clean and people are in very good economic class. The weather is also very good."

I nod. I will believe it when I see it.

"By the way," he adds, "I am back early because I faint three times when I am away."

The next day he goes to the doctor and returns with a vial full of new pills.

"Moe, I worry about all the pills you take. I don't think they help you very much."

He looks at me and I see his frown deepen into furrows all around his forehead.

I have said too much.

"So, now you are my doctor?" He sighs deeply, and I step forward attempting to put an arm around him.

"Get away, woman. You don't care if I die," he shouts, "You always criticize poor Moe."

"I don't mean to criticize you, Moe," I argue. "I just think you need to take fewer pills. They make you tired and grumpy."

"I think it a good thing for you to take children and go back to States. I think this place not good for anybody."

I just look at him. "I won't do that and leave you here sick. You don't know me at all, do you?" I hold the tears that threaten to spill out.

He looks at me for a moment longer. Then he turns and goes to lie down on the living room mattress. He closes his eyes.

I go into the bedroom and shut the door.

The following weekend, we are invited to visit the family of a man who works with Moe. I expect his house will be a small shack in the countryside like the other workers, but I am surprised when Moe pulls up to a large villa complete with an electric gate and a beautiful garden.

"He works with you?" I ask.

"Yes, but his family has money." Moe replies. "He was a governor during the French time."

"Wow! Look at this palace he lives in," I gush.

Moe pushes the buzzer and a voice comes at us loud and booming. Moe gives his name and the iron gate swings open so that we can drive in. Moe parks at the front door and before we can get out, his friend is there to greet us. He takes my hand and smiles into my face. I am startled. He looks exactly like my father. Moe smiles at me as I stare rudely, unable to take my eyes off him.

"This is weird," I finally whisper.

"Yes, that's what I thought," Moe says, nodding.

We follow our host into the house and admire the exquisite tile floors and lovely furniture. The place shines with cleanliness.

Moe stops in the foyer and turns to me. "By the way, he owns two houses like this," Moe tells me quietly, "One for each wife."

"One for each wife?" I ask incredulously. I have heard that Moslem men sometimes maintain more than one household, but have never met anyone with two wives before.

"Yes. He has two." Then Moe adds, "I tell you this now so when you meet them you not be surprised."

Moe's friend tries to talk to me in Arabic but realizes I can't understand. Moe translates that his friend wants me to come to the kitchen to meet his wives. "I cannot go with you," Moe adds. "I am not a relative."

I follow the man to the kitchen. Two women, who look very much alike, except that one is quite old and the other young, come forward smiling. They greet me with kisses and bouncing curls and then trundle back to their duties. Moe tells me that having two wives is unusual in Algeria. He explains that the Koran says a man can have two wives, but only if he can treat them equally.

Moe looks at me and then adds, "What man can do that? In this case he really loves his first wife but she never has children, so he ask her to pick a second wife for him. So far the second wife give him fourteen children. He says she is very happy and the house is filled with children and the children have two mothers. Everybody is happy with this arrangement."

"If they are so happy with this arrangement, why do they have two houses?" I ask.

Moe says, smiling, "Well, maybe, they not that happy."

I laugh. Sometimes Moe's sense of humour is the best thing about him.

We are served a five-course meal of expensive exquisitely prepared food. We even have a specialty dish – a dish prepared to honour special guests. A sheep's head complete with the eyes, brains, tongue and jaw, is cooked in a special sauce. When it is time to leave, Moe's friend brings out gifts for all of us: two necklaces, a gold bracelet and a beautiful prayer rug.

Moe is overwhelmed. He spends a long time expressing his gratitude.

We drive home in silence. Moe is deep in thought. Finally, he wonders aloud, "Why we receive so much attention from this man? He is my co-worker. I am not his boss. Maybe he know something I not know."

"Maybe you are about to get a raise or a promotion or something," I tease.

"I hope not," Moe snaps. "I not want to be boss there."

The next day when Moe is finishing his breakfast before going to work, he faints and falls off his chair and onto the floor. I bend over him, at first wondering if he is dead. But he immediately starts to moan and he opens his eyes.

"You have to see a doctor, Moe. I will go with you," I offer. But he just shakes his head, gets to his feet, and heads for the bedroom. He climbs into bed and covers his head with the blanket. A few hours later, he gets up again and walks to the kitchen. He faints again, this time falling face first on the hard kitchen floor, barely missing the edge of the table. This time, he comes to more slowly. He looks at me groggily. His face is bruised and he has a cut on his lip. I help him to his feet and hang onto him while he again stumbles back to bed.

The next day he stays in bed until noon. When he finally struggles to get up, I attempt to help him. He pushes me away.

"You are going to the doctor today," I tell him, exasperated by his stubbornness. "I insist. You cannot go on like this, Moe. It's not fair to me or to the children. What if you fall and can't get up? I can't lift you and I don't know who to talk to that would take you to the hospital."

He looks at me for a few minutes and then nods. Within a few minutes, he is dressed and, before I can stop him, he heads out the door.

"Wait a minute," I call after him. "You can't go by yourself."

"Yes, I can," he answers as he disappears down the stairs.

I watch him drive away and wonder what will happen to us. Now, I need my willow.

 A Mishwee

Moe doesn't return from Algiers for two days. When he finally comes home, I don't know whether to be happy or sad or angry. Mostly, I am so worn out from worry that I can barely ask him where he has been or what has happened to him.

"I sorry I am gone so long," Moe says. "I go to my friend Mohamed G and he take me to see the doctor the American Embassy recommend. I have to wait for appointment. Doctor says I take wrong medicine. He says I have a problem in my mind and it comes out in my body. He calls it the *shock of culture*. He is seeing many students with this condition coming home from studies in the West. He says I need different medicine and much rest. I try what he says. Maybe it help."

Moe is back to work within two weeks, feeling much better, but still determined to find another job. He makes arrangements for us to go to Tiaret again. This time he will decide whether or not he wants to live there. We plan to stay with Abdullah and Ishiah again. We are travelling with Aouf and his wife Yarka, and their twins. At the last minute, Little Ahmed and his wife Rashida, Hushmoaui and Fatiha and two kids are added to the group. Ahmed and Mohamed G are going with us as well, but they will travel in a different car.

We pull our sleepy grumpy children out of bed at four o'clock in the morning. Moe insists on the early hour so that we can be in Tiaret before noon. He says it is necessary because he has a surprise.

Silently, I hope the surprise involves sleeping. Otherwise, by nightfall we will all be exhausted.

We stop in Algiers and pick up Aouf and Yarka and the twins.

Our trip is uneventful, meaning we don't encounter any road-blocks. We arrive at Abdullah and Ishiah's at Moe's appointed time and an hour later, the rest of the group arrives. Ten of us leave Abdullah's in a four-car convoy and drive fifty miles into the countryside. We stop at the farm owned by Mohamed G and his four brothers. After parking in the farmyard, we walk down a small grassy hill to a large fire pit where our lunch is being pre-pared. Two whole sheep are being slowly roasted over hot coals by four men, each holding long thick wooden spits, two men to a spit. They turn the spits inch-by-inch, minute-by-minute inside the pit. The heat is unbearable, even from our vantage point above and away from the edge of the pit. I see sweat pour off the men's bodies and I wonder how they can stand the heat.

The roasting meat gives off a wonderful smell of hot fat min-gled with garlic and onion. My morning meal of melon and toast suddenly feels like it wasn't enough. Moe puts his arm around my shoulders and whispers, "This is my surprise. This lunch in hon-our of you. We call it *Mishwee*."

"What does that mean?" I ask Moe.

"It means my friends want to welcome you to this country with special feast. I show you what to do when it is time. Just do what I say. Okay?"

"Okay," I nod, wondering what is in store for me this time, and understanding why everyone wanted to come on the trip with us.

Before we step back from the edge of the pit, I ask Moe about the large package that I see inside the lamb's body.

"It is liver," he explains. They roll it in sheep fat and roast it inside the belly of lamb. It most tasty treat you ever eat."

It is early afternoon before the cooking is done and we are led into a long building that is used as a storage shed in the summer. For this special occasion it has been emptied, cleaned and set up as a dining room. A long low table covered in a clean coloured cloth extends the length of the shed. Tucked under the edge of the table are large, soft, plump pillows for sitting. I am directed to the head of the table and given the seat of honour. Moe is on my right and Abdullah on my left.

As soon as we are seated, the roasted lambs are brought in, still on the spits, and laid directly on the table. Abdullah says a few words and in unison, everyone reaches out and pulls bite-sized pieces of meat from the nearest carcass. The toasted brown meat goes from greasy fingers to opened mouths, like some pre-programed dance. After a few moments the picking gives way to a rapid feeding frenzy. It reminds me of a flock of vultures, ripping the meat off the bones of a carcass, anxious to get at some juicy morsel of meat that promises to be better than the last. Moe nudges me with his elbow and tells me to try some. I reach out tentatively, watching everyone else. The meat comes off the body easily and I feel its oily texture on my fingers. I put the morsel to my lips. The taste is like nothing I can describe. As I reach for a second piece, Moe whispers that there is no taste like the taste of freshly killed, freshly roasted, young tender lamb, especially when it is cooked over an open pit in the countryside. I become as vulture-like as the rest.

Once we have slowed our meat eating fervour, large bowls of green salad and giant loaves of Algerian bread are brought to the table. A few minutes later, everyone stops eating and watches Abdullah, who approaches carrying a large container. He walks over to me, and places it directly in front of me. I look inside. It looks like meat with bits of grey-white gristle floating in a thick oily yellow-red liquid. The smell is not unpleasant, tomatoes and cinnamon, but the look of it turns my stomach. I swallow.

"Moe what is this?" I ask, curious, and hoping I won't be expected to eat it.

"It is Algerian delicacy and our host gives you the honour to start. It is tradition."

"O-kay," I say slowly. Then I ask again, "What is it?"

"Eyes," Moe says quickly, as if saying it quickly will elevate the meaning of the word to something that I would find tasty. I detect a small smirk crossing his lips. He tries to erase it, but fails.

"Eyes – eyes?" I ask, horrified.

"Yes, you not eat the whole thing, just reach in and take one eye and eat it. Then you pass pot to next person."

"With my fingers?" I ask.

"Do you see spoons here?" he asks, losing his patience and looking at me like I am stupid.

I look into the red tomato mess one more time and then plunge my meat-greasy fingers in, hoping it will be impossible to even get the glob out of its container. Then, feeling something rubbery, I take what I think is an eyeball between my thumb and forefinger, pull it out of the pot and push the gelatinous mass into my mouth trying not to think about what I am doing.

Twelve pairs of living eyes are watching me. I think, "Do I swallow or do I chew?" I notice that the sauce that comes with the glob is very tasty – a spicy combination of cinnamon, cumin, mint, tomato and strong pungent garlic. I decide to chew. The glob has the consistency of soft rubber. It doesn't really taste much different than the octopus Moe made me eat from the restaurant by the sea. A few more chews and I swallow.

Twelve people break into a cheery round of spontaneous applause and, just as abruptly as they started, turn back to their eating. Moe smiles at me.

I feel like I have passed some sort of test, but then I think, "Perhaps it's not a test at all, but just another joke on the Americanea."

Abdullah again leaves his seat and goes off in the direction of the pit. This time Moe pokes me in the ribs to get my attention. "Now come real treat," he laughs sarcastically. "Good luck to you now."

"This has to be a joke," I think.

Again, Abdullah appears at my side, but this time he carries a large basket. He sets it down carefully in the space just in front of me. He reaches into his pocket and pulls out a hand-whittled wooden spoon with a small rounded end on it and hands it to me. I take the implement and roll it over in my hand. I find its small rounded edges are imbedded with sharp metal. It is some kind of cutting tool. I look at Moe to find out what is coming next. He suggests I look inside the basket.

I take a deep breath, expecting the worst. I am not disappointed. In the basket is a sheep's head, eye-less, skinned of all its wool, but with the muscles still attached. It smells like it has been cooked.

"Thank heavens," I breathe. The sheep's teeth are worn and chipped and the lip, nose, and ears are all intact. Moe reaches into the basket and turns the head around so that I can see down through the top of its open skull, so that I can see what I will be eating, the greyish brown- coloured brains.

Moe whispers, "Use cutting spoon and scoop out what you want. Then pass the spoon and the head to Abdullah."

I look into Moe's face and again I see a smirk. This time, however, I have a smirk of my own. As a child growing up with my grandmother, we always ate eggs and brains every single Sunday morning. I thank God for my granny and her Sunday morning buffets.

I relax, take the spoon and scoop out as generous a portion of the mess as I can fit on the small spoon. I put it on my plate, then pop a bite into my mouth, sit back, smile and chew. I swallow and reach for another spoonful. It is delicious.

When I reach for a third spoonful, Moe, astonished at my performance, pokes me again. "You not be greedy. You leave some for other people."

"Sorry, Moe," I tell him, smiling, "I love brains. Didn't you know?"

Moe's friends are all staring at me, wide-eyed and amazed that *Americanea* would actually eat such countryside delicacies.

"One small victory for me," I think. In my mind, I nod at the willow. It bows back to me.

After lunch we get back into the cars and are driven to the foot of a timeworn, rock-covered, scruffy-looking mountain. Moe tells me that we will climb up this mountain for some exercise and a beautiful view.

I tell him I would rather eat brains.

He doesn't find that funny.

"How do you expect me to climb in these high-heeled shoes?" I ask.

"If you can eat brains, you can find a way to climb in high-heels," he throws back at me good-naturedly.

The men leave us behind and climb to the top where they stand looking out over the countryside. In high-heels, it is difficult. I constantly stumble on stones and trip over thick tree roots. Fatiha and I walk together, half dragging both our Tareks. Zohra goes ahead with the men and she yells down encouragement from above, her little voice echoing over the countryside.

Fatiha and I sit down to rest. I am sure I cannot go another step. She agrees. A cold wind is blowing and I am glad I wore my woolly white coat. I wonder what my parents would think if they knew I was climbing a mountain in high-heels and a straight skirt.

When I finally get a chance to look, I see the beautiful landscape of the whole valley, and over my shoulder, a bit farther up the mountain, I spy an old structure. Abdullah says it is an old French fort used long ago for defence. Looking out over the valley again, I see a man standing on a rock, far below me. He is holding a long rifle. Surprised, my eyes move again, and I spot four more men, strategically located, up and down the mountain at various distances from our little group, They all carry long black rifles and wear the headdress and robes of the Tourag, a desert people. Two of the men stand tall and straight and gaze off into the distance. The ones that are closer sit on large boulders, their eyes looking into the distance, as if they are deliberately not looking at us. I point them out to Moe.

He whispers that there are many bandits in these hills just looking to rob people or kidnap women.

"Really?" I ask, suddenly worried.

"I not sure they kidnap women," says Moe, laughing. "I make up story but I know that Mohamed G's family hire these men because they have some concern about local tribesmen." Moe, the eternal joker. But I know there must be a reason for our guards. Perhaps it is just as well that I don't know what it is.

We return to Abdullah's house before dark and carry the children into the room where they all sleep in the same bed. It is more than a bed, it is the biggest feather mattress I have ever seen and it sinks down low and comfy when each child is placed on it. The children, about a dozen of them, make no fuss. They are so tired from their day on the mountain that they sink into oblivion the moment their little heads hit the pillows. It is quite the sight to see a dozen children in one bed, all asleep.

Ishiah has been cooking since we returned. This is her time to shine. Even though it is now ten o'clock at night, we are about to embark on another feast. We sit at a magnificent solid mahogany table with room for twenty or more, men on one side and women on the other. We begin with a salad made of beets, carrots, artichoke hearts, and potatoes, which is followed by a pastry full of meat and potatoes and spices. Next, we have chicken with carrots and peas and a red tomato sauce that smells of cinnamon, cumin and garlic. The fourth course is a large bowl of buttered rice with sugar and then a selection of different kinds of puddings. Every course is served with homemade bread and a kind of punch that I don't recognize. I am so full I cannot breathe.

After dinner everyone adjourns to a large sitting area full of couches and comfortable chairs. The men gravitate to one end of the room and the women to another. It feels nice to have a group of men and women at least in the same room. The woman talk quietly to each other and the men are into their own conversations.

Even though I am mostly left out as Moe is busy solving the problems of Baba Ali and discussing his recent decision to move to Tiaret, I feel content in this group. I have a sense of belonging and acceptance. I know that eventually I will understand. I just have to live here a bit longer and work on my language skills. I already understand a lot more than I can say. I think of that as a good sign.

It is after midnight when the talking winds down. The men are all directed as a group to the first level where blankets and quilts are piled on the floor. The women climb the beautiful marble staircase to a large room with two huge beds. Three of us climb into one, and two into the other. We pull up the feather quilts over our clothes and, like the children, fall immediately into a deep sleep. No one stirs until the children wander into our room late the next morning.

One by one, we roll off the bed and head to the bathroom to

wash up. As we descend the long marble staircase, we are engulfed by the wonderful smells of baking bread. We say hello to the men who are just awakening and reseat ourselves around the table like the night before. Family servants arrive with arms loaded with freshly baked bread, homemade sweet rolls of a dozen different kinds and sweet rich Algerian coffee served in demitasse cups. I never want to leave. It is profoundly peaceful, even with a dozen active children and as many adults sharing the space.

Throughout the morning, people gradually disappear, going their own way with their families. Some men go walking and some ride around the city. Moe and I take the children and drive to the farm where Moe hopes to work. We are met by Abdullah's cousin who gives us a tour of some of the three thousand acres of green grass and beautiful gardens. It is the largest horse breeding and selection farm in North Africa. Horses from all over the world are brought here to be bred. As part of that process, the workers conduct research on the various breeds. Abdullah's cousin says there are two *Engineur Agronome* positions opening up in the near future. He encourages Moe to apply immediately to the ministry.

We leave the horse farm and drive out to Abdullah's farm, which is forty miles from Tiaret. When we park on the road near the farm, we notice the cars of the others in our party also parked along the road. We walk for a mile. The children are tired by the time we finally arrive at a large grove of cherry trees. We find our friends sitting under the trees, all seated on beautiful coloured padded blankets. A wonderful cooking smell is wafting in the air, and before we join our friends, we follow the aroma to a pit further inside the orchard. It appears we are about to have another *mishwee*. The ten of us eat another lamb. When the meat is finished, we eat bowls of traditional couscous with sour milk called *Elben*. Then we visit until late in the afternoon, when everyone exchanges long goodbyes and many wishes that we will all be together again in the future.

We drop off Aouf, Yarka and the twins in Algiers and drive back to Birtouta. It has been a wonderful weekend with all our dearest friends. The children are happy and tired. Moe and I are hopeful that things will work out for us in Tiaret. I am hopeful that we will be able to move where Moe will finally be happy.

Three days after our holiday in Tiaret, Abdullah's relative who is the head of Animal Science in Algeria calls Moe in for a job interview. Moe dresses in his best suit and as he leaves the apartment, he is hopeful and smiling.

"I do my best," he says.

The interview goes well.

"Now all I do is wait," he says.

I decide to write to my father about Moe's experience with the interview.

April 14, 1967

Dear Daddy:

Just want to tell you about Moe's job interview on Tuesday with the head of Animal Science in Algeria. This is all according to Moe, remember, so I will try to quote him. Evidently the man was so nice. He asked Moe first about his work at Baba Ali and Moe told him he was very discouraged. The man said, "Well, Mr. Chaabane, you are lucky you have only been here 1½ years. I arrived here in 1963 and things were really bad then. So many times I wanted to quit but I came to Algeria to help. It takes a lot of patience I know, but we need all of you young engineers. If you all stick out the bad times and work together, you will have everything much better before too long. He said the new minister is aware of the problems at Baba Ali and the sabotage that is going on. He also said that Mr. Shelig is in very bad trouble already. The new Secretary General is a young dynamic man who is also on the side of the young engineers. He stressed that it is difficult for everyone, but they are trying as best they can to solve the problems. That is why he said they begged Ahmed and Mohamed G not to resign and they withdrew their resignations. Anyway Moe told him that he wanted out of research (Shelig) for health reasons and the man said, "Give me your application and I will do all I can for you." So here we go again. Moe and I are much encouraged. Like Moe says, as long as there is some indication that we are needed and wanted, we will stay. I will let you know how things go, of course.

Much love, Susie

I put my pen away and climb into bed next to Moe. He is sleeping and I hear his breath, easy like it used to be long ago. I fall asleep and dream of going to America. I awake several hours later. Moe isn't there. I stumble out and turn on the light in the hallway. I look in the living room and find him sitting at the table reading something. He doesn't acknowledge me and I go back to bed.

On the morning of Zohra's birthday, Moe loads the children and their suitcases into the car and goes to Mascara to visit his family. He plans to pick up Big Ahmed and Mohamed G somewhere along the way.

I can't bear the thought of going to Mascara again. The thought of it makes me sick. It is much easier for him to go without me.

Moe agrees.

My plan is to sleep the entire time they are gone and enjoy my time alone.

At noon, as I am settling in for what I hope will be a nice long nap, there is a knock on my door. It is Fatiha and Mustapha Hushmoui with their children. I explain that Moe has gone to Mascara with Mohamed G and Ahmed. They tell me they already know that. They met him on the highway and told him that they would take me with them for the weekend to Cherchell, a seaport town that is a vacation spot. It is 55 miles west of Algiers. Mustapha will go from there to Mascara to see his brother. I can stay with Fatiha until everyone gets back.

I say good-bye to my time alone and happily pack a bag. Fatiha is quickly becoming the best friend I have in Algeria. I have found a way to understand her broken French laced with easy Arabic. She is very patient with me. She is interested in everything I do and she is happy to help me understand things. I also like Mustapha. He and Moe grew up together in Mascara and went away to school together. However, Mustapha returned to Algeria in 1956 and spent seven years fighting for independence while Moe went off to school in America. Now they are back together. Moe calls it fate.

Mustapha is attending the Military Academy in Cherchell and in eight months will be an army captain. Fatiha's baby, also named Tarek, is only a year old. She is razor thin, and pregnant with her fourth child. I want to tell her about birth control, but I decide I should ask Moe before I do.

I stay in Cherchell with Fatiha and her husband for the weekend. They are kind to me, taking me to the beach and out for nice meals in lovely restaurants. They spend many hours trying to understand my broken French-Arabic. We have several great conversations, but each one takes a long time. I learn many new words in both languages.

To me, Mustapha and Fatiha are educated and modern in their thinking. Compared to some other couples I have met, this is true – but in their sleeping arrangements they are as traditional as the poorest villagers. While Mustapha is in the house, I sleep with Fatiha in her bed. Mustapha sleeps on a cot in the children's room. I feel like I am intruding on their privacy. Unfortunately, I don't have the vocabulary – or the courage to even try to broach this subject.

The sleeping arrangements straighten themselves out on Monday when Mustapha leaves for Mascara with two of the children. I get the cot in the children's room. We spend our entire time cooking. She teaches me how to make the paper thin dough that goes around *bruek*, a meat pie with hamburger, potatoes, and spices. I work diligently to make my pile of dough paper thin, but I fail. Her dough is thinner than mine every time. She also teaches me how to make other Algerian delicacies and I eagerly write the recipes down so I can make them as a surprise for Moe when he gets home.

Moe is expected to arrive at Fatiha's house by Friday. But, there is no sign of him. The next day, Fatiha and I busy ourselves, taking short walks to the market and playing with her baby. The day passes slowly as our cooking is finished, and we have less and less to talk about. I feel that I have out-stayed my welcome.

When Moe hasn't returned by Saturday night, I begin to worry that he has taken the children and gone away forever. Late in the evening, I feel the tears forming and eventually, I can't hold them in.

Fatiha comforts me by hugging me and bringing me hot sweet tea to drink. "He will come soon." she says in French, "Soon."

She says this over and over again until I think she is trying to convince herself as well.

"It is the way of men in my country," she adds finally. "Sometimes they come home and sometimes they don't."

I understand what she is saying perfectly, but it doesn't make me feel any better.

Moe arrives with the children at noon on Sunday. He looks tired and angry and he doesn't offer any excuse for arriving two days late. He orders me to get my things and get in the car. Zohra is very sick and we need to go home right away and get her to the doctor.

As we reach the curb where the car is parked, I ask him why he is two days late.

"I not late," he says harshly. "I never tell you when I return."

I sigh and say nothing further. It is no use to argue.

As I climb into the little Renault, I see Zohra sitting groggily in the backseat, looking red-eyed and pale.

She can barely speak and only manages, "Hi, Mommy."

Tarek whines to sit on my lap for the trip home and I let him climb over the seat. He hugs me the whole way. "I miss you, my Mommy," he says over and over.

We arrive home without being stopped at a single roadblock. It is a relief. I am happy to see my little apartment. It is beginning to feel like it is really home.

As soon as we are inside and shut the door, I take Zohra to the bathroom to wash her down. She smells like urine and vomit. I lift her into the tub, and she suddenly grabs her stomach and screams in pain.

"Honey," I ask, "what's wrong?"

Moe tells me he is going to take her to the clinic. "She throw up and cry this whole trip," he says, concerned but impatient. "I come home early. I think she have appendix trouble."

I ignore his remark about coming home early and carry her to the bedroom for clean clothes.

"I think you should take her to the hospital, Moe. She looks so sick."

Moe picks her up in his arms before I can get her socks on her feet and carries her to the car. He insists I stay home and look after Tarek.

In three hours, Moe returns with the news that she doesn't have appendicitis, just a nasty virus. We put her to bed with aspirin and hot water bottles. I sit holding her hand until she goes to sleep. Looking down at her sweet face, I realize that with everything that has happened, we forgot to celebrate her birthday. A huge box of presents has arrived at the post office from my parents. When she is better, we will have a party.

# Two Stories –
One Funny, the Other Not

The next day, Moe returns to work. It only takes a few days for him to be sick again. His friend, Djibalis has been fired.

Moe can't believe it. "He was good man. Baba Ali is such a mess! You not believe it. I think I be next," he adds.

Five days later, Moe is next, but he is not fired. He is transferred. He receives his official letter stating that he is being transferred, as of next Monday, out of Baba Ali and into a new job. His title will be Director of Forage and his office located in *Maison Carrie*, an upscale area of Algiers.

The commute will be difficult but the ministry has agreed to pay for his gas until they can find us an apartment. Housing has always been a problem in Algiers. It could take a long time.

We celebrate by taking the children to see Moe's new office and then out for ice cream at our favourite shop. On the way home, we stop at the beach. While sitting in the sand watching the children play with their shovels and buckets, Moe talks to me about his expectations for his new job. After a few minutes he laughs and says he might be embarrassed to go to work on Monday.

"Why will you be embarrassed?" I ask.

"Well, funny thing happen to me when I go to interview for this job. I see it funny now. But not so funny then."

He pauses, and I wonder if he has decided not to tell me the story. But, when I look at him, I see he is trying hard not to laugh.

"Okay, Moe. Can you share your joke?"

"Oh, it not a joke. It funny, funny story."

He settles more firmly into his seat in the sand, bending his legs up under his chin as he begins his tale.

I can't help but think how handsome he is with his thick black curly hair and enchanting smile. He has never lost that crooked wonderful smile. I remember how one of our favourite songs before we were married was *A Certain Smile* by Johnny Mathis.

Moe looks at me and asks, "Why are you smiling? I haven't started my story yet."

"Sorry. I was just thinking back to before we were married and our favourite songs," I pause. "Never mind, Moe. Tell me your funny story."

"Okay, I go to Ministry couple of months ago for interview for job. When it over, I go to bathroom. When I try to leave, the door is locked. I pound on it. I scream. I yell. Nothing. After ten or more minutes, I yell again and this time the secretaries in the office hear me shouting. These secretaries are ladies.

"They yell, 'What do you want?'

"I answer back, 'Halloo, Halloo.' I not know why I shout, halloo, halloo. Maybe I too shy to yell, 'Help! I locked in bathroom.'

"So the ladies think I am big joker and they do nothing.

"I wait twenty minutes more until somebody come to bathroom. This way, I get rescued. Now I go work in that building with those ladies." He shakes his head, but I see that he is smiling. It is a good sign.

On June 5, 1967 as I am getting Tarek dressed to go for a walk, I hear the apartment door open and then slam shut. Concerned, I call out, "Moe is that you?"

Moe enters, carrying a small radio. "Things very bad," he says breathlessly, "very sad and very bad."

"What? What's happening?" I ask.

"Listen. Listen," he says, pointing to the radio, which is on full blast with what sounds like the news. He knows I don't understand Arabic, yet he keeps pointing to the radio as though he thinks that I know what is being said. He listens intently. I can tell by his focus and his frown that something terrible has happened.

"I need to get short wave," he suddenly announces. "I need to hear what BBC says."

"Moe, for heaven's sake, what is going on? Tell me," I plead.

"War. War is going on," he shouts. "Israelis catch Egyptians sleeping in their airplanes and bomb them all and kill many people. It is terrible time. I know about this. I was in Cairo in 1956 when British and French bombers attack. Now it happen again. I can't believe this! They surprise us! They soon bomb all the Middle East! Soon it will be here! We must be ready!"

He stops suddenly and looks at me intently. His eyes widen with fear. "I not know what to do with you. This very dangerous time. Not good time for American wife to be here. National radio is calling all the young men and women of Algeria to get ready for war and to join the army to liberate Palestine. I not believe this is happening. At work we listen to BBC. It says the Israelis strike first because Arabs are going to strike."

By the time Moe gets to the end of his angry, fear-filled tirade, he is out of breath and his eyes are swimming in tears.

I feel both his fear and his passion like a pain deep inside my chest. I think of my children and the Arab blood that runs in their veins. What will become of us?

On the second day of the war, the music starts. It is the music of war. Strong, loud, military march music that slides up your backbone and makes you want to grab a gun and march into battle. It is piped from some mysterious central place and booms out night and day from power poles in the streets of Birtouta.

Zohra and Tarek think it is wonderful. They march endlessly around the house singing at the top of their lungs. Moe watches them, but says nothing.

Everything in the country shuts down. No government business. No school. Everyone is at home listening to the radio. Moe leaves the apartment for hour-long sessions in the village square, listening to shortwave radio piped there for the general population. These programs talk about the progress of the war. He returns, disillusioned and full of angry anti-Israeli, anti-American slogans.

On the third day of the war, Radio Paris announces the

American Embassy in Algiers is calling for all American citizens to leave Algeria as soon as possible. However, I hear nothing directly from the embassy. I know I am registered and they have my address, but there is no word from them.

Algeria breaks diplomatic relations with the U.S.

On one of his breaks from radio listening, Moe tells me I should go home.

"What do you mean, I should go home?" I ask him. "This is my home."

"No. No, it not." He shouts at me.

I can't figure out if he is shouting to be heard above the children's voices and the music or if he is shouting in anger.

"This never your home." he continues. He pauses and then retracts his statement. "I not mean that, but I think this situation too dangerous for you and maybe for our children." The anger in his voice fades into sadness.

"I never feel afraid here," I tell him quietly. "I want to stay."

On June 10th we learn from the Algerian press that American and British planes have bombed Cairo and Damascus. The war is over. The Israelis have won.

Moe goes to the market and returns carrying a package. It is wrapped in butcher paper and looks like something to eat. He holds it clutched to his body while he talks. "I cannot stay in this house one more minute. We go to Algiers. I hear many people run in the streets. We go to see."

The idea of walking in the streets of Algiers makes me anxious. There is so much anti-American feeling about the war and the bombs. "Why don't you go by yourself?" I suggest.

"No," he answers, "it not safe for you to stay by yourself here in the village. You come with me. You wear this."

Without warning, he winds up like a baseball player and throws the package at me with all his strength. It is aimed at my head. I duck and it hits the wall, falling to the floor with a soft thump. Moe turns away with disgusted resignation. "You have to cover yourself," he mutters.

I bend down and take the now-ripped package in my hand.

Tearing it open further, I find a new white veil with a white lace face piece like the one I wore in Mascara.

"So, it has come to this," I think. If Moe wants me to cover up in Algiers, a place where I always walked free, he must be afraid. I hold the veil as I answer him. "Okay. I will take it with me to the city in case I need it."

Just outside of Birtouta, we are stopped by armed militia. As usual, Moe shows them his old Arizona driver's license and they let us pass. Moe and I have talked about why we get by with just this piece of documentation when most of our friends are subjected to much greater scrutiny when they are on the road. We have come to the conclusion that the militia, police or soldiers must consider this license as some secret police trick or test, and they are afraid not to let us through. These roadblocks, while becoming almost normal, still feed my fear that one day we will be shot and left by the side of the road. We hear about killings like that every day.

Ten miles further, we are pulled over by another group of armed men – this time, only four camouflage-dressed young commandos. They are all straining to listen to a small portable radio blaring war news from the back of an old military-green pick-up truck. They carry automatic weapons. But, they smile at the children. One of them even walks to the window to pat Tarek's blond head. We are waved through after only a minute of conversation.

As we accelerate onto the highway, Moe sighs and with a voice wrapped in bitterness says, "I hope that is all today. I am sick of this stupid roadblock business."

We speed towards the city and after what seems like forever, we pull into Ahmed's driveway. Moe jumps out, leaving us in the car. A few moments later, he returns with the news that Ahmed has been called to the embassy on an emergency due to the war.

"We go for drive downtown now," Moe says suddenly as he slides back behind the wheel.

"I'd rather not," I answer.

But Moe isn't asking for my opinion.

We approach the government buildings in the centre of the

city, and he pulls the little Renault into a parking stall next to a small store. The streets are filling up with people.

"I-I don't like this, Moe," I stutter. "It doesn't feel safe for the children."

"Of course, it safe for children. Do you think we would have riot?"

I look at him, about to say more.

But he isn't interested in what I am thinking. "You stay here and I come back for you," he says, head down and grumpy-voiced. He trots away and disappears into the crowd.

I stare at his departing back in disbelief. Disbelief that he would abandon me and the children in the middle of a war, in the middle of a hot June afternoon in a car on a side street in Algiers. My hands shaking, I reach into the back seat and take out the veil. The material feels soft and cool between my fingers. I drape it over my body the best I can in a sitting position. I decide the face piece will be too hot and leave it sitting on the seat. I roll down the windows for a minute to let some of the heat out. The sun is beating down and it is getting hotter in the car by the minute.

"He will return," I think, trying to maintain some sense of optimism even while my sense of outrage overflows and I mutter angrily, "But what good will that do if we are all cooked alive?"

Suddenly, the sound of a huge explosion assaults my ears and its vibration rocks the car. Flashes of light and flying debris ricochet off a nearby building and bounce off the car. The children scream and come tumbling over the back seat on top of me. Clutching them to me, I sink down in the front seat as low as I can.

"Mama, what's that noise? Boom! Boomy!" yells Tarek, burrowing his little face into my neck.

Zohra crawls on top of us. She whimpers, "Mommy, I'm scared."

"Me too, honey," I whisper, trying not to show how frightened I really am. "I don't know what is happening. Let's just sit still for a few minutes. Okay?"

Both children just nod and snuggle up to me more tightly.

I smell smoke. I loosen myself from the arms of my children and struggle to sit up so I can see what is happening around us.

As I raise my head up enough to see the street, I hear what sounds like a thousand running feet.

I peer out anxiously. "Where are they?"

Suddenly, around the corner a huge mob comes running like a herd of uncontrolled animals. I stare, transfixed. They are men, young and old. Some are dressed in white tunics of the countryside, others in T-shirts and jeans. Some men jump on cars and smash the windshields. This mob is running straight toward us.

I pull the veil up over my face so that only my eyes can be seen.

Suddenly, a man with dark hair, dressed in a dark shirt and jeans jumps onto the hood. The car rocks. I hug my children to me, trying to keep their faces burrowed into my chest. They both push against me and sit up to see what is going on.

Through the side window, I look straight into the eyes of an angry young man with an iron railroad tie in his hand. He is about to smash it down on the windshield. The second he sees my eyes – and my children looking at him, he stops, his arm in midair. He looks away, drops his arm and goes on to the next car.

I am glad I have covered my face.

More men pour into the street. The crowd moves in a thick stream away from the centre of the city. A few minutes later, as the mob disappears in the distance, hundreds of police brandishing batons, surge after it.

I sit with my children in frozen silence. No one else approaches us. No one sees us. It is as if we don't exist.

The heat inside the car becomes unbearable. We must find shade. I grab the door handle to get out of the car. But, it swings wide open on its own, and I nearly tumble out.

Moe's strong arm catches me. "The bomb was for American Information Agency! Good thing you have veil! Good thing you are in car." His words say that he is concerned about our safety but his voice reveals that he is excited by the danger of it all.

His eyes are wide and glassy and he has a funny look about him. "My God, this whole thing is a joke to him," I think. My head spins. Tears stream down my face. I sob uncontrollably. The absurdity of it all is too much for me.

"Shut up," Moe snaps as he climbs into the car. "Just shut up. Stop crying. You are crazy woman." He speeds as fast as he can through traffic towards Birtouta. We drive in silence. For once, there are no roadblocks.

At six o'clock the next morning, a post office worker delivers a letter by *Special Delivery*.

"*Special Delivery*? I didn't know Algeria has a special delivery system," I remark as Moe signs for the letter.

Moe laughs, "It from your father. I think your Mother and Father can do anything," Moe exclaims, "Even use Algerian post office system in war. It is miracle."

I smile. It is true. All forms of communication have been shut down because of the war, yet my parents manage to send a special delivery letter.

Moe hands me the letter. I open it to find four airplane tickets on Air France from Algiers, Algeria to Tucson, Arizona, U.S.A. They are open-dated. A note is attached.

Susie: Please come home, all of you. You don't have to stay forever. Just come home for a little while.

Love Daddy

I look at Moe and hand him the note.

He reads it silently. "Good," he says matter-of-factly. "You must take children and go."

"But – what about you?" I ask, horrified at the thought of leaving him here, remembering the mob in Algiers, the men running through the streets and smashing cars, and Moe's strange excitement about the whole thing.

He smiles, "You know I not able to leave. It is announced on radio. No Algerian nationals can leave country. They want foreigners to leave for safety reasons." He looks at the tickets in his hand, and adds, "I like that your father send ticket for me. He respect me."

"Foreigners?" I say softly. It is the only word I really hear. Somehow, Moe's words convince me of a fact that I have never accepted before – that everyone here sees me as a foreigner, and they will always see me as a foreigner. I will never belong. "Perhaps this is how Moe felt when he lived in America," I think, as the full understanding of my situation floods over me.

"What about the children?" I ask. "Will they be able to get out of the country?"

"I think so," Moe answers slowly, "I have to give my permission. It be very difficult thing. We will have to make some plan."

He turns to me suddenly and looks in my eyes. "This is good thing for you – and for my children. You can return when this war is finish and there is peace in the Middle East."

# Other Plans

From the day the tickets arrive, Moe is on a mission to get us away. He is up at five the following morning, waking up the children and hustling them out the door even before they have breakfast.

I keep asking him, "Why are you in such a hurry?"

He keeps answering me, "I think this *getting out* business will take very long time and I want to go back to work in three days. We start now."

"But if you are letting me out, why would there be so much trouble?" I ask, confused.

"Because I know about this. You and children need exit visas and sometimes exit visas not easy. This not America where you just go out and come back whenever you want."

We arrive at the government office at 8 a.m. The line of people seeking exit visas from Algeria runs down the block and around the corner. We get in line and wait. At noon Moe goes to find a phone to see if he can get one of his friends to take the children for the rest of the day. They are restless and bored and we have not come prepared for this wait.

Eventually a car pulls up. It is Rashida. She happily takes Tarek and Zohra, agreeing to bring them back in a few hours. The line inches toward the door. People sit down in the street or lean against the building to rest. We listen to the conversations around us and realize there are many foreigners who want to go home. They are afraid the war might spread and they want out.

Moe and I stand in line saying little to each other. Ever since he decided I should go home, he has few words for me.

Several times, I try to start a conversation, but I get little or no response. Finally I ask, "Do you want me to come back?"

He bows his head and I can't see his eyes. "Of course," he says, his voice tinged with impatience. "Of course."

Late in the afternoon, Abdullah brings the children back. We are close to the head of the line. They are laughing and bright-eyed and can't stop talking about all the things they did at Auntie Rashida's house.

Abdullah talks to Moe for a few minutes. Then, unexpectedly, Abdullah ends the conversation with loud angry words and stomps out of the building.

I stare in disbelief. "What was that about?" I ask.

"Abdullah not happy I let you leave. He tells me you never come back. I tell him he is crazy. He not like that."

"Why would he say that, Moe? I want to stay. You know that."

"I know, but my friends think I am crazy to trust you."

"Moe, I don't want to go. I don't think I should leave you now anyway. It is you that seems to think we should go. Are you telling your friends that it is me that wants to go? Is that why they don't trust me?"

"You go. It is best decision for my little family. When all this problem is fixed, you come back. You have visit with parents and they will be happy. I know they want me to go to America with you but you tell them why I cannot go. I hope they get money back from my ticket."

As Moe finishes his statement, we find ourselves at the head of the line. I understand the man behind the counter when he asks us for the *Livre de Famille*.

Moe answers immediately in Arabic and a long back and forth conversation ensues. Eventually Moe turns to me and says in English, "This is hopeless. We not get married in Algeria and so we have no *Livre de Famille*. Without this *Livre de Famille*, we have no proof of our marriage. We go to airport now and talk to my cousin. Maybe he can send you off."

The man behind the counter has been listening to us and he asks Moe another series of questions. He disappears into an office and when he returns he has a piece of paper, which he stamps and gives to Moe.

"So, is that my exit visa?" I ask as soon as we are in the car and on our way.

"No, I have to drop this off at some other government office. We have an appointment in two days and then they will decide."

"In two days?"

"Yes. I tell you before, it will take time to get you out. I have to swear you are my wife and these are my children. They don't like that all the documents are in English."

I spend the next two days packing what I will need for a short stay in Tucson. The tickets my father sent are open ended. I can use them any day when there are enough seats on the plane. Because I am uncertain as to what day I will get my exit visa, I can't book a definite flight. I write to my parents that I can't get out of Algeria until at least June 20. I hope the letter and the information will get to them before I leave. I am not sure, but I mail it anyway

On the day of our appointment, we arrive ten minutes early. We are shown to a small room and told to wait. It isn't long before a man dressed in army fatigues enters and takes a seat at the desk in the middle of the room. He has a large file folder in his hand and he is smiling. He leafs through the information and stamps a few pieces of paper. Getting up, he hands the papers to Moe and tells him we don't need an exit visa. We just have to present these papers at the airport. The three of us are cleared to leave Algeria any time in the next three days.

On the way home we stop at the Air France office to book three of the four tickets. The lady behind the desk smiles at me and then says in English, "We have been trying to get hold of you for days about these tickets." She laughs. We even called the local Birtouta police but they said they don't know you. Then she adds, "Your parents must have influence. They phoned our head office and insisted we find you. We decided, finally, to send a special delivery to the only address we had. I am glad to see that you got the tickets."

As she talks, she is busy checking her papers. She turns to me,

"Okay, the first booking I have is for June 19, arriving in Phoenix on June 20."

We take it. I am glad I mailed the letter to my mother.

All the way back to Birtouta, Moe and I laugh about the influence of my parents. Leave it to them to go to the highest authority of the airline to find us. I can see my father calling in all his government favours.

We have seven days to wait. I tell Zohra and Tarek that we are going to see Mi-Mi and Papa. Tarek looks at me with unknowing eyes, but Zohra is excited. "We go see my Mi-Mi and my Papa," she sings happily for the next week. Every morning she talks to their photograph as if she is already with them. She has an amazingly clear memory of who they are.

The week is spent packing up the last of my things. I don't want to take too much as I anticipate I will return within the month. In the end we fill two suitcases, which makes me happy as two suitcases and two children will be all I can handle through Customs.

According to my itinerary, I will have a six-hour wait in New York. This time Uncle Marshall and his friend won't be there to help me. Uncle Marshall hasn't been well in the past year and his girlfriend has gone away.

The night before our departure, we put the children to bed early, and despite the excitement of the trip, they both fall asleep quickly. Moe and I spend the hours saying good-bye to each other. Part of me wants to cry, but I keep reminding myself that I will be back as soon as possible.

Moe assures me that it is best that I go home. It isn't safe for us in Algeria right now. "You did well in my crazy country and I happy you go back home for visit. I know what it is to miss family." We fall asleep wrapped around each other, wondering what the next few weeks will hold.

We are on our way to the airport by seven o'clock the next morning. We leave the parking lot of HLM #36 *Batiment*, Birtouta for the last time. Moe drives at Mach speed and we race for the last time down the highway to Algiers. We both pray that we don't encounter any roadblocks. Both gods seem to be listening. The road is clear.

Moe is strangely quiet, and I also have no words. Before we get out of the car at the airport, he hugs me and says softly, "Goodbye Sewzie."

"Moe, you are so funny. That name still makes me laugh," I speak softly as he does, trying to keep my voice light. He doesn't like to see me cry.

"I know," he answers. "Moe funny forever. You have good trip. *Inshallah!*" he whispers. "We enter strange times. A beginning and an ending. When I think of you, you will always be my willow."

I feel tears well up and threaten to overflow. A pain pierces my heart. "That's the loveliest thing you have ever said to me." I concentrate on not crying.

Then Moe takes the faces of each of his children in his hands. He kisses them on their little noses. "Daddy will miss you too much," he says. He can barely speak.

The airport is full of travelers. We stand in line to check our bags through to Paris and then on to New York. The woman behind the counter tells us that she will hold our baggage until we make our way through another line to check our papers.

The line we are told to join has only one other person in it and we are quickly called forward. The uniformed police officer looks at me, then the children, and then Moe. His tone is dark and his motions menacing as he indicates he is not happy with whatever Moe is telling him.

Moe is also not happy. The two seem to be locked in a dispute, Moe fighting to keep his temper, the policeman fighting to keep the power.

Finally, I hear Moe mention the name of his cousin who is the head of the gendarmes at the airport. The dark menacing man looks at Moe with fire in his eyes and tells us to go sit down.

I ask Moe what is happening.

"Same story. This idiot think I not married to you and he says these not my children. He says if I married to you I can produce the *Livre de Famille*. He says I steal other man's children and lie to get them out of Algeria. He calm down when I mention my cousin. You see that. He told us to sit down. Big man is going to get in big trouble when cousin gets here."

Fire flashes in Moe's eyes. "I hate these people of arrogance," he rages. "I tell them to get my cousin but this idiot tell me my cousin gone out of office for business. I pray he get back soon."

I look at my watch. In the background, a crisp French female voice announces the first boarding call for Air France Flight 2320 leaving at 10:40.

"We are probably going to miss the plane," I think. Anger builds inside me at the thought of missing the flight when we are so close. "What will happen now?"

Suddenly, bursting through the door like a sunbeam, Moe's cousin enters, followed by the dark nasty official. Moe's cousin walks up and greets Moe eagerly with embraces. Then he kisses both my cheeks. He goes over to the children and presents them with candy and other gifts – a large bag for each child. He presents me with a wrapped present and tells me to open it on the plane. Then, he speaks briefly to Moe. The dark nasty official stands in the background looking at the floor.

Moe turns to me, grinning. "My cousin will take you to the plane. He say they hold plane for you and children. My cousin went out to buy gifts for you. He see your name on passenger list and want to show respect."

Moe's cousin takes Zohra from my arms. She is fascinated by the shiny buttons on his uniform jacket. Moe takes Tarek and together the five of us walk through the security station, down the tarmac and up the steep, wobbly metal stairs to the waiting plane. We board with the captain and crew waiting at the door as I am led to my seats. The men place the children in their seats and stand in the aisle until we are all are buckled in.

Moe follows his cousin down the aisle and out the door without saying another word or turning back. The three of us stare after him until he disappears.

The doors close and shortly, I feel the plane taxi down the runway. The stewardess gives her safety speech in French. Zohra holds on to my hand and Tarek stares straight ahead in sheer terror as the noise of the plane accelerates. I am still without speech when the plane levels out in the air.

"It's over," I think. "My Algerian adventure is over and I am going home."

A beautiful French stewardess leans down and asks me in French, "Coffee? Tea? Milk for the children?"

I burst into tears and cannot stop.

Zohra and Tarek are shocked. "Mommy, Mommy why you cry?" asks Zohra looking so sad. "Are you crazy, Mommy?"

I shake my head. "I-I don't know," I stammer. "Maybe."

The stewardess returns, carrying Kleenex for me and juice for the children. She smiles and asks if I am okay.

My voice harsher than necessary, I tell her that I don't speak French or Arabic. I don't speak anything but English.

She looks at me, puzzled at my outburst, and returns to her other passengers.

At 12:30 we land in Paris. As the plane taxies to a stop, there is an announcement in French. A uniformed man comes on board and calls my name. I answer. He tells me to come forward. Before anyone else is allowed to disembark, he helps me and the children off the plane. He escorts us to a place for women with children. He tells me to wait for two hours and someone will come and help me to my flight to New York.

I feel like a movie star or someone equally special. A uniformed woman arrives a short time later and shows us where we can eat and go to the bathroom. At 4:00 p.m. a land stewardess leads us to TWA Flight 801 to New York.

We are the first passengers on board. The children snuggle into their seats and fall asleep shortly after take off. It has been a long day. I feel worn out myself. Sleep, however, is far away.

Sometime during the long night in the air, a booming voice calls out over the loudspeaker, "Will Madame Chaabane please turn on her call button?"

At first I think I am dreaming, but when the command is repeated, I reach out and push the silver button above my seat. Heads turn to look at me from as far down the aisle as I can see. A stewardess walks towards me with a paper in her hand.

"Madame, is this you?" she says sweetly in English, showing me the paper with my name written in fine even handwriting.

I nod.

"The captain has had a message for you," she gives me the paper and smiles.

"Thank you," I stutter.

I unfold the paper and read: "Susan Glasier: Parents will meet you in Phoenix, Arizona. Do not go on to Tucson."

Leave it to my father to phone an airplane with a message for me. I turn off the light and settle back into my seat looking out at the night sky and the stars that undoubtedly shine over my home in Tucson, Arizona.

The children sleep until we reach New York City seven hours later. I wake them up and they are both grouchy little bears. But, I don't care. I am nearly home again. We disembark, immediately pick up our baggage and carry it to Customs, which seems to be at least a mile from where the bags come off the carriage. With no land stewardess to help me, I struggle to get both bags off. Then I stand there, surrounded by bags and children, unsure of where to go.

Another passenger comes up and smiles at me. "I'd be happy to carry those bags for you, Ma'am, if you like," he drawls, half-stating and half-asking. His accent is cowboy-thick.

I want to kiss him. I smile. "Thank you" I say. "I'd be ever so grateful." I wonder why I am drawling.

Picking up the suitcases, he leads us down the ramp and through the long tunnel of a building and through the door marked Customs. He puts the suitcases down, tips his white Stetson and trundles off. I have no idea where he goes or who he is, but I decide that I love cowboys in white Stetsons. And the irony of it all is that this is New York, not Phoenix.

Tarek decides to scream and whine through the entire Customs ordeal. The officials ask a long series of questions and try to understand where I have come from. After ten minutes of listening to my son wail at the top of his lungs, they pass us through, and this time there is a stewardess to help me with the children, and to make sure my bags get onto the plane for Phoenix.

I leave New York City around midnight and arrive in Phoenix at four in the morning. I exit the plane with my children, groggy and muttering. As I step onto the tall stairway that leads to the tarmac, I see my mother with her nose pressed up against the window in the terminal doorway. She is crying and smiling and waving. I hurry down the stairs as fast as the legs of two little kids can go and I run into her arms. My father stands smiling in the background. He moves forward only when we have had our fill of mother hugs and gathers us all at once into his big wide arms.

"Oh God, it's good to finally see you all," he says, hardly able to keep down the sob that wells up in his throat.

"So," my mother finally says, after all the welcomes and hugs are done, "When do you have to go back?"

"Never!" The word flies out of my mouth before I can stop it. Shocked, I cover my mouth.

"Never?" my father asks. "What does that mean?"

"I – I'm not sure," I tell him. "I suppose it means – I'm really not sure."

We walk silently to the car listening to Zohra chatter.

Finally my mother says, "Let's just play it day-by-day, shall we?"

I agree.

The next day I write a letter to Moe. I tell him that I am thinking of staying in America. I ask him to come. I tell him that my father will get him a job. I tell him that he doesn't have to be so involved in politics and all the bad things that are happening in his country.

I receive no word from him for more than a month. I am frantic. I wonder if he is sick. I tell my parents that I should get ready to go back.

My mother looks at me with surprise. "Are you sure that's what you want?" she finally asks. "You know, he let you out once. He might not do that again." She bursts into tears. "I'm sorry," she sobs, "but I hate the thought of you and the kids going back to that place."

The next day I phone the airlines to see if I can get a ticket to Algiers. They tell me I have to have an entry visa and a sponsor.

I write Moe another letter. I tell Moe that I have changed my mind and I am coming back to Algeria. I explain that I need him to sponsor me so I can get an entry visa.

Two weeks later I get a reply. All it says is this:

Dear Susie

You too late. I make other plans. I get married yesterday.

Yours truly,

Mohamed Chaabane

P. S. Give my respect to your parents. I will write to the children when I can.

As I read his words, I see my willow in my mind's eye. I reach out for it, but all I touch are falling leaves.

 EPILOGUE

He never did write to us again. At least, that's what I believed for 14 years.

I remarried in 1969 and immigrated to Canada with a new husband and three children. In 1976 my mother died of cancer. My father informed me that she was gone and there would be no funeral. He had the funeral home bury her under a tree in a Tucson cemetery and asked that no one attend the burial. He stayed locked in grief for the next five years, unable to make even the smallest attempt at cleaning out her personal belongings.

Then, suddenly one day in 1981, he called me, asking that I fly to Tucson to help him distribute my mother's things and to clean out the house. He announced he had married his housekeeper in a Las Vegas ceremony and wanted to get the house in shape to sell.

Stunned, but not surprised, I flew back to Tucson to help. When I arrived I found him relaxed and happier than I had ever seen him in my life. When I asked why he didn't tell us he was getting married, he said he was afraid I'd be upset with him. I told him that I wanted him to be happy and it was good to see him smile again. This was the beginning of the close relationship I always dreamed of having with my father, but that always eluded me because of my mother's need for all his attention.

In the process of helping him dispose of my mother's belongings, I opened one of her dresser drawers and discovered a stack of letters. When I pulled them out for a closer look, I recognized many familiar onion-skin envelopes. Each was neatly addressed to me at my parent's home in the distinctive black ink that could have only been scripted by Moe.

The minute I realized what they were, I yelled for my father to come and see. He looked from the letters to my face and I will always remember his words, "Your mother thought it would be better if we didn't tell you he was writing. She thought it might be troubling for your new marriage."

Anger surged through my body. I couldn't catch the sudden fury before it exploded out of my mouth! "How could you? How the hell could you?" I heard myself saying over and over again. "How the hell could you not tell me and his children that he really did care and really did try to stay in touch? This was my business! Not yours to make such decisions for me! How could you leave us to believe that he had abandoned us forever?"

With tears running down his face, my father looked into my eyes and said, "I'm so sorry dear. We just thought it would make it easier for you." With that, he turned and left the room.

I read every letter that night. There were 36 of them: One card for every New Year and a letter on each of the children's birthdays. They were sad epistles, and every one began with the line, "Why don't you write to your poor, miserable father who miss you very much?"

In between the sadness and the blame for not writing, there is news about his life. One letter tells about his new wife and then another about a new baby son. The following year, he has another child, a daughter.

Then the letters stop. He doesn't write anything to us for two years. When the letters start up again, they contain the news that his young wife has died of typhoid because he could not get her to the hospital in time. He bemoans the fact that now he needs to search for another wife to look after his children. Another letter informs us that he has married his cousin and has moved back to the village of his birth, Mascara.

When I finish helping my father clean out my mother's closets and cupboards, I say good-bye and return home to Canada. The first thing I do is to give all of the letters to Zohra. In 1981, she is eighteen and engaged to be married. She is overjoyed with my gift and immediately writes to the address on the last letter, inviting Moe to her wedding. She hears back from him in a heartfelt letter full of joy and amazement that after all these years he has heard from his daughter. He assures her he will come to the wedding.

For the next several months she hears nothing more. As her wedding day approaches, she decides that he is not coming after all. Even with all the happiness of her special day, she can barely hide her sadness and disappointment.

Then, the day before her wedding, in the middle of the night, she gets a phone call from the Calgary airport. An Air Canada employee asks if she is expecting a visitor from Algeria.

When she screams yes, he tells her that a man claiming to be her father has been roaming the airport, distraught over the fact that he cannot remember the name of the people he is supposed to call in order to get a ride from the airport. The Air Canada employee has been going through the phone book phoning all the names that are even close to what the Algerian man remembers. Zohra and her new in-laws all drive off into the night to pick him up.

Moe enjoys his two weeks in Canada and participates in all the wedding activities. He has kept up with his English and it seems the same as when I left. Zohra is a happy daughter.

My only discussion with Moe during this visit involves him questioning me as to why I never answered his letters. I try to explain that I didn't know he was writing because my mother hid the letters from me. He keeps saying, "Your parents wouldn't do that." In many ways, I can't blame him for not believing they would do such a thing. I can barely believe it myself.

The best thing that comes out of this visit is that Zohra is able to establish a relationship with her father. When the first of Zohra's six children, a daughter, is a year old, she packs her up and goes to Algeria for a whole summer. When they return, Zohra talks about her adventures and tells me she now understands why I left.

In the summer of 2000, Moe died of heart failure after many years of sickness. A part of me wonders if perhaps it was more heartbreak than heart failure. I still feel sadness for this man who was so dedicated to improving the lives of his countrymen. He had such expectations, such hope. It had to have been a terrible loss when he discovered his expectations were mere illusions.

Today when I think of my time in this culture and with Moe, I am grateful. Grateful for what it taught me about other people, other religions and other ways of living a life. And, of course, I am eternally grateful for my children from this relationship. I grew up in this story. It has taken me many years to put it all in perspective.